Communication
and mental health
disorders

Communication and mental health disorders

Developing theory, growing practice

Caroline Jagoe and Irene P. Walsh

(Eds)

J&R Press Ltd

A dedication to our mentors, teachers and friends

This book is dedicated to the memory of **Professor Claire Penn**. Claire supported my early interest in communication and mental health, mentoring me in my very first piece of research. Perhaps the most important lesson Claire taught me was the relevance of context – the communicative context of an utterance, the psychosocial context of the client, the sociocultural context of the healthcare system – context in all its wonderful complexity.

Caroline Jagoe

I would like to dedicate this book to the memory of **Jenny France**. Jenny, one of the first Speech and Language Therapists in psychiatry, was my long-time mentor, teacher and friend. Jenny inspired me to always look beyond the person's 'diagnosis', in order to bear witness to that person's lifeworld and 'living' experience of language and communication. Such inspiration has guided me through my career, a gift I will be ever-thankful for.

Irene P. Walsh

Contents

About the authors

Jennifer Brophy is a Clinical Specialist Speech and Language Therapist in the area of adult mental health based in Dublin, Ireland. She has worked in community and acute adult mental health services for over 10 years. She established the first SLT service to adults with mental health disorders in the health service in the Republic of Ireland. Her research interests have focused on exploring the lived experience of people with schizophrenia of speech, language and communication difficulties. She is interested in developing and advocating for SLT services for adults with mental health difficulties.

Professor Karen Bryan, OBE, has worked as a consultant speech and language therapist in forensic psychiatry. Her research interests are in communication difficulties in young offenders and in forensic populations, and the impact of communication difficulties on access to healthcare. Karen is involved in the development of Registered Intermediaries working for the Ministry of Justice in the UK, and was previously a member of the Health Professions Council. She is a Visiting Professor in the Department of Neuropsychology at the University of Warsaw, and is a Fellow of the Royal College of Speech and Language Therapists.

Dr Judy Clegg is a Senior Lecturer in the Division of Human Communication Sciences at the University of Sheffield, UK. She trained as a Speech and Language Therapist at the University of Manchester and completed a PhD in developmental language disorders at the University of Nottingham. Her research interests focus on the developmental trajectories and outcomes of children with language and communication needs, the impact of social disadvantage on children's language and communication development, the complex co-morbidity between children's social disadvantage, their developing language and communication and their behaviour and mental health, and evaluating the effectiveness of interventions designed to facilitate children and young peoples' language and communication abilities. Judy is a Fellow of the Royal College of Speech and Language Therapists (RCSLT) and a Trustee of ICAN, the Children's Communication Charity. Judy is also co-editor of the journal, *Child Language Teaching and Therapy*.

Patricia Delmar contributes to the undergraduate programme in Clinical Speech and Language Studies, at Trinity College Dublin. She is also a co-researcher and co-author on a number of publications with the editors of this book, Caroline Jagoe and Irene Walsh. As a person with a diagnosis of Autism Spectrum Disorder, Patricia is an advocate for respectful consideration for differences in communication.

Dr Caroline Jagoe is Assistant Professor in the Department of Clinical Speech and Language Studies, Trinity College, The University of Dublin. She has worked as a clinical Speech and Language Therapist and a researcher in the fields of neurorehabilitation as well as in acute, community and forensic psychiatry. Pragmatic language is a particular focus of her work and she situates herself as a Relevance Theorist, working on applications to conversational data involving people with schizophrenia, aphasia and those who use alternative and augmentative communication. She has a particular interest in optimizing communication access within the context of mental health and psychosocial support and has been involved in projects in countries as diverse as Ireland, South Africa and Iraq.

Dr Sinéad Kellaghan is a practising Senior Speech and Language Therapist working with people with Intellectual Disabilities in the Health Service Executive (HSE), Ireland. Her doctoral work focused on the area of clinical pragmatics and uncertainty management. Sinéad has a keen interest in qualitative research methodologies and working collaboratively to even out the conversational floor for people with disabilities in clinical interactions and beyond.

Sarah McGlinn is a Senior Speech and Language Therapist, with vast experience working with children who have speech, language and communication disorders in community settings. Sarah spent an extensive part of her career working as an Infant Mental Practitioner as part of an Area Based Strategy in Dublin to tackle childhood poverty. She has a special interest in prevention and early intervention and supporting language development in the early years. In her work, Sarah is particularly attuned to supporting healthy social-emotional development and early communication by attending to the important role of the parent-child relationship and parenting in the early years.

Dr Ramin Nilforooshan is a Consultant Psychiatrist for older adult psychiatry in Surrey and Borders Partnership NHS Foundation Trust and a Visiting Professor at University of Surrey. He is the CRN Speciality Dementia research Lead in Kent, Surrey and Sussex and is the Principal Investigator for several national and internationally clinical trials in dementia and mental health. His special research interest is using technology to provide better care for people with dementia.

Dr Jane O'Connor is a Consultant Psychiatrist who has worked in a variety of psychiatric settings, including forensic services and mental health services for people with intellectual disability. She has an interest in interdisciplinary working and ethical and legal issues pertaining to mental healthcare. She has spearheaded initiatives to optimize communication in the settings in which she works.

Stephanie O'Connor is a Clinical Specialist Speech and Language Therapist working on an adult mental health team in Dublin, Ireland. She has worked for many years with adults with both mental health difficulties and intellectual disability, and is passionate about finding ways to ensure that all people using mental health services have the opportunity for their voices to be heard.

Áine Sheehy is a clinical Speech and Language Therapist working in a community setting in the Health Service Executive (HSE), Ireland, and has previously worked in inpatient neurorehabilitation and acute settings. Her M.Sc. research focused on the psycho-emotional impact of communication difficulties arising from stroke. She has a particular interest in the relationship between communication and wellbeing as it relates to people with acquired brain injury, progressive neurological disorders, and psychiatric disorders.

Professor Pamela Snow is both a Speech-Language Pathologist and a registered psychologist. Until late 2019, she was head of the La Trobe Rural Health School at La Trobe University (Australia) and as of January 2020 has taken up a new appointment as Professor of Cognitive Psychology in the School of Education at the same institution. Pamela has conducted extensive research on the language and literacy skills of vulnerable children and adolescents, particularly those in youth justice, out of home care, and flexible education settings.

Dr Irene P. Walsh is an Associate Professor in Speech and Language Pathology at Trinity College Dublin, Ireland. Her clinical background is in the area of child and adult psychiatry. Her research interests reflect this background and include communication and language (dis-)ability within the context of mental health and disorder (e.g., schizophrenia); the analysis of talk in clinical and non-clinical interactions, and first and other-person accounts of the living experience of psychiatric conditions. In the area of allied healthcare education, she is interested in how professional identity emerges in the social interaction of teaching and learning contexts and in exploring how health humanities can be incorporated into such educational contexts.

Introduction

Irene P. Walsh and Caroline Jagoe

Communication and mental healthcare are inseparable. The relationship is complex and bidirectional, although the precise nature of the association is not yet fully understood. In *Communication and Mental Health Disorders: Developing Theory, Growing Practice* we address this complex relationship from a number of perspectives, including considerations across the lifespan, theoretical advances within communication and mental healthcare and, ultimately, how such information can help grow and inform practice in clinical and educational domains of mental healthcare.

The influence of communication on mental health and wellbeing and, conversely, the influence of mental health disorders on communication is evident from the very earliest stages of development and persists across the lifespan. Part I takes a lifespan perspective on communication and mental health, through four chapters spanning infancy, childhood, adulthood and older adulthood. In Chapter 1, 'Communication and infant mental health', Mc Glinn explores how the foundations of communication development are laid down in the first days and months of an infant's life, building relationships which will form the cornerstone of social and emotional development and contribute to long-term mental health. Parent-infant relationships are at the heart of developing communication. However, communication is also the medium through which these relationships are nurtured. Moving beyond infancy, in Chapter 2, 'Children's communication and their mental health', Clegg highlights the multifactorial and interdependent nature of children's development, arguing that it is useful to consider how communication mediates the development of social-emotional competence, thereby influencing mental health. Chapter 3 (Walsh, Jagoe & Brophy), 'Language and communication in adults with mental health disorders', focuses on the communication difficulties that can be intrinsic to, or associated with, mental health disorders in adulthood, specifically schizophrenia, mood disorders and anxiety disorders. A thorough understanding of the nature of the communication difficulties with which some individuals with mental health disorders present is essential if services are to be appropriately designed to meet their needs. In Chapter 4 of Part I, 'Language and communication in psychiatry of old age: A UK perspective', Nilforooshan explores some connections between language and communication and psychiatry of older people. This chapter includes a brief discussion on dementia, which is covered by psychiatry of old age in some countries, including the UK.

The centrality of communication to mental health and in mental health services has been long recognized. The argument which emerges across the chapters of this book is that considerations of communication support needs should be central to the delivery of all mental health services. The Speech and Language Therapist has a unique role to play, both through directly addressing communication difficulties as well as intervening at broader environmental and organizational levels. Realizing these changes within mental health services is a challenge of service improvement across the sector. The specific application of theory to developing healthcare interventions, specifically complex interventions, is increasingly recognized. Part II of this book explores some of the developing theory pertinent to communication and mental health. In Chapter 5, 'Pragmatic language and social conversational skills intervention for children with mental health disorders', Kellaghan provides an outline of how pragmatic theory can inform clinical practice. A parallel argument is made in Chapter 6, 'Developing theoretically grounded approaches to pragmatic intervention in people with schizophrenia', in which Jagoe explores how two specific pragmatic theories (Cognitive Pragmatics Theory and Relevance Theory) could inform speech and language therapy practice with this population. In order to grow practice and incorporate a greater appreciation for the role of communication in mental health, the education of the next generation of healthcare professionals must reflect the communication needs of service users. Walsh explores, in Chapter 7, how a medical humanities framework using literary autobiographies might inform a communication-inclusive approach to mental healthcare education. Chapter 8 of Part II explores theories of hope and recovery, where Jagoe, Delmar, Sheehy and Walsh draw concepts of hope within healthcare and the particular considerations raised when communication difficulties are evident.

In the almost 20 years since the publication of the book, *Communication and Mental Illness* (France & Kramer, 2001) there have been significant strides in the field. This growing practice is the focus of Part III of this book. This part of the book is more particularly focused on the profession of speech and language therapy and its place within mental healthcare. These chapters reflect the domains of mental health services in which speech and language therapy provision has grown in particular ways. Speech and language therapists continue to be well-established members of the multidisciplinary team in child and adolescent mental health services (CAMHS) – the wealth of input in this domain is reflected in earlier chapters of the book (particularly Chapters 2 and 5). The role within infant mental health (Mc Glinn, Chapter 1), is an area of growing practice, and one which is invaluable in nurturing the communicative foundation of relationships. The role of the Speech and Language Therapist within adult mental health services is an area of growing practice, although service provision continues to be patchy at best, with anecdotal evidence suggesting that dedicated speech and language therapy input is lacking for the majority of adult mental health services. Speech and language therapy practice within adult mental health is currently being deepened and broadened, with an increasingly holistic view addressing not only the individual, but their communication support needs from an environmental and societal perspective (explored in Chapter 9 by Brophy and O'Connor). Significant developments have occurred in the provision of speech and language therapy services to young offenders, particularly in the UK and Australia, with the role discussed in Chapter 10 by Bryan and Snow, while provision within forensic mental health services is also an area of growth, discussed in Chapter 11 (O'Connor). Chapter 12 illustrates how speech and language therapists can extend their own practice through incorporating approaches developed in other disciplines. In this final chapter, Brophy addresses how cognitive behavioural approaches may be usefully applied to addressing the language and communication needs of clients, whilst also allowing the clinician to incorporate the psychological issues which will inevitably surface in this context.

Communication is a core human capacity and, as the contributors to this book demonstrate, is interwoven with mental health and wellbeing. The centrality of communication suggests that an appreciation of the communication difficulties is important for all members of the multidisciplinary team. It is hoped that this book will not only nurture multidisciplinary interest but promote increased reflection on the unique and complex relationship between mental health and disorder, and language and communication. Shining a spotlight on this field of practice ensures that careful attention is paid to the application of theoretical developments to clinical practice, while at the same time charting the innovative and ever-growing practice in this field.

Reference

France, J. & Kramer, S. (2001). *Communication and Mental Illness: Theoretical and Practical Approaches*. London: Jessica Kingsley.

Section 1

Communication and mental health across the lifespan

1 Communication and infant mental health

Sarah Mc Glinn

Introduction

The development of early communication skills is firmly rooted within an infant's primary relationships. Relationships are the building blocks of healthy development, including language and communication. Infant mental health is about the promotion of healthy social and emotional development in the crucial first three years of life, supporting secure attachment and healthy parent–child relationships. If infants and toddlers have positive, predictable and emotionally attuned relationships with their parents or other caregivers, they will feel safe from harm and secure that their basic needs will be met. Therefore, their energy can be spent on exploring the world around them and having positive early experiences that will nurture their developing brains and help them achieve healthy growth and development including, of course, language and communication.

Early communication development

Language and the developing brain

A child's interactions with their caregivers during the earliest days and months of life have a lasting impact on the architecture of their developing brain (Fox, Levitt, & Nelson, 2010). Genes provide the basic blueprint, but interactions and experiences determine whether a child's brain will provide a strong or weak foundation for all future learning, behaviour and health (National Scientific Council on the Developing Child, 2010). When an infant experiences interactions, such as holding eye gaze with his mother or exchanging smiles with his father, neurons become active or 'fire' (Siegel & Bryson, 2012). When neurons fire together, new synaptic connections are formed between them.

Astonishingly, in the first few years of life, more than one million synaptic connections form every second (National Scientific Council on the Developing Child, 2007). In a child's first years of life, the brain exhibits extraordinary neuroplasticity, refining its circuits in response to environmental experiences (Murgatroyd & Spengler, 2011). Synapses are built, strengthened, weakened and pruned away depending on the frequency and quality of an infant's interactions with their caregivers and environment (Tierney & Nelson, 2009). Positive parent–child interactions, such as talking, cuddling, reading, singing and playing, not only help tune babies into language but these interactions also build the foundation for developing attention, cognition, memory, emotional regulation, social-emotional development, language and literacy, sensory and motor skills that will help them reach their communicative potential (Siegel, 2001).

The key to forming strong brain architecture is what is known as '*serve and return*' interactions between infants and their caregivers (National Scientific Council on the Developing Child, 2004). Nugent (2011) highlights how newborn babies are already equipped with a wide range of stunningly precocious communication strategies: some cues that are clear and unambiguous like a loud cry saying "help me" or other cues that are not so easy to interpret like a faint change in facial colour, perhaps communicating "I'm slightly stressed, please give me a short break" (Nugent, 2011, pp.xiii, xiv). Invoking a tennis match analogy, new neural connections form in the brain as infants instinctively '*serve*', for example through cooing, a puckering of the brow, a quickened pace of breath or a bright-eyed look, and adults '*return*' the serve by responding in a sensitive and meaningful way (National Scientific Council on the Developing Child, 2007, p.6). An infant who smiles and gets snuggled in return has received positive reinforcement and will smile again, inviting additional nurturing responses from her caregiver. With regards to the development of language and literacy skills, for example when an infant sees an object, the parent says its name. Not only is this an emotionally satisfying experience for the baby who senses their parent's interest in his/her focus and attention, it also provides the context in which the infant can link the auditory word and the corresponding object (Woodward & Hoyne, 1999). Later, adults show young children that these objects and sounds can also be represented by marks on a page in the form of graphemes, leading to reading and then writing skills (Neuman, Copple, & Bredekamp, 2000). Each stage builds on what came before. Ensuring that children have adult caregivers who consistently engage in 'serve and return' interactions (National Scientific Council on the Developing Child, 2007, p.6) beginning in infancy, builds a strong foundation in the brain for building all of the future communicative skills that follow.

The critical period for language experience

The last decade has brought an abundance of research in neuroscience examining young children's early processing of language (Kuhl, 2009, 2010; Kuhl & Rivera-Gaxiola, 2008). Language, like vision and most other brain functions, exhibits a 'critical period' for learning (Eliot, 2001). The infant brain is immensely better at learning language than a cognitively superior older brain because of the remarkable plasticity of the young nervous system. Within a child's first years, there is the greatest opportunity for selecting optimal neural pathways for acquiring language as the number of synaptic connections in a child's brain is at its peak (Eliot, 2001). Johnson and Newport (1989) highlight the relationship between the age of acquisition of a second language and language skill accomplished. What is evident is that our brain is most equipped to learn a second language under the age of 7 years old, and after this time there is a systematic decline in our language acquisition ability (Johnson & Newport, 1989). Furthermore, not all aspects of language learning exhibit the same temporally-defined critical 'windows'. Kuhl (2010) highlights, for example, that the critical period for phonetic learning occurs prior to the end of the first year, whereas syntactic learning flourishes between 18-36 months. Vocabulary development 'explodes' at 18 months of age but does not appear to be as restricted by age as other aspects of language learning – one can learn new vocabulary items at any age. What has been established without doubt is the critical importance of the birth-to-3 years phase for children's language development. These findings have theoretical and clinical implications showing that appropriate experiences which encourage optimal communication development are crucial during the relatively brief critical period for language learning in early life.

The centrality of relationships

The role of relationships in language development

The remarkable journey from pre-linguistic communication to verbal language is rooted in the caregiver-infant relationship in which both parties play crucial roles. Right from birth, babies are equipped with a rich behavioural repertoire that allows them to engage and connect with their caregivers (Brazelton, 2009). Newborns possess a wide range of visual, auditory and perceptual abilities that allow them to explore their world and to engage in face-to-face, eye-to-eye mutual exchange (Nugent, 2015). From the beginning, babies show their individuality and are making choices about what they want to look at and listen to. Above anything else, a baby's preference is to look at his mother's face and listen to her voice (Sullivan, Perry, Sloan, Kleinhaus, & Burtchen, 2011). A baby's early behaviours are the window into their mind, brain and emotions. Whether it is a contented smile, a subtle facial expression, a splaying of the fingers or tightening of the leg muscles, these are babies' cues that communicate important messages to us. Their behaviour is their language and they are reliant on their caregiver's acute attention and sensitivity to tune into their behaviours, and interpret their thoughts and feelings, so that their innate desire to form a synchronous relationship with their caregiver is fulfilled (Hong & Park, 2012). Infants are completely reliant on this relationship for their growth, learning and wellbeing. It seems that parents too are pre-programmed to behave in ways to ensure the unique parent–infant bond (Swain, Lorberbaum, Kose, & Strathearn, 2007). Mother's unconditional admiration and natural preoccupation with their newborn baby contributes to building this special relationship (Lothian, 1999). When parents are tuned into and respond sensitively to their baby's cues, it has an important impact on how babies actively seek to invest in this relationship and learn to find mutual meaning through their language and communication skills (Lally & Mangione, 2017). This pleasure and joy in feeling accepted, understood and responded to by their most significant other sets the foundation for optimal learning and communication and is the bedrock of positive mental health.

The verbal and nonverbal interactions that caregivers have with their babies provide infants with much more than a language model for acquiring adequate communication skills. While caregiver–infant conversations are rooted in the desire to share meanings together, they are the basic ways that parent–infant attachment styles are formed (Roseman, 2008). Moreover, these parent–child interactions are the channel through which infants acquire models for forming future relationships (Roseman, 2008). It is in this critical phase that the baby is forming his internal working model of what relationships are about, what he can expect from them and how much he can trust them to meet his needs (World Health Organisation, 2004). The strategies for encouraging babies and toddlers to engage with adults in communicative interactions give the baby a sense of who he/she is as an individual in his/her own right, as someone worthy of love, attention and social connection. These experiences foster a strong, emotionally secure relationship between baby and parent. Caregivers who are sensitive to their infant's interests and needs, who recognize the baby's role in their relationship and who allow the child to lead interactions, are using effective strategies for supporting their child's language and communication skills and helping their baby develop a template for satisfying secure relationships (Roseman, 2008).

The relevance of communication breakdown and repair in the parent–child relationship

Early interaction within the parent–infant dyad is often described as a synchronous 'dance' (Leclere et al., 2014). Nugent acknowledges, however, that this is an idealized description and highlights that parent–infant interactions can be complex and challenging (Nugent, 2011). Missed communicative opportunities can occur frequently and are to be expected. The important factor is a parent's capacity to repair these communicative mismatches and to re-establish synchrony in the dyad (Beeghly & Tronick, 2011). The experience of reparation contributes to a sense of trust in the infant and to the development of a secure attachment relationship (Beeghly & Tronick, 2011).

A healthy view of the transition to parenthood includes the notion of parents forming a 'good enough' relationship with their infant – a process that begins in pregnancy and progresses into the baby's first days, weeks, months and beyond – whilst at the same time maintaining or enhancing their own wellbeing (Slade, Cohen, Sadler, & Miller, 2009, p.22). Winnicott's concept of 'good enough' parenting acknowledges that parenting is a complex task and that children do well enough when they are nurtured within a relationship that is sensitive, attentive and predictable enough to provide healthy maturational processes in the baby (Winnicott, 1953). This strengths-based model of 'good enough' parenting recognizes the foundational qualities needed for healthy infant development and wellbeing and disregards the concept of the hyper-critical 'perfect parenting'. Appreciation of this concept holds important clinical implications in working compassionately with parents and young families. For this reason, the term 'good enough' as it relates to parenting and relationships will be used in this chapter.

Risk factors to parent–infant bonding and relationship

The birth of an infant marks a major transition stage in the life of his/her parents, and for the infant the first three months of life are disproportionately important in setting their developmental trajectory. This developmental trajectory is heavily dependent on the quality of the relationship with their parents (Nicolson, 2015). However, for some parents and babies, there are factors that get in the way of forming 'good enough' relationships. Some examples might be a parent's early attachment trauma, a current or past abuse, parenting in a new culture, medical concerns in pregnancy affecting the mother or baby's wellbeing, substance dependence, lack of support, depression, anxiety or other mental illness, younger or older parenthood, premature birth, unplanned pregnancy and unanticipated birth complications to name but a few (Nicolson, 2015). Negative experiences and unresolved losses may gravely affect a parent's capacity to attend to or 'fall in love' with their baby and alter the developing relationship in the infant's first years (Weatherston, 2000). Fraiberg's concept of the "ghosts in the nursery" describes how the arrival of a baby, with all the challenges and opportunities it presents, has the capacity to reawaken the parent's deeply-buried suffering (Fraiberg, Adelson & Shapiro, 1975, p.389). Past and current challenges or suffering pose a risk to parent–infant bonding.

Some new parents experience healing of their childhood pain through the experience of bringing a child into the world. They may describe their child as their 'saving grace' and have the desire and ability to give "something better for my child than I have had" (Fraiberg et al., 1975, p.389). As Selma Fraiberg points out, the baby "stands for the renewal of self; his birth can be experienced as a psychological rebirth for his parents" (Fraiberg, 1980, p.54). However, for other new parents, their myriad complex emotions and maladaptive coping strategies obstruct their ability to offer a 'good enough' relationship to their child. To prevent these risk factors from negatively impacting on the parent–child relationship, with the likely outcome of insecure attachment for the baby, an infant mental health intervention is required. Such intervention may involve the practitioner providing a safe space for exploring the unresolved psychological experiences of the parent's past. In conjunction to this, it is imperative that these parents are offered timely support in enhancing their capacity to tune into, build understanding and empathy for their infant's developmental needs from parent–child interactions and the relationship they offer to their child. This type of support is core to the expertise of speech and language therapy.

Speech and language therapy in infancy

Babies can't wait – timing is crucial for the development of early communication

In most instances, a Speech and Language Therapist (SLT) is first introduced to a parent and their child when a communication delay is already suspected. More often than not in these circumstances, the child is already of preschool age, by which time the critical window of the first two years of life has passed and the therapist's capacity to support children's early communication may be compromised.

A significant amount of brain shaping has already taken place by preschool age, which is largely dependent upon the well-established interaction and communicative patterns between the child and his caregivers (National Scientific Council on the Developing Child, 2010). These patterns of parent–child interaction could be augmented through parents being supported earlier in the process about the potential of their role in supporting their child's communication development (Brockmeyer Cates, Dreyer, Berkule, White, Arevalo, & Mendelsohn, 2012). Coaching parents on positive interaction styles during the critical period for language learning gives children a much better opportunity to reach their communicative potential.

Without a doubt, prevention and early intervention is key. The earlier in children's lives that the profession of speech and language therapy shares its knowledge and expertise in early communication development, through information sharing, coaching and building the capacity of important people in children's lives including parents, caregivers and early years practitioners, the more effective this investment of time and resources will be. The later the input of interventions in terms of a child's age, the longer it takes to effect positive changes (Wachs, Georgieff, Cusick, & McEwen, 2014). Consequently, this also negatively impacts on the cost of interventions.

If the speech and language therapy profession is to share expertise on nurturing early language and communication, there is a need to implement ways of working with infants, parents and other caregivers through evidence-based universal programmes much earlier in children's lives. For those concerned about children's early interactions, early communication and their mental health trajectory, Nugent (2015) suggests that the earliest months of life may be the most relevant and optimal intervention point across the lifespan.

Infusing infant mental health practice into speech and language therapy

The field of speech and language therapy has so much to learn from, and contribute to, the practice of infant mental health. Hawthorne (2015) highlights that no single profession has taken the lead in establishing standards or requirements for practitioners working with infants and young children around their social and emotional wellbeing. Yet a guiding principle of infant mental health is that every practitioner involved in the lives of families plays a role in the social and emotional wellbeing of infants and young children (Wechsler & Woodlock, 2006). Generally speaking, apart from paediatric medical or special needs services, there are few SLTs working with children under the age of 2 years old. Yet from the field of speech and language therapy there is a powerful contribution that could be made to children's learning and long-term wellbeing by engaging with concerned parents from the earliest days and months. This opportunity is unequalled and one that cannot be replicated at any other stage of a child's life.

Speech and language therapy plays a key role in supporting parents to observe their child with curiosity, listen attentively to their communicative attempts, and follow their lead in order to offer sensitive interactions that best nurture their child's innate propensity towards language and communication. However, the availability of this support is so often offered all too late. It is so important for speech and language therapy to be integrated into the multidisciplinary healthcare services offered to parents and babies right from the earliest stages because the foundations of language and communication development are laid in the very earliest days and months of a baby's experiences. When SLTs are in a position to work with parents right from the beginning, parents are being supported in tuning into their baby's 'language' and establishing interactions that are socially reinforcing, regular, familiar, intimate and predictable. Indeed, these interactions are the matrix for language growth. The well-known face-to-face gazing and back-and-forth smiling between parents and infants in the early months is the essential foundation for each baby's growing communication (Brockmeyer Cates et al., 2012). In these moments, a baby's appreciation of communication and language is being established (Nugent, 2011). Their 'language' is being understood, responded to and valued by their most important communication partner and consequently their appetite for investing in communication grows from strength to strength.

Even more than this, the foundations of a relationship that will last a lifetime are being laid down, contributing to sound long-term mental health.

Relationships: The heart of developing communication

As discussed earlier, relationships play a critical role in early development across all domains, including communication. For this reason, the status of a child's relationships with their primary caregivers is of significant interest and should be a primary focus for all concerned with the healthy development of children. Interactions between infants and their parents are central to a child's growing language and communication skills. A toddler learns to say the word 'book' when he shows his book to his sensitive mother and hears, "You love this *book*. Let's sit together and read your *book*. This is so much fun!" In order to set strong foundations for the development of healthy communication, the role of the SLT is to support the parent–child relationship from the earliest months and beyond.

With the task of fostering the development of early communication, it is as important for the SLT to offer a relationship that is as attuned to the parent as it is to the young child. Failing to get the balance with this may result in a disservice to the child. A focus on the child throughout assessment gives information on their style of communication and their stage of language development. However, an assessment focusing on the parent–child dynamic enlightens the practitioner on the established interaction styles within the dyad. For instance, observations of a parent's sensitivity towards their child, a child's proximity or comfort seeking from their parent, and how a parent plays and talks with their child and talks about their child, all contribute to an understanding of this early caregiving relationship and its capacity to build healthy social-emotional development – an important precursor to the development of early language and communication skills (Mares & Woodgate, 2017). However, it is also very relevant to explore the expectations, perceptions and attributions parents have of their child as well as exploring parents' own life experiences and wellbeing through the practitioner–parent relationship. An appreciation of these factors is necessary in order to better understand, or at least wonder about, the wider context of the parent–child relationship. Within a trusting practitioner–parent relationship, revelations about a parent's own childhood experiences may be shared. Examples of difficult childhood experiences that parents may have encountered include abuse (i.e., physical, emotional and/or sexual), neglect, exposure to domestic violence, having a parent who was incarcerated or experiencing psychiatric illness. Indeed, these are examples of adverse childhood experiences that negatively impact on a parent's ability to be emotionally available and to establish interactions that best support their child's development across domains, including language and communication (Kolomeyer, Renk, Cunningham, Lowell, & Khan, 2016). Hence, by attuning to parents in the assessment process, services can offer more holistic and meaningful interventions with the support of interdisciplinary team members. It is important to note that if parents are invited into a relationship-based assessment process that aims to connect with their child's needs in such a trusting and holistic way, the provision of timely intervention and appropriate supports needs to be prioritized if there is to be any value to such a comprehensive assessment process.

Just as the style of interaction between a parent and child holds great significance for a child's learning outcomes, the style of interaction between the practitioner and parent holds equal importance to the outcomes of therapy. One of the most important ways to positively influence the parent–child relationship is to place utmost importance on the practitioner–parent relationship. This concept of a parallel process is captured by the phrase "Do unto others as you would have others do unto others" (Pawl & St John, 2004, p.7). This process implies that feelings and interactions from one relationship can be carried forward into another relationship. With regard to early childhood development, the assumption is that the relationship between the practitioner and parent impacts on the relationship between the parent and child. One way to support infants and toddlers to thrive through effective and healthy parent–child relationships is to ensure that parents are also 'held' in nurturing, effective relationships with practitioners working with their family (Slade, 2007). By listening to parents, following their lead and recognizing their strengths, practitioners are offering a trusting relationship which becomes the foundation for pivotal change (Slade, 2007). Parents who feel heard, understood and respected by the practitioner can accordingly become more able to offer the same to their young child: listen to them, follow their lead and recognize their strengths – all essential components in supporting early communication.

A strengths-based model of care

Relationship-based care models within the field of infant mental health are innately strengths-based (Weatherston & Tableman, 2002). According to Powell and colleagues (1997), a strength-based philosophy is a critical belief, an all-encompassing attitude that informs a professional's interactions with clients. Ideally, an entire agency will adopt the approach and, through ongoing training, this attitude change will transform the way practitioners view their work, their colleagues and, of course, the people and communities they work with (Roebuck, Roebuck, & Roebuck, 2011). A core principle of infant mental health practice is that parents are the experts on their child. The practitioner's role is to remain open, curious and reflective in order to appreciate each parent's individual capacities and offer a tailored, supportive, therapeutic framework, possibly involving other disciplines, in order for each child to achieve their developmental potential across all domains, including language and communication (Weatherston, 2000). In the words of Pawl and St John (2004), the principle is "Don't just do something – stand there and pay attention" (p.7). In this light, the reflective practitioner may consider more tailored supports than, for example, a prescriptive or manualized parent–child communication programme. This is particularly relevant when other social or environmental factors may be getting in the way of a parent's capacity to enrich their child's language and communication through a nurturing parent–child relationship.

Delighting in parents' achievements and reinforcing what is going well within parent–child interactions are other key principles of Infant Mental Health practice (Weatherston, 2000). Highlighting strengths in each parent–child relationship is incredibly powerful. For example, commenting "I notice how you copy Joshua's sounds. This builds Joshua's confidence with language as he knows you are so interested in what he has to say" or "I see Joshua has learned that song because you take the time to sing it with him every day" communicates explicit appreciation of the individuality of each parent and child. Such strengths-based comments or feedback contribute well to a parent's involvement in the therapeutic process and can result in often allegedly 'hard-to-reach' families becoming enthusiastically engaged in parent–practitioner collaboration. Moreover, these 'hard-to-reach' families may indeed have little experience of trust and security in their lives. Therefore, these are the families that deserve an offering of a trusting and secure relationship the most.

Building adult capacity to support early communication

Supporting the early communication of infants, toddlers and preschoolers is best served through building the capacities of the important adults in a child's life including parents, extended family members and early education practitioners (Rafferty, 2014). Educating parents, right from the start, on the impact of nurturing interactions on their infant's brain development is absolutely critical to helping families focus on what is most important in developing their child's communication skills. Healthcare services provide ample information and support for parents around managing infants' diet, nutrition and physical development. However, there is, broadly speaking, very little focus on helping parents nurture their baby's social-emotional development. There is a need to develop a 'language' for parents and practitioners in which early social and emotional development is better understood and expressed. The cutting-edge knowledge now available to us through scientifically-grounded theory needs to be translated into accessible, effective and up-to-date services for parents and infants. Instead of only giving information and advice to parents, there is a need for active skill building through teaching, practice and coaching (National Scientific Council on the Developing Child, 2015). The field of Implementation Science informs us that the extent to which newly-learned skills are utilized substantially differs depending on whether coaching has been part of the training process or not (Joyce & Showers, 2002). Coaching involves teaching in context, giving feedback and providing emotional support (Spouse, 2001). Parents who are offered this kind of support in fostering their infant's language and communication skills are much more likely to show active use of these skills throughout everyday interactions (Kaiser & Hancock, 2003).

In order for services to infuse infant mental health theory into clinical or community practice, it is of utmost importance to build on the capacities of practitioners. Yet many practitioners who work with very young children and their families have not received training in infant mental health (Wechsler & Woodlock, 2006). For all professionals working with families, there is a need to access infant mental health training in order to better understand and support the parent–child relationship, which in turn promotes early social and emotional development, learning and wellbeing. In a quest for such professional growth, an infant mental health learning group in Chicago, called *Ounce*, was formed. The reported outcomes of this learning group included changes in the way staff related with one another, thought about families and placed importance on the new infant's experiences (Wechsler & Woodlock, 2006). Reflective supervision also plays an important role in professional development and building expertise in the practice of infant mental health (Watson & Neilson Gatti, 2012). Once again, it is the relationship that is central to the process of reflective supervision; all professional growth and capacity to reflect and learn takes place within a trusting supervisor-practitioner relationship (Parlakian, 2001).

The future of speech and language therapy in infant mental health

Translating attachment research to clinical interventions

Given the substantial longitudinal research highlighting the risks associated with insecure attachment (e.g., poorer mental and physical health and lower social competence), the need to intervene to reduce the risk of insecure attachment is clear. In the past 20 years, researchers and clinicians have developed numerous therapeutic programmes to prevent or reduce insecure attachment (Cassidy, Jones, & Shaver, 2013). Despite the fact that a handful of attachment interventions have shown initial success (e.g., Bujia-Couso, O'Rourke, & Cerezo, 2010; Cassidy, Woodhouse, Sherman, Stupica, & Lejuez, 2011), we have as yet only a collection of individual initiatives with little replication. More research is needed to identify the critical components of attachment and infant mental health interventions and to understand the process of implementation and replication. SLTs, with their expertise in human communication, are ideally placed to contribute to this clinical research.

Supporting secure attachment by embedding infant mental health constructs into speech and language therapy interventions

Parents of very young children whose attachment trajectory and social-emotional development are at risk more often than not never see a mental health practitioner (Shahmoon Shanok & Geller, 2009). However, with the frequent co-occurrence of early communication concerns in the first years of life, often SLTs are amongst the first professionals to work with these parents and young children and sometimes the only practitioners to do so in an ongoing process. Given how the internal workings of the parent–infant relationship directly impacts on a child's growing language and communication, as discussed throughout this chapter, best practice requires that SLTs integrate infant mental health constructs into their clinical practice in order to work with a certain 'mental health mindedness' and maximize the opportunity for clinical growth and change (Shahmoon-Shanok, Lamb-Parker, Halperin, Grant, Lapidus, & Seagle, 2005). Relationships have two inseparable sides – an *interactive* side, which involves the behavioural, observable patterns of interaction between participants, and also an *intersubjective* side, which involves internal intentions, feelings and meanings between participants (Fivaz-Depeursinge, Corboz-Warnery, & Keren, 2004). Traditionally, within speech and language therapy practice the interactive side of relationships takes the primary focus of attention. However, building capacity to also attune and attend to intersubjective states would enhance the SLT's appreciation of how relationship experiences, past and present, affect client change and growth (Shahmoon-Shanok & Geller, 2009). This broadening of theoretical paradigms within the field of speech and language therapy would support the practice of a relationship-based and reflective working model, supporting early attachment and social-emotional development as the essential foundation in building healthy language and communication skills. Costa (2006) highlighted that non-mental health professionals, like SLTs, can be trained in integrating specific mental health constructs into discipline specific work. Through the assimilation of such a transdisciplinary model, it is proposed that children's emotional security and communication development could be nurtured more effectively through such enhanced speech and language therapy practice.

Role of the SLT in the development and evaluation of infant mental health interventions

The development of attachment interventions often involves considerable resources, extensive training and supervision of staff, videotaping individual parent–infant interactions and providing individualized parental feedback (e.g., Bujia-Cousoet al., 2010; Klein Velderman, Bakermans-Kranenburg, Juffer, & van Ijzendoorn, 2006). Given the social and economical value of such preventative interventions, continued attempts to develop interventions that are widely and affordably implementable are important. Continued development of infant mental health interventions should include protocols that can be provided through existing service delivery mechanisms, like speech and language therapy services, with the provision of support for organizational and systems change. Given its expertise in parent–child interactions and communication, the field of speech and language therapy is well placed, with relevant training and support, to contribute to this clinical development. There is also a subsequent need for evaluation of parent–infant relationship interventions developed with the aim of supporting wider implementation amongst families whose children are at elevated risk for developing insecure attachments, compromised social-emotional development and poor development of language and communication. Intervention testing can be enormously expensive yet is crucial in order to justify replication of effective attachment interventions developed.

Another worthwhile aspect to evaluate further is how the infusion of infant mental health principles into pre-existing parent-child interaction programmes, delivered by SLTs, impacts on outcomes for parents and outcomes for children's communication and social-emotional development. Infant mental health practices and principles are highly compatible with community programmes that are already broadly in use, bringing the experience for parents and practitioners to a deeper level. Using comparison groups, it would be important to explore any post-programme differences in factors such as parents' experience of a service, parental engagement, parental sensitivity, incorporation of newly-learned skills, parental sense of efficacy and satisfaction and, ultimately, any differences in children's communication and social-emotional outcomes.

Conclusion

The first three years of life present an enormous opportunity to set a strong foundation for children's communication, learning and life-long mental health. During this critical period, 80-90% of the infant brain develops, growing from 50 trillion synapses at birth to 1000 trillion synapses (Schore, 1997). This brain development is highly vulnerable to environmental influences and research confirms that early relationships and parental caregiving play a critical role in the developing architecture of the brain (Shonkoff, Boyce, & McEwen, 2009). All areas of development, including language and communication, flourish in the context of a synchronous parent-child relationship, in which an infant's individual abilities are recognized, appreciated and nurtured. Trevarthen (2011) asserts that babies have an innate capacity to share states of mind and communicate with sympathetic others. With repeated, regular, positive interactions with their caregivers, infants' means of communication soon evolve from behaviours that require much decoding by their sensitive parents, such as crying or a subtle facial grimace to using elaborate verbal language to communicate their wants and needs. Sensitive and attuned parent-child interactions not only foster early language and communication, but also are central to the development of secure attachment and to the establishment of positive parent-infant relationships. Indeed, these interactions set a strong foundation for life-long positive mental health (Shonkoff et al., 2009).

The remarkable plasticity of the infant brain means the younger the child, the more vulnerable their brain is to the effects of their environment. Adverse experiences, involving deprivation, abuse or neglect, for example, can be particularly harmful to a child's developing brain, their learning and their mental health trajectory. Where there is a combination of risk factors such as maternal depression, parental substance dependence, homelessness or lack of social support, for example, the impact on a child's learning and mental health outcomes are greater (Sameroff, 2010). Taking a life-span approach to mental health necessitates early intervention from the prenatal period, birth and onwards. Through various settings, the field of infant mental health offers a critical role in providing preventative, strengths-based models of intervention, with a central focus on nurturing positive and protective parent–child relationships.

SLTs, with their specific expertise in early parent–child interactions, are well placed as key contributors to the development and implementation of early attachment-based interventions. Important aspects to the foundation of a secure parent–child relationship include parents' ability to attune to their infant's 'language' and respond sensitively to their baby's communicative behaviours, right from the earliest days and months. The discipline of speech and language therapy is key to promoting and supporting these protective parent–child interaction patterns. Prevention and early intervention are of utmost importance for infants who are at risk of developing an insecure attachment. For this reason, there is a need for universal infant screening programmes to assess and support early social and emotional development in the context of the parent–child relationship. Ideally, universal infant screening programmes could be multidisciplinary in nature, with speech and language therapy offering very relevant expertise. Moreover, for SLTs working within more traditional models with young children, incorporating insights from the field of infant mental health would contribute to an important paradigm shift in which language and communication development are more holistically nurtured through a relationship-based, reflective model of intervention.

Being mindful of infants and their parents within the individual context of their relationship ensures that important prerequisites for the development of language and communication are being attended to. Through the influence of infant mental health, all practitioners working with families – including SLTs – can be better equipped to bring about transformational changes to children's early learning, communication and mental health.

References

Beeghly, M. & Tronick E. (2011). Early resilience in the context of parent infant relationships: A social developmental perspective. *Current Problems in Pediatric and Adolescent Health Care, 41*(7), 197–201.

Brazelton, T.B. (2009). The Neonatal Behavioural Assessment Scale (NBAS). In J.K. Nugent, B. Petrauskas & T.B. Brazelton (Eds), *The Newborn as Person: Enabling Healthy Infant Development Worldwide* (pp.278–286). Hoboken, NJ: John Wiley & Sons.

Brockmeyer Cates, C., Dreyer, B.P., Berkule, S.B., White, L.J., Arevalo, J.A. & Mendelsohn, A.L. (2012). Infant communication and subsequent language development in children from low income families: The role of early cognitive stimulation. *Journal of Developmental and Behavioural Pediatrics, 33*(7), 577–585.

Bujia-Couso, P., O'Rourke, A., & Cerezo, M.A. (2010). Criteria based case review: The parent-child psychological support programme. *Irish Journal of Applied Social Studies, 10*(1), 6–19.

Cassidy, J., Jones, J.D., & Shaver, P.R. (2013). Contributions of attachment theory and research: A framework for future research, translation and policy. *Development and Psychopathology, 25*(402), 1415–1436.

Cassidy, J., Woodhouse S.S., Sherman, L.J., Stupica, B., & Lejuez, C.W. (2011). Enhancing infant attachment security: An examination of treatment efficacy and differential susceptibility. *Development and Psychopathology, 23*, 131–148.

Costa, G. (2006). Mental health principles, practices, strategies and dynamics pertinent to early intervention practitioners. In G.M. Foley & J.D. Hochman (Eds), *Mental Health in Early Intervention: Achieving Unity in Principles and Practices* (pp.113–138). Baltimore: Brookes.

Eliot, L. (2001). *Early Intelligence: How the Brain and Mind Develop in the First Five Years of Life*. London: Penguin Books.

Fivaz-Depeursinge, E., Corboz-Warnery, A., & Keren, M. (2004). The primary triangle: Treating infants in their families. In A.J. Sameroff, S.C. McDonough & K.L. Rosenblum (Eds), *Treating Parent-Infant Relationship Problems: Strategies for Intervention* (pp.123–151). New York: Guildford Press.

Fox, S.E., Levitt, P., & Nelson, C.A. (2010). How the timing and quality of early experiences influence the development of brain architecture. *Child Development, 81*(1), 6–22.

Fraiberg, S. (1980). *Clinical Studies in Infant Mental Health: The First Year of Life*. New York: Basic Books.

Fraiberg, S., Adelson, E., & Shapiro, V. (1975). Ghosts in the nursery: A psychoanalytic approach to the problems of impaired infant-mother relationships. *Child & Adolescent Psychiatry, 14*(3), 387–421.

Hawthorne, J. (2015). Influencing health policy in the antenatal and postnatal periods: The UK experience. *Zero to Three, 36*(1), 21–27.

Hong, Y.R. & Park, J.S. (2012). Impact of attachment, temperament and parenting on human development. *Korean Journal of Pediatrics, 55*(12), 449-454.

Johnson, J. & Newport, E. (1989). Critical period effects in second language learning: The influence of maturation state on the acquisition of English as a second language. *Cognitive Psychology, 21*(1), 60-99.

Joyce, B. & Showers, B. (2002). *Designing Training and Peer Coaching: Our Needs for Learning*. Virginia, VA: ASCD.

Kaiser, A.P. & Hancock, T.B. (2003). Teaching parents new skills to support their young children's development. *Infants & Young Children, 16*(1), 9-21.

Klein Velderman, M., Bakermans-Kranenburg, M.J., Juffer, F., & van Ijzendoorn M.H. (2006). Effects of attachment-based interventions on maternal sensitivity and infant attachment: Differential susceptibility of highly reactive infants. *Journal of Family Psychology, 20*(2), 266–274.

Kolomeyer, E., Renk, K., Cunningham, A., Lowell, A., & Khan, M. (2016). Mothers' adverse childhood experiences and negative parenting behaviours – Connecting mothers' difficult pasts to present parenting behaviour via reflective functioning. *Zero to Three, 37*(1), 5-12.

Kuhl, P.K. (2009). Early language acquisition: Neural substrates and theoretical models. In M.S. Gazzaniga (Ed.), *The Cognitive Neurosciences*, 4th ed. (pp.837-854). Cambridge, MA: MIT Press.

Kuhl, P.K. (2010). Brain mechanisms in early language acquisition. *Neuron, 67*(5), 713-727.

Kuhl, P.K. & Rivera-Gaxiola, M. (2008). Neural substrates of language acquisition. *The Annual Review of Neuroscience, 31*, 511–534.

Lally, J.R. & Mangione, P. (2017). Caring relationships: The heart of early brain development. *Young Children, 72*(2), 17-24.

Leclere, C., Viaux, S., Avril, M., Archard, C., Chetouani, M., Missonier, S., & Cohen, D. (2014). Why synchrony matters during mother-child interactions: A systematic review. *PLoS One, 9*(12), 1–34.

Lothian, J.A. (1999). Maternal-infant attachment, naturally. *The Journal of Perinatal Education, 8*(4), viii-xi.

Mares, S. & Woodgate, S. (2017). The clinical assessment of infants, preschoolers and their families. In J.M. Rey (Ed.), *IACAPAP e-Textbook of Child and Adolescent Mental Health*. Geneva: International Association for Child and Adolescent Psychiatry and Allied Professions.

Murgatroyd, C. & Spengler, D. (2011). Epigenetics of early child development. *Frontiers in Psychiatry, 2*(16), 1-15.

National Scientific Council on the Developing Child (2004). Young children develop in an environment of relationships. Working Paper No. 1. www.developingchild.harvard.edu

National Scientific Council on the Developing Child (2007). The science of early childhood development – Closing the gap between what we know and what we do. www.developingchild.harvard.edu

National Scientific Council on the Developing Child (2010). Early experiences can alter gene expression and affect long-term development: Working Paper No.10. www.developingchild.harvard.edu

National Scientific Council on the Developing Child (2015). Supportive relationships and active skill-building strengthen the foundations of resilience: Working Paper 13. www.developingchild.harvard.edu

Neuman, S.B., Copple, C., & Bredekamp, S. (2000). *Learning to Read and Write: Developmentally Appropriate Practices for Young Children*. Washington DC: National Association for the Education of Young Children.

Nicolson, S. (2015). Let's meet your baby as a person: From research to preventative perinatal practice and back again, with the newborn behavioural observations. *Zero to Three, 36*(1), 28-39.

Nugent, K.J. (2011). *Your Baby is Speaking to You: A Visual Guide to the Amazing Behaviors of Your Newborn and Growing Baby*. Boston: Houghton Mifflin Harcourt Publishing Company.

Nugent, K.J. (2015). The newborn behavioural observation (NBO) system as a form of intervention and support for new parents. *Zero to Three, 36*(1), 2-10.

Parlakian, R. (2001). *Look, Listen and Learn: Reflective Supervision and Relationship-Based Work*. Washington, DC: Zero to Three.

Pawl, J.H. & St John, M. (2004). *How You Are is as Important as What You Do...In Making a Positive Difference for Infants, Toddlers and Their Families*. Washington, DC: Zero to Three.

Powell, D.S., Batsche, C.J., Fox, L., & Dunlap, G. (1997). A strength-based approach in support of multi-risk families: Principles and issues. *Topics in Early Childhood Special Education, 17*(1), 1-26.

Rafferty, M. (2014). *A Brief Review of Approaches to Oral Language Development to Inform the Area Based Childhood Programme*. Dublin: Centre for Effective Services.

Roebuck, B., Roebuck, M., & Roebuck, J. (2011). *From Strength to Strength: A Manual to Inspire and Guide Strength-based Interventions with Young People*. Cornwall: Youth Now Intervention Services.

Roseman, M. (2008). Early language development and adult/child relationships. In M. Renck Jalongo (Ed.), *Enduring Bonds: The Significance of Interpersonal Relationships in Young Children* (pp.39-54). Boston, MA: Springer.

Sameroff, A. (2010). A unified theory of development: A dialectic integration of nature and nurture. *Child Development, 81*(1), 6-22.

Schore, A.N. (1997). *Rethinking the Brain: New Insights into Early Development*. New York: Families and Work Institute.

Shahmoon-Shanok, R. & Geller, E. (2009). Embracing complexity across disciplines: Reflective supervision and postdegree training integrate mental health concepts with speech-language therapy and graduate education. *Infant Mental Health, 30*(6), 591-620.

Shahmoon-Shanok, R., Lamb-Parker, F., Halperin, E., Grant, M., Lapidus, C., & Seagle, C. (2005). The Relationships for Growth Project: A transformational collaboration between head start, mental health and university systems. In K.M. Finello (Ed.), *Handbook of Training and Practice in Infant and Preschool Mental Health* (pp.402-424). San Francisco, CA: Jossey-Bass.

Shonkoff, J.P., Boyce, W.T., & McEwen, B.S. (2009). Neuroscience, molecular biology and the childhood roots of health disparities: Building a new framework for health promotion and disease prevention. *Journal of the American Medical Association, 301*(21), 2252–2259.

Siegel, D.J. (2001). Toward an interpersonal neurobiology of the developing mind: Attachment relationships, "mindsight", and neural integration. *Infant Mental Health, 22*(1-2), 67-94.

Siegel, D.J. & Bryson, T.P. (2012). *The Whole-Brain Child: 12 Revolutionary Strategies to Nurture Your Child's Developing Mind*. Brunswick, Victoria: Scribe Publications.

Slade, A. (2007). Reflective parenting programs: Theory and development. *Psychoanalytic Inquiry, 26*(4), 640–657.

Slade, A., Cohen, L.J., Sadler, L.S., & Miller, M. (2009). The psychology and psychopathology of pregnancy: Reorganization and transformation. In C. Zeanah (Ed.), *Handbook for Infant Mental Health*, 3rd ed. (pp.22–39). New York: Guilford Press.

Spouse, J. (2001). Bridging theory and practice in the supervisory relationship: A sociocultural perspective. *Journal of Advanced Nursing, 33*(4), 512–522.

Sullivan, R., Perry, R., Sloan, A., Kleinhaus, K., & Burtchen N. (2011). Infant bonding and attachment to the caregiver: Insights from basic and clinical science. *Clinics in Perinatology, 38*(4), 643–655.

Swain, J.E., Lorberbaum, J.P., Kose, S., & Strathearn, L. (2007). Brain basis of early parent–infant interactions: Psychology, physiology, and *in vivo* functional neuroimaging studies. *Journal of Child Psychology and Psychiatry, and Allied Disciplines, 48*(0), 262–287.

Tierney, A.L. & Nelson, C.A. (2009). Brain development and the role of experience in the early years. *Zero to Three, 30*(2), 9-13.

Trevarthen, C. (2011). What is it like to be a person who knows nothing? Defining the active intersubjective mind of a newborn human being. *Infant and Child Development, 20*(1), 119–135.

Wachs, T.D., Georgieff, M., Cusick, S., & McEwen, B. (2014). Issues in the timing of integrated early interventions: Contributions from nutrition, neuroscience and psychological research. *Annals of the New York Academy of Sciences, 1308*, 89–106.

Watson, C. & Neilson Gatti, S. (2012). Professional development through reflective consultation in early intervention. *Infants and Young Children, 25*(2), 109-121.

Weatherston, D. (2000). The infant mental health specialist. *Zero to Three, 21*(2), 3-10.

Weatherston, D. & Tableman, B. (2002). *Infant Mental Health Services: Supporting Competencies / Reducing Risks*, 2nd ed. Southgate, MI: Michigan Association of Infant Mental Health.

Wechsler, N.D. & Woodlock, K.K. (2006). The infant mental health learning group: Infusing infant mental health practices into community–based programs. *Zero to Three, 26*(3), 14-19.

Winnicott, D.W. (1953). Transitional objects and transitional phenomena – A study of the first not-me possession. *The International Journal of Psychoanalysis, 34,* 89-97.

Woodward, A.L. & Hoyne, K. (1999). Infants' learning about words and sounds in relation to objects. *Child Development, 70,* 65–72.

World Health Organisation (2004). The importance of caregiver-child interactions for the survival and healthy development of young children: A review. Geneva: World Health Organisation.

2 Children's communication and their mental health

Judy Clegg

Introduction

When children start school between the age of 4 and 5 years, they are expected to be 'school ready'. The term 'school ready' is currently much used by policymakers as a marker for children having achieved adequate development and acquisition of skills to be able to engage in their learning in the school context. Being 'school ready' not only involves being competent communicators ready to use their speech, language and communication skills to learn but also having adequate social-emotional competence to manage their emotions to behave in a way considered acceptable to the school context. Both areas of competency are considered essential for effective engagement and learning in the classroom and later psycho-social adjustment and mental health. Yet we know very little about how development in speech, language and communication interacts with children's social-emotional development, and their subsequent overall mental health.

It can be difficult to accept that children as young as 5 years of age can be in receipt of Child and Adolescent Mental Health Services (CAMHS) as this means they are experiencing severe and complex social, emotional and behavioural difficulties impacting on not just their own development and adjustment but the lives of those around them. There is some acknowledgement now that children's speech, language and communication abilities have a role to play in their mental health (Clegg, Law, Rush, Peters, & Roulstone, 2015; Law, Rush, Schoon, & Parsons, 2009; Petersen et al., 2013; Yew & O'Kearney, 2013) but how this proposed association operates within known biological, psychological and social risk factors such as gender, parenting and socio-cultural contexts is not well understood. Such knowledge has the potential to further understand the needs of these children and ultimately to provide more effective provision.

From reading this chapter, the reader will learn more about how the association between children's communication development and their mental health may operate; how communication profiles in children with mental health difficulties have been documented; how a dynamic perspective about the interaction within children's development over time can inform our understanding of the association between children's communication and their mental health, and the value of identifying these children's communicative competence to further understand and meet their needs, illustrated using a case example.

Children's communication and socio-emotional competence

It is well documented that the pattern and rate at which children develop their speech, language and communication abilities vary (Bates, Dale, & Thai, 1995; Buckley, 2003), with many accessible publications reporting on the milestones to be achieved from birth and their approximate ages (e.g., ICAN, The Children's Communication Charity, www.ican.org.uk and The Communications Trust, www.thecommunicationtrust.org.uk). In terms of speech, language and communication, children are considered 'school ready' when they have speech that is clear and easy to understand, are able to speak in sentences linking these sentences into narratives, use their language to communicate for a range of reasons such as reasoning, negotiating, empathizing and predicting, are confident and appropriate in their interactions and conversations with other children and adults and know some letter names and the sounds that go with these.

Social-emotional competence is a complex psychological construct. Denham and colleagues (2006, 2009) in the USA offer an accessible approach for professionals to understand how this is defined and how it develops in relation to children's school readiness. Children who are able to positively engage with those around them and are able to regulate or manage their emotions and how they express these emotions are those who are considered to be more school ready and so able to learn and manage the demands of the classroom. Denham goes further to explain five key dimensions of social-emotional development that underpin social-emotional competence in children's early development. In summary, these are: *social competence* where the child is able to engage in social interactions appropriate to the context;

attachment where the child has established a secure attachment or connection with a primary caregiver usually from birth, which then enables the child to develop secure attachment and relationships with key people in their lives; *emotional competence* where the child is aware of not only their emotions but those of others and is able to manage or regulate how they express or show these emotions to others; *self-perceived competence* where the child is aware of their own strengths and weaknesses in relation to their peers and are then able to use this awareness to drive their own motivations to engage and achieve; and finally *temperament* which refers to the child's intrinsic personality in how he or she reacts to experiences and then how the child manages these. Disruptions to these dimensions of development can put the child at greater risk of social, emotional and behavioural difficulties.

This brief overview of both the communication and social-emotional skills needed to be school ready highlights the interaction between these two domains. Two important questions can be posed here: to what extent are children's developing communication skills needed for social-emotional competence, and to what extent is social–emotional competence necessary for children to be cõmpetent communicators? There is very limited theoretical evidence as to the interaction involved but increasing anecdotal evidence supports how closely linked these areas of competency are. In *social competence,* children need to be competent communicators with adequate and appropriate social communication skills or pragmatic language skills in order to engage appropriately in social interaction. The process of *attachment* (Bowlby, 1969) necessitates the infant to have the prerequisite intent to be communicative and to encourage their caregivers to communicate with them. The process of attachment also requires caregivers who are able to communicate and who have the capacity – both communicative and emotional – to communicate with their infant. To have *emotional competence,* the child needs to learn the vocabulary of emotions and how this vocabulary maps onto their emotions in order to be able to understand and express these to others. To develop *self-perceived competence,* children need to be effective communicators who can then have strengths in effective interactions, friendships and relationships. Children all have different *temperaments* often expressed through being shy, quiet or more talkative and communicatively confident. To answer the questions posed above, it is proposed that these interactions are dynamic involving within-child factors and factors external to the child (Cohen, 2001). It is probably the interaction between all these factors that is most important in understanding the association between communication competence, social-emotional competence and effective psycho-social adjustment and subsequent mental health.

A culture of evidence-based practice necessitates knowledge of the theories underpinning the association between children's development in their communication and their social emotional competence and mental health. This knowledge then determines how to identify communication difficulties and inform intervention to facilitate communication with a potential impact on the child's mental health, thus making a valuable contribution to the overall multidisciplinary management of children and young people in receipt of mental health services.

A note on terminology

Much terminology is used by the speech and language therapy profession describing children who have some sort of difficulty in their speech, language and communication development. Some children have difficulties understanding spoken language, others in their talking, and for some children difficulties in both their understanding and their talking. Children can have difficulties in their speech where they find it difficult to say the speech sounds in words clearly; in their language development where they may not have enough vocabulary to say what they want to or to put words together in a meaningful way; and in their communication development where they may not know how to communicate effectively following conventions of social interaction, which as we know vary according to social contexts and cultures. Terminology will refer to children having delays in some or all of these areas where these children are expected to 'catch up' with typical development at some point. Other children may be described as having a specific or primary impairment, usually indicating more pervasive and chronic longer-term difficulties with less chance of resolution. Speech, language and communication difficulties are often co-morbid with other developmental disorders (Mueller & Tomblin, 2012).

There is rightly much debate about the best terminology to use to understand the nature and trajectories of these children's communication difficulties and the impact of these on the child's life. This has most recently been demonstrated in the discussion of the terminology to use to refer to children with primary or specific impairments in language development and ability, traditionally referred to as Specific Language Impairment (SLI) (Bishop, 2014; Bishop et al., 2016). A new term of 'Developmental Language Disorder' is now proposed (Bishop et al., 2017). There is no doubt that terminology is important and indeed the field of Child Psychiatry has its own complex system of terminology and diagnostic classification, most recently illustrated by the debates around and the subsequent publication of the revised *Diagnostic and Statistical Manual of Mental Disorders*, 5th edition (DSM-5) (American Psychiatric Association, 2013) (see Ozonoff, 2012 and Norbury, 2014 for recent relevant discussion around children's social communication difficulties). However, the translation of this terminology to understanding children with mental health difficulties is complex, and for the purpose of this chapter the emphasis will be on understanding these children's communication development and abilities, the potential impact of communication difficulties on social-emotional competence and subsequent mental health, and how professionals working with children with mental health difficulties can understand the role of children's communication in their everyday professional practice.

To clarify, the term *mental health* will be used as a general term to refer to children's social, emotional and behavioural functioning and the term *communication* to cover children's development and abilities in speech, language and communication.

A historical perspective

Research in this field dates back over 40 years when eminent child psychiatrists such as Professor Sir Michael Rutter, Professor Dennis Cantwell and Professor Lorian Baker started to investigate the psycho-social development of children with pervasive communication difficulties such as developmental receptive language disorders, finding that these children were at an increased risk of child mental health difficulties (Cantwell & Baker, 1977, 1987; Howlin & Rutter, 1987). Over time, these findings were replicated in other studies looking at the longer-term psychosocial outcomes of children with diagnoses such as Specific Language Impairment (SLI) (Beitchman et al., 2001; Botting, Durkin, Toseeb, Pickles, & Conti-Ramsden, 2016; Brownlie et al., 2004; Clegg, Hollis, Mawhood, & Rutter, 2005; Clegg, Ansorge, Stackhouse, & Donlan, 2012; Conti-Ramsden & Botting, 2008; Snowling, Bishop, Stothard, Chipchase, & Kaplan, 2006). Research also advanced to investigate previously 'undetected' communication difficulties in children with primary diagnoses of child mental health difficulties (Cohen, Davine, Horodezky, & Lipsett, 1993; Cohen, Menna, Vallance, Barwick, Im, & Horodezky, 1998a; Cohen, Barwick, Horodezky, Vallance, & Im, 1998b; Giddan, Milling, & Campbell, 1996; Hollo, Wehby, & Oliver, 2014; Prizant, Audet, Burke, Hummel, Maher, & Theadore, 1990; Van

Dahl, Verhoven, & van Balkom, 2007). Mechanisms were proposed to explain these findings including a shared neurodevelopmental delay explaining both the communication difficulty and the child mental health difficulty, with common antecedents such as low intelligence and environmental deprivation and the psycho-social rejections and academic failure experienced by children with communication difficulties leading to difficulties in emotional reactivity and regulation (Beitchman, 1985; Howlin & Rutter, 1987). The researchers varied in their methodologies from cohorts of children with specific communication difficulties studied longitudinally to cross-sectional studies, from cohorts of all children in a child psychiatry service (Cohen et al., 1993; 1998a,b) to smaller cohort studies (Petersen et al., 2013), and case studies of children with specific mental health difficulties (Clegg & Hartshorne, 2004; Cross, Blake, Tunbridge, & Gill, 2001; Heneker, 2005). Much has been reported and discussed in relation to this research literature (see Benner, 2002 and Hollo et al., 2014 for comprehensive reviews).

Children and young people who have been excluded from mainstream school or at risk of exclusion due to their behaviour are less well understood. Studies indicate higher-than-expected rates of communication difficulties in pupils at risk of school exclusion/excluded from school (Clegg, Stackhouse, Finch, Murphy, & Nicholls, 2009; Ripley & Yuill, 2005), yet communicative competence had not previously been considered a factor in the young people's behaviour and engagement with their education. Research into the communication profiles of young offenders has also offered some insights into the role of communication abilities in the trajectories of social-emotional development and resulting behaviour in young people (see Chapter 10 in this book and Bryan, Freer, & Furlong, 2007; Bryan, Garvani, Gregory, & Kilner 2015; Snow & Powell, 2011).

Communication profiles of children and young people with mental health difficulties

Identifying communication profiles for specific mental health difficulties remains challenging. Many children have more than one diagnosis of mental health difficulty; a child with a mental health difficulty (such as a conduct disorder or attachment disorder) may also have a co-occurring language difficulty not previously identified and so any profile detected is not necessarily attributable to the identified mental health difficulty. The varied language assessments used in research differ across studies, so establishing sensitivity and specificity across these assessments and studies is problematic (Redmond, Thompson, & Goldstein, 2011). Profiling also involves the child engaging in detailed assessment, which children with mental health difficulties are often reluctant to engage in, requiring considerable attention and concentration (Clegg et al., 2015; Redmond et al., 2011).

Research has attempted to identify specific profiles of communication abilities in a range of children's mental health difficulties such as Attention Deficit Hyperactivity Disorder (ADHD), Conduct Disorder, Selective Mutism and others (Benner, 2002 and Hollo et al., 2014 offer reviews of previous research). In ADHD, many and wide-ranging speech, language and communication difficulties have been reported. Walsh and colleagues (2014) failed to detect a general ADHD-specific language profile in a cohort of 40 children between 9 and 12 years of age attending a CAMHS, although there were some trends across the group as a whole. Gilmour et al. (2004) found evidence to support their hypothesis that children with conduct disorder have social and communicative skills deficits, which may underlie or contribute to the anti-social and disruptive behaviour demonstrated. In Selective Mutism, generally defined as the persistent refusal to talk in certain situations (e.g., school) despite being able to talk in others (e.g., usually home), preliminary research has suggested that some of these children have a range of previously-existing speech and language difficulties and history of autism spectrum disorders that may contribute to the children's reluctance to talk (Baltaxe, 1994; Sharkey & McNicholas, 2014; Steinhausen & Juzi, 1996).

Much less is known about children who are identified with attachment disorders even though this is a group of children who receive much provision from CAMHS, and communication between the caregiver and the child is intrinsic to the process of attachment. As discussed in Chapter 1 of this volume, *attachment* is the term used to refer to the process by which a caregiver/parent establishes a relationship with their child which makes the child feel safe, secure and protected (Benoit, 2004; Bowlby, 1969). Secure attachment is considered the foundation of a child's development, specifically their psychosocial adjustment over their lifetime. Disruptions to the attachment process are considered to result from *seriously inadequate caregiving environments* (Chase Stovel & Dozier, 2008), a broad term used to describe significant physical and emotional neglect, abuse, being removed from the biological home to experience many foster care placements, and growing up away from a family unit in institutions. Where disruptions in attachment are experienced, this is typically described as insecure attachment with three sub-categories: insecure-avoidant, insecure-resistant and insecure-disorganized. Insecure attachment can lead to attachment disorders identified by behaviours that are grouped into two clinical patterns (Zeanah & Gleason, 2015). The first is Reactive Attachment Disorder (RAD) and the second Disinhibited Social Engagement Disorder (DSED) (Zeanah & Gleason, 2015). In brief, children identified with RAD are those who are considered emotionally withdrawn and inhibited, who seek little comfort from others and/or little response when comfort is given and do not seek to engage in interactive activity with others. Children with DSED have socially indiscriminate behaviour where they are overly familiar with unfamiliar others including strangers (Zeanah & Gleason, 2015). Common examples of behaviours across RAD and DSED include: difficulties in attention and concentration; wanting to be in control and therefore behaving in an oppositional, defiant and aggressive manner; and difficulty in showing affection to others including being unable to show remorse.

Children with attachment disorders have been identified with expressive language and social communication difficulties (Sadiq, Slator, Law, Skuse, Gillberg, & Minnis, 2012). Differentiating the socially-indiscriminate behaviours constituting attachment disorders from the social communication difficulties found in autism spectrum disorders (ASD) has directed current research. Sadiq et al. (2012) compared children between 5 to 8 years with RAD to children with autism spectrum disorders to find the children with RAD had similarly severe difficulties in their use of social context, establishing social rapport and relationships. The study employed *The Children's Communication Checklist* (CCC) (Bishop, 1998, 2003), a parent and/or teacher report measure to assess social communication and pragmatic language skills in these children, rather than any direct assessment. The nature of the social communication difficulties in RAD remains unknown and it is not clear if these are linked directly to the child's early attachment experiences, the child's early language and communication development, part of wider developmental difficulties or some combination of all of these factors.

As attachment disorders are a consequence of seriously inadequate caregiving environments, we need to know more about what factors in these environments are involved. Caregiving quality and positive caregiving with an emphasis on the mother's capacity to parent is often highlighted. Here, various aspects of the mother's capacity to parent are identified such as maternal substance abuse, maternal mental health and limited social support. The impact of maternal depression is known to be a significant risk factor for impoverished attachment in the first few years of a child's life (Paulson, Keefe, & Leiferman,

2009). Maternal depression significantly reduces the mother's capacity to care for her child, to stimulate her child's general development and to form a robust attachment. Very little is known about if and how maternal depression specifically affects a young child's language development and the role of the attachment process in this. One proposal is that maternal depression impacts negatively on the attachment process which then leads to a reduction in the amount of shared time a mother will interact with her child and, ultimately, resulting in fewer opportunities for a child to develop their language skills (Paulson et al., 2009). Pan et al. (2005) found maternal depression had a negative impact on a child's rate of vocabulary growth between the ages of 1 and 3 years of age in children of low-income families. On the other hand, Paulson et al. (2009) found an association between both maternal and paternal depression and the amount of parent-to-child reading that took place, but only the father's depression impacted on child language development at 24 months of age. Some of the literature around child neglect and child language has some relevance here (Sylvestre & Merette, 2010). The few studies indicate that severe parental neglect has more of an impact on children's language development than physical abuse (Allen & Oliver, 1982; Culp et al., 1991; Eigsti & Cicchetti, 2004). Explanations propose that children who are neglected are more likely to stay in the home where language stimulation is poor, whereas children who are physically abused are usually removed from the parental home into a more verbally stimulating environment (Culp et al., 1991).

Whilst establishing specific communication profiles should not be ruled out, another way forward is to look at how children with mental health difficulties who have communication difficulties respond to speech and language therapy intervention. The first published study of a randomized controlled trial (RCT) for children with Selective Mutism aged 3 to 9 years showed that intervention incorporating defocused communication (i.e., enabling the child to feel more comfortable in a hierarchy of verbal and nonverbal communicative situations), along with behavioural intervention was effective when delivered by child and adolescent mental health (CAMH) practitioners (Oerbeck, Stein, Wentzel-Larsen, T., Langsrud, O., & Kristensen 2014; Oerbeck, Stein, Pripp, & Kristensen, 2015). CAMH practitioners were trained to deliver the psychosocial intervention consisting of defocused communication along with behavioural intervention. The defocused communication was based on the principles of intervention advocated by Speech and Language Therapists Maggie Johnson and Alison Wintgens (2007; 2016). The intervention lasted for three months (21 sessions) and was delivered in the children's homes and or schools/preschools with parents/carers and school staff also participating. The primary outcome measure was a teacher-reported questionnaire rating the child's frequency of talking. A significant increase in frequency of talking was found in the intervention group compared to the control group. The home- and school-based intervention was effective and proved to be more effective for the younger children, emphasizing the need for early detection and intervention. In a much smaller study, Clegg et al. (2014) evaluated the effectiveness of a school curriculum vocabulary intervention for children with special, emotional and behavioural difficulties (SEBD) with previously unidentified communication difficulties who had been excluded from school. The children were able to learn new vocabulary but the pace of learning was much slower than expected. The children used the expected semantic strategies (learning the meanings of the words) but were less able to employ phonological strategies (learning the first sound and syllable structure of the words) as other children do to help them with new word learning. These preliminary findings indicate that these children need intensive speech and language intervention over a considerable period of time but respond as other children do to intervention.

In summary, research supports an association between children's communication development, their social-emotional competence and their mental health. There is much to learn, though, about the nature of this association and how it operates over time, in not only the clinical populations discussed but also for the wider population as well.

A dynamic perspective

From the above discussion, the complexity of the association between communication and social/behavioural factors is clear, highlighting how children's development is multifactorial and interdependent. Therefore, a more dynamic approach is adopted whereby it is the interaction within development that needs to be more or better understood. A bio-psychosocial or bio-ecological framework (Bronfenbrenner & Morris, 2006; Dodge & Petit, 2003) is informative here in identifying the role of *within child*, *interpersonal* and *environmental* factors in the association with an emphasis on the dynamic nature of how these factors interact at multiple levels through a child's development.

Within child factors are usually biological in that they are intrinsic to the child, such as gender. Other relevant biological factors include family history and health at birth. *Interpersonal* factors generally refer to the dynamic relationships between the child and the people in their world, often with an emphasis on parents/caregivers and usually the mothers, such as maternal education, maternal stress and parenting (including attachment). *Environmental* factors often identify level of socio-economic status as key but should also include the socio-cultural environment of the child and the different expectations of children that arise across varying socio-cultural contexts. Inherent issues with definition and measurement are highlighted within this theoretical framework: for example, the potential over identification/reporting of developmental difficulties in boys than girls, if and how bilingualism and multilingualism are involved, and how parenting and material wealth are not mutually exclusive.

Clinical populations of children and young people with primary diagnoses of either communication difficulty or mental health difficulty have historically been the focus of the research. More recently, employing a bio-psychosocial framework to understand if and how the association operates (in general population cohorts rather than clinical populations) have moved understanding forward. Longitudinal birth cohort studies are very large cohorts representative of the general population. These include the Millennium Cohort of approximately 19,000 infants born in one week in the millennium year (Millennium Cohort Study, www.cls.ioe.ac.uk), the Avon Longitudinal Study of Parents and Children (ALSPAC) cohort of approximately 14,000 infants born between 1991 and 1992 in the Bristol area of England (www.bristol.ac.uk/ alspac), and the 1970 British Cohort Study of 17,000 infants born in one week in 1970 (British Cohort 1970, www.cls.ioe.ac.uk). These studies collect a wealth of data about children's development across many domains and then enable detailed study of the developmental trajectory of children over time into adult life. The advantages of these cohorts for studying the association between children's communication and their mental health is that by studying general populations rather than clinical populations, there is not an over-representation of the clinical difficulties which are the focus of the study. Studying clinical populations brings an array of potential methodological difficulties such as whether all the diagnostic labels assigned to a child use consistent criteria and how any variation here is accounted for, (e.g., how representative the clinical population is in terms of demographic factors such as level of socio-economic status, family structure and other factors). General population studies are larger and therefore much more representative of all children, and if an association is found in a general population cohort as well as a clinical population then this is more evidence to support the association. An important advantage is that the within-child, interpersonal and environmental factors, and the interaction between these over time, can be studied and so moves research and understanding forward.

The issue of causality versus association is central here. Many of the clinical studies reported are only really establishing association at that point in time in the children's lives. In these cross-sectional studies, no temporal component is accounted for so the children are studied at one point in time and an association found *only* at that time. Longitudinal birth cohort studies are able to consider the extent to which children's language and communication ability is involved in the association, specifically as a potential predictor or contributor in the development of later mental health difficulties (e.g., looking at children's language ability at 2 years and then statistically evaluating whether it predicts or contributes to mental health difficulties in later childhood and adolescence more than other developmental factors, such as intelligence). It is the approach of looking at language ability as a *predictor of* or *contributor to* rather than being *associated with* mental health that is most important here. Complex statistical analyses such as regression modelling are typically used in these studies where mental health or behavioural functioning is a dependent or outcome variable and earlier language ability is one of several independent or predictor variables. These analyses involve looking at if and how the dependent variable changes according to the independent or predictor variables. It is then possible to see if and how early language ability predicts later behavioural functioning more or less than other developmental factors such as gender, intelligence and early social risk or disadvantage. This is still not necessarily about children's language and communication ability as a cause of mental health difficulties but understanding more about *if and how* early language and communication development is involved in children's mental health rather than just being associated at one time point.

In the Millennium Cohort Study, the longitudinal associations between children's vocabulary development, gender and emotional and behavioural functioning were explored (Hartas, 2011). Moderate rather than strong associations were found between vocabulary development at 3 years of age and problem behaviour two years later, at 5 years of age. A strong predictor of teacher-reported behaviour difficulties at 5 years was early literacy development. Rescorla, Ross and McClure (2007) measured parent-reported expressive vocabulary development and behaviour in children aged 18 months to 3 years who were attending child development clinics in the USA. Once neurodevelopmental delay and pervasive developmental disorders were excluded from the analyses, no associations were found between language development and behaviour indicating that the association identified earlier in the analyses only held due to the presence of other developmental disorders.

No association between early vocabulary development and later emotional and behavioural functioning were identified in the Western Australia Pregnancy cohort (a sample of 1623 children) (Whitehouse et al., 2011). Caregivers completed a parent-report measure of expressive vocabulary called the Language Development Survey (LDS) (Rescorla, 1989) when the children were 2 years old and the Child Behaviour Checklist (CBCL) (Achenbach, 1991), a parent-report measure of child behaviour. Children with a score on the LDS at or below the 15th percentile for their age and gender were categorized with an expressive vocabulary delay and formed the late talker's subgroup. The CBCL was then repeated at ages 5, 8, 10, 14 and 17 years. At 2 years of age, the late talkers were more likely to have clinically-significant behaviour difficulties when compared to a typical language group (i.e., children with no expressive vocabulary delay from the same birth cohort). Yet at all the later follow-up points (including at 5 years of age), there was no difference between the late talkers and the typical language group on the CBCL suggesting that any behavioural difficulties disappeared over time. In conclusion, the study stated that early expressive vocabulary delay is not a specific risk factor for later emotional and behavioural difficulties in childhood and through adolescence.

Clegg et al. (2015) used the children in the focus sample from the ALSPAC cohort to look at the role and contribution language comprehension and production ability at 2 years and at 4 years of age make to emotional and behavioural functioning at 5 years of age. In contrast to the previous studies, the language assessments included direct child assessment rather than relying only on parent report data. The statistical analyses found that early language ability at 2 years, specifically expressive vocabulary and later receptive language at 4 years, both made a moderate but important contribution to emotional and behavioural functioning at 5 years, over and above that predicted by biological and social risk. The study concluded that children's language development does have a predictive role in children's behavioural functioning. However, it is one of many developmental factors involved in the association between children's communication and later mental health.

Role of pragmatic language ability

Children's structural language ability has been the focus of these studies, therefore specifically investigating vocabulary and grammatical production and understanding. The pragmatics of language has become a more recent focus and looking at the role of pragmatic language as a component of children's communication ability in children's mental health (as discussed earlier in the communication profiling section). Pragmatic language is defined as a group of behaviours that are concerned with how language is used to convey meanings and refers to a range of communication skills including being able to appropriately initiate conversation, take turns in a conversation and share a relevant topic of conversation (see Adams, 2002 for a comprehensive review). Such communicative behaviours necessitate a higher level of understanding of what constitutes what is 'appropriate' according to the immediate context of the interaction, as well as being able to understand and respond to intended meaning conveyed by a conversational partner. Rather than looking at pragmatic language as a predictor, Law et al. (2015) analyzed general population data from the ALSPAC cohort to determine if pragmatic language operates as a mediator between children's social disadvantage and their behaviour. The theoretical rationale here acknowledges the robust research confirming that social disadvantage and behaviour are associated, that is, children who experience significant social disadvantage are more likely to develop behavioural difficulties later on in childhood (Piotrowska, Stride, Croft, & Rowe, 2015). This is a complex relationship and the way in which social disadvantage might predict behavioural difficulties is not entirely understood (Davis, Sawyer, Lo, & Wake, 2010), as already discussed.

Law et al. (2015) analyzed the trajectories of 2915 children from the ALSPAC cohort, using data pertaining to their level of social disadvantage at birth, a teacher-rated strengths and difficulties questionnaire as a measure of children's behaviour at 13 years, and a teacher report measure of the children's pragmatic language using the Children's Communication Checklist (CCC) (Bishop, 2003) at 9 years. Here, the CCC is the mediator with early social disadvantage as an independent variable and the children's behaviour (the SDQ) as the outcome variable. The CCC was used here to determine – or further understand – the nature of the relationship between social disadvantage at birth and behaviour at 13 years. The hypothesis was that pragmatic language at 9 years would mediate between social disadvantage and later behaviour at 13 years and potentially heighten the relationship. The study accounted for gender, age, early developmental health and verbal and nonverbal intelligence. The study confirmed that pragmatic language does mediate between social disadvantage and adolescent behaviour. The mechanics by which this operates is less clear but potentially points to children from more socially disadvantaged backgrounds being more likely to have communication difficulties (including pragmatic language difficulties) which then makes them more susceptible to behaviour difficulties in adolescence. It may be that pragmatic language difficulties make children more susceptible to disengaging from and being able to relate positively to those around them, thus impacting on learning, engaging effectively in communication and developing relationships. There is a methodological issue here in that it may be the same set of social communication-type behaviours which are being measured but from different perspectives, a pragmatic language perspective that is more linguistic compared to a more behaviorally-defined perspective.

Although the advantages of longitudinal birth cohort studies have been highlighted, it is important to also reflect on their limitations. Namely, the measures used are often parent or teacher report measures rather than direct assessment of the children with the exception of the Clegg et al. (2015) study. This is simply due to the size of the cohorts where it is not feasible in terms of resources to assess thousands of children on standardized language and communication assessments.

Research has established an association between children's language and communication, their social-emotional competence and their mental health. More recently, the role of language and communication as a predictor and mediator has been identified. Language and communication is certainly involved but not as a direct causal factor and instead it is part of a dynamic interplay within a biopsychosocial framework. The nature of this interaction will most likely have to be understood at the level of the individual child and their environment.

A case perspective: A reluctant talker

A case study is presented here from the author's own clinical experience. The aim of this case study is to highlight how a biopsychosocial framework can be used to help understand the child. The case study is not exhaustive in its detail but does aim to highlight the complexity of the child's needs and how this complexity can be understood. Nor does the case study aim to offer a detailed and in-depth psychological analysis of the child. There then follows some discussion of the role of speech and language therapy in the case in terms of what it could offer and, importantly, what it could not, all as part of the multidisciplinary management.

Jake was 8 years old and in year 4 at a mainstream primary school in the UK when he was referred to a tier 4 Child and Adolescent Mental Health Service (CAMHS) in a large city in the North of England. Tier 4 services cater for children and young people with the most serious problems, such as day units, highly specialized outpatient teams and inpatient units. Jake already had a statement of Special Educational Need for learning difficulties, speech difficulties and a diagnosis of Autism Spectrum Disorder (ASD). He was in a mainstream classroom with one-to-one support from a teaching assistant for much of the time. At school, Jake was reported to be two years behind in his academic attainment. He had some emerging literacy skills, writing some words and short sentences. Jake's behaviour at home and school had become increasingly challenging leading to several temporary exclusions from school. Professionals described Jake as having selective mutism, which Mum reported started when he was about 3 years old. The main aim of the referral to CAMHS was to understand Jake's needs, with a view to locating more appropriate educational provision for him and to improve family life at home by enabling Jake's parents to understand and manage his behaviour.

At home, Jake was one of four siblings, being the second youngest. Jake's parents described him as very aggressive and challenging at home. There were frequent episodes during the day of violent outbursts that were described as usually culminating in Jake being physically aggressive to his siblings and his Mum. Mum had a history of mental health difficulties and was managing a long-standing diagnosis of bipolar disorder at the time, being fully engaged with the local mental health services. During Jake's attendance at CAMHS, Mum reported that she was expecting another child. Jake's Mum talked openly about her experiences with bipolar disorder and, as a result, how she was often absent as a parent. Jake was born 11 weeks early requiring a long period of three months in intensive care. She also talked about Jake's early development as very challenging, including feeding and sleeping difficulties and his delays in reaching the developmental milestones his siblings had all achieved easily. She reported finding him much more difficult to parent, demanding much more of her in terms of time and energy. She also talked about a very difficult time when Jake was 2 years old where she gave birth to a fourth child who died at 2 weeks. At this time, Mum took Jake to various bereavement support groups, which is when she first reported that Jake started to stop talking, becoming a reluctant talker.

Jake's communication profile was complex. It was at school that his selective mutism was most apparent. He was reported not to have spoken at school for the previous three years. He did not speak to his peers or any staff or adults at school (including during verbal activities such as reading aloud and singing). His mutism had significant implications for his learning, not only in being able to engage in learning activities but also in being able to assess his level of learning. Jake was not able to engage in assessment as this involved talking (i.e., reading aloud to a teacher to determine how much he could read). In stark contrast, at home Jake was his usual talkative self and described by his parents to be as talkative and communicative as all his other siblings. Videos taken of Jake at home confirmed this fact as reported. Jake received the diagnosis of ASD at 3 years of age due to developmental difficulties he was experiencing. Details on these difficulties were limited but pointed to a developmental delay in speech and language development and limited play, with some evidence of repetitive behaviour. Speech difficulties (described as 'unclear speech') were also identified at this time. Due to Jake being unable to talk away from the home environment and with unfamiliar people it was not possible to determine how unclear his speech was at 8 years of age. The limited observations of Jake on video at home indicated that his speech was clear and his parents reported that they could understand him.

A biopsychosocial model offers a framework to understand some of the complexity of Jake's needs. Taking the biological component first, research indicates that being a boy, being born prematurely and having a history of mental health difficulties in the family (i.e., through Mum's diagnosis of bipolar disorder) increase the risk of children developing mental health difficulties. Jake was very much part of a strong family unit; however, the interpersonal component was still very relevant to him in terms of how his development had impacted on his relationship with Mum, how Mum considered she could be a parent to him, and the extent and quality of the attachment with Mum. Contributing to the complexity was the death of Mum's fourth child and Jake's younger sibling, again challenging the interpersonal dynamic between Mum and Jake and the family. Locating Jake's communication needs in the *interpersonal* can help us to understand how his delayed communication abilities may have had a negative impact on his interactions with Mum. For example, the difficulty in interacting and communicating with Jake due to a combination of not understanding his speech, his refusal to speak in situations outside of the home and his more challenging behaviours (linked to the label of ASD), all manifested themselves as reduced time spent with Jake. The result was, perhaps, Jake not feeling he had his needs met when he attempted to communicate these, further impacting on the attachment between Mum and Jake. (It is interesting to note here, how much Mum was the focus rather than

Dad, even though Dad needed to take on much of the parenting when Mum was unwell and unable to parent as she would have liked to.)

The environmental component is less clear in that, although the family was from an area of low socio-economic status, they were a strong family unit who were clearly committed to all their children. The role of expectations is relevant here in that there will have been expectations of Jake particularly in comparison to his other siblings which Jake – due to his needs – was unable to meet. The consensus from the CAMHs team was that there were many challenges within the interpersonal component for Jake and for his parents to understand and manage.

As Jake attended the CAMHS unit on a part-time basis while continuing to attend his mainstream provision, it became easier to understand his needs. He was always willing to attend and engaged fully in the school and therapeutic activities. Jake's parents engaged in family therapy at the same time. It was only when he was challenged that Jake would start to show challenging behaviour, for example in situations where he was being asked to complete school work that he found too hard, being in a situation where there was a lot of pressure on him to communicate with others, and being expected to complete a task that he felt unable to do even with support. Through the therapeutic activities he engaged in, such as the Art and Play therapies, it emerged that he was also very angry about life at home and his place in the family.

The role of speech and language therapy was very much part of the multidisciplinary management. The overall aim of the SLT input was to enable Jake to communicate to the best of his abilities while attending CAMHS. A secondary aim was for Jake to use these communication abilities to enable him to participate in the school and other therapeutic activities, thus enabling him to maximize his participation in his management. The approach involved working with Jake directly to increase his communication with all the children and staff on the unit and working with the staff and the children to enable them to understand how to communicate with Jake. Direct work with Jake essentially involved enabling Jake to find communicating with people less anxiety inducing and so desensitizing him to communicating per the approach advocated by Johnson and Wintgens (2007, 2016). Communication here is seen in its broadest sense and so can be verbal and nonverbal. Initially Jake was able to point and then over time became more comfortable to use gesture, drawing, writing and then some non-sounds such as giggling, laughing, noises to indicate dissatisfaction, and finally, one word which was 'no'. A graded approach was used where he would meet one of these goals such as using gesture with a more comfortable adult (i.e., the Speech and Language Therapist), then his key worker and then another adult. The next goals would be achieved in the same graded way. Jake's key workers and other staff were encouraged to use visual support in all activities with Jake (such as visual timetables) so Jake knew what was going to happen and what was expected of him during his time at the unit and also through other significant times (such as family meetings and when moving on was being discussed). Staff were also able to reduce the pressure on Jake to talk and to encourage and accept all forms of the nonverbal communication from Jake. This approach served to lessen the pressure around verbal communication for Jake. At the time of Jake moving on, he was able to communicate using various nonverbal means often by initiating written messages and being able to use a 'yes' or 'no' when asked direct questions with four staff members. However, such responses did not generalize to all the staff or to all the children on the unit at the time.

After attending the unit for eight months, Jake moved on to a different mainstream school on a full-time basis where he was able to access an integrated resource for children with speech, language and communication needs. Here, for the first time, he was reported to talk freely with adults and children and was engaging well with the school and his learning.

Speech and language intervention was one small part of Jake's overall management and offered an opportunity to Jake and the team for more effective communication, thus enabling Jake to engage in his overall management. Speech and language therapy was never viewed as a solution to his complex needs but by focusing on his communication it was possible to see how his communication difficulties were having an impact on his social-emotional competence, primarily through the interpersonal component of the biopsychosocial model taken. By enabling Jake to be the best communicator he could be at that time, staff were able to establish an effective means of communication with him and thus facilitate his engagement in his overall therapeutic management. Hopefully, it has been shown that the issue of whether his communication difficulties were a cause of his mental health difficulties or vice versa is not particularly helpful and, instead, it is about the dynamic interaction between the child, their interpersonal relationships and their environment.

Conclusion

There is a long-standing association between children's communicative competence and their mental health, with children's social-emotional competence as an integral component in this association. Rather than understanding children's communicative competence as a causal factor, it is more fruitful to consider how children's communication is involved in their developing social-emotional competence and subsequent mental health. Children's level of communicative competence may simply make them more or less resilient to developing mental health difficulties, in conjunction with other known risk factors. Much more needs to be known about how this mechanism operates in children over time. Specific profiles of communicative competence in mental health difficulties have not been reliably identified; instead, investigating how children with mental health difficulties respond to interventions targeting their communicative competence is potentially more informative for both research and practice.

References

Adams. C. (2002). Practitioner review: The assessment of language pragmatics. *Journal of Child Psychology & Psychiatry, 43*(8), 973-987.

Allen, R.E. & Oliver, J.M. (1982). The effects of child maltreatment on language development. *Child Abuse & Neglect, 6*(3), 299-305.

American Psychiatric Association. (2013). *Diagnostic and Statistical Manual of Mental Disorders*, 5th ed. Washington, DC: APA.

Avon Longitudinal Study of Parents and Children (ALSPAC). www.bristol.ac.uk

Baltaxe, C.A.M. (1994). Communication issues in selective mutism. Paper presented at the meeting of the American Speech-Language-Hearing-Association, New Orleans, LA.

Bates, E., Dale, P.S., & Thal, D. (1995). Individual differences and their implications for theories of language development. In P. Fletcher & R. MacWhinney (Eds), *Handbook of Child Language*. Oxford: Basil Blackwell.

Beitchman, J.H. (1985). Speech and language impairments and psychiatric risk: Toward a model of neurodevelopmental immaturity. *Symposium on Child Psychiatry, 8*(4), 721-735.

Beitchman, J.H., Wilson, B., Johnson, C.J., Atkinson, L., Young, A., Adlaf, E., Escobar, M., & Douglas, L. (2001). Fourteen year follow up of speech/language impaired and control children: Psychiatric outcome. *Journal of the American Academy of Child & Adolescent Psychiatry, 40*(1), 75-82.

Benner, G.J. (2002). Language skills of children with SEBD: A literature review – emotional and behavioural disorders. *Journal of Emotional and Behavioural Disorders, 10*(1), 43-56.

Benoit, D. (2004). Infant-parent attachment: Definition, types, antecedents, measurement and outcome. *Paediatrics and Child Health, 9*(8), 541-545.

Bishop, D.V.M. (1998). Development of the Children's Communication Checklist (CCC): A method for assessing qualitative aspects of communicative impairment in children. *Journal of Child Psychology & Psychiatry, 39*(6), 879-891.

Bishop, D.V.M. (2003) *The Children's Communication Checklist* (CCC), 2nd ed. London: The Psychological Corporation Ltd, Harcourt Assessment.

Bishop, D.V.M. (2014). Ten questions about terminology for children with unexplained language problems. *International Journal of Language & Communication Disorders*, *49*(4), 381-415.

Bishop, D.V.M., Snowling, M.J., Thompson, P.A., Greenhalgh, T., & the CATALISE Consortium. (2016). CATALISE: A multinational and multidisciplinary Delph consensus study. 1. Identifying language impairments in children. PLOS One, *11*(12), e0168066.

Bishop, D.V.M., Snowling, M.J., Thompson, P.A., Greenhalgh, T., & the CATALISE -2 Consortium. (2017). Phase 2 of CATALISE: A multinational and multidisciplinary Delphi consensus study of problems with language development: Terminology. *Journal of Child Psychology & Psychiatry*, *58*(10), 1068-1080.

Botting, N., Durkin, K., Toseeb, U., Pickles, A., & Conti-Ramsden, G. (2016). Emotional health, support and self-efficacy in young adults with a history of language impairment. *British Journal of Developmental Psychology*, *34*(4), 538-554.

Bowlby, J. (1969). *Attachment and Loss*. New York: Basic Books.

British Cohort Study 1970. www.cls.ioe.ac.uk

Bryan, K., Freer, J., & Furlong, C. (2007). Language and communication difficulties in juvenile offenders. *International Journal of Language & Communication Disorders*, *42*(5), 505-520.

Bryan, K., Garvani, G., Gregory, J., & Kilner, K. (2015). Language difficulties and criminal justice: The need for earlier intervention. *International Journal of Language & Communication Disorders*, *50*(6), 763-775.

Bronfenbrenner, U. & Morris, P.A. (2006). The bioecological model of human development. In R.M. Lerner (Ed.), *Theoretical Models of Human Development. Volume 1 of the Handbook of Child Psychology*, 6th ed. (pp.993-1028). Hoboken, NJ: John Wiley & Sons.

Brownlie, E.B., Beitchman, J.H., Escobar, M., et al. (2004). Early language impairment and young adult delinquent and aggressive behavior. *Journal of the Abnormal Child Psychology*, *32*(4), 453-467.

Buckley, B. (2003). *Children's Communication Skills: From Birth to Five Years*. London: Routledge.

Cantwell. D. & Baker, L. (1977). Psychiatric disorder in children with speech and language retardation. *Archives of General Psychiatry*, *34*(5), 583-591.

Cantwell, D.P. & Baker, L. (1987). Prevalence and type of psychiatric disorder and developmental disorders in three speech and language groups. *Journal of Communication Disorders*, *20*(2), 151-160.

Chase Stovel, K. & Dozier. M. (2008). Infants in foster care: An attachment theory perspective. *Adoption Quarterly*, *2*(1), 55-88.

Clegg, J. (2014). Curriculum vocabulary learning intervention for children with social, emotional and behavioural difficulties (SEBD): Findings from a case study series. *Emotional and Behavioural Difficulties*, *19*(1), 106-127.

Clegg, J. & Hartshorne, M. (2004). Speech and language therapy in hyperactivity: A United Kingdom perspective in complex cases. *Seminars in Speech and Language, 25*, 263-271.

Clegg, J., Ansorge, L., Stackhouse, J., & Donlan, C. (2012). Developmental communication impairment in adults: Outcomes and life experiences of adults and their parents. *Language, Speech and Hearing Services in Schools, 43*(4), 521-535.

Clegg, J., Hollis, C., Mawhood, L., & Rutter, M. (2005). Developmental language disorders – a follow up in later adult life. Cognitive, language and psycho-social outcomes. *Journal of Child Psychology & Psychiatry, 46*(2), 128-129.

Clegg, J., Law, J., Rush, R., Peters. T.J., & Roulstone, S. (2015). The contribution of early language development to children's emotional and behavioural functioning at 6 years: An analysis of data from the Children in Focus sample from the ALSPAC birth cohort. *Journal of Child Psychology & Psychiatry, 56*(1), 67-75.

Clegg, J., Stackhouse, J., Finch, K., Murphy, C., & Nicholls, S. (2009). Language abilities of secondary age pupils at risk of school exclusion: A preliminary report. *Child Language Teaching & Therapy, 25*(1), 123-140.

Cohen, N. (2001). *Language Impairment and Psychopathology in Infants, Children and Adolescents*. London: Sage.

Cohen, N.J., Davine, M., Horodezky, N., & Lipsett, L. (1993). Unsuspected language impairment in psychiatrically disturbed children: Prevalence and language and behavioral characteristics. *Journal of the American Academy of Child & Adolescent Psychiatry, 32*(3), 595-603.

Cohen, N.J.R., Menna, R., Vallance, D.D., Barwick, M.A., Im, N., & Horodezky, N.B. (1998a). Language, social cognitive processing and behavioral characteristics of psychiatrically disturbed children with previously identified and unsuspected language impairments. *Journal of Child Psychology & Psychiatry, 39*(6), 853-864.

Cohen, N.J., Barwick, M.A., Horodezky, N.B., Vallance, D.D., & Im, N. (1998b). Language achievement and cognitive processing in psychiatrically disturbed children with previously identified and unsuspected language impairments. *Journal of Child Psychology & Psychiatry, 39*(6), 865-877.

Conti-Ramsden, G. & Botting, N. (2008). Emotional health in adolescents with and without a history of specific language impairment (SLI). *Journal of Child Psychology & Psychiatry, 49*(5), 516-525.

Cross, M., Blake, P., Tunbridge, N., & Gill, T. (2001). Collaborative working to promote the communication skills of a 14-year-old student with emotional, behavioural, learning and language difficulties. *Child Language Teaching and Therapy, 17*(3), 227-246.

Culp, R.E., Watkins, R.V., Lawrence, H., Letts, D., Kelly, D.J., & Rice, M. (1991). Maltreated children's language and speech development: Abused, neglected and abused and neglected. *First Language, 11*(33), 377-398.

Davis, E., Sawyer, M.G., Lo, S.K., & Wake, M. (2010). Socioeconomic risk factors for mental health problems in 4-5-year-old children: Australian population study. *Academic Pediatrics, 10*(1), 41-47.

Denham, S.A. (2006). Social-emotional competence as support for school readiness: What is it and how do we assess it? *Early Education and Development*, *17*(1), 57-89.

Denham, S.A., Wyatt, T.M., Bassett, H.H., Echeverria, D., & Knox, S.S. (2009). Assessing social-emotional development in children from a longitudinal perspective. *Journal of Epidemiology & Child Health*, *63*(Suppl I), 37-52.

Dodge, K.A. & Petit, G.S. (2003). A biopsychosocial model of the development of chronic conduct problems in adolescence. *Developmental Psychology*, *39*(2), 349-371.

Eigsti, I.M. & Cicchetti, D. (2004). The impact of child maltreatment on expressive syntax at 60 months. *Developmental Science*, *7*(1), 88-102.

Giddan, J.J., Milling, L., & Campbell, M.D. (1996). Unrecognized language and speech deficits in preadolescent psychiatric inpatients. *American Journal of Orthopsychiatry*, *66*(1), 85-92.

Gilmour, J., Hill, B., Place, M., et al. (2004). Social communication deficits in conduct disorder: A clinical and community survey. *Journal of Child Psychology & Psychiatry*, *45*(5), 967-978.

Hartas, D. (2011). Children's language and behavioural, social and emotional difficulties and prosocial behaviour during the toddler years and at school entry. *British Journal of Special Education*, *38*(2), 83-91.

Heneker, S. (2005). Speech and language therapy support for pupils with behavioural, emotional and social difficulties (BESD) – a pilot project. *British Journal of Special Education*, *32*(2), 86-91.

Hollo, A., Wehby, J.A., & Oliver, R.M. (2014). Unidentified language deficits in children with emotional and behavioural disorders: A meta-analysis. *Exceptional Children*, *80*(2), 169-186.

Howlin, P. & Rutter, M. (1987). The consequences of language delay for other aspects of development. In J. Yule & M. Rutter (Eds), *Language Development and Disorders*. Oxford: Mackeith Press.

ICAN, The Children's Communication Charity. www.ican.org.uk

Johnson, M. & Wintgens, A. (2007). *The Selective Mutism Resource Manual*. Brackley, UK: Speechmark.

Johnson, M. & Wintgens, A. (2016). *The Selective Mutism Resource Manual*, 2nd ed. Abingdon: Routledge.

Law, J., Rush, R., Schoon, I., & Parsons, S. (2009). Modelling developmental language difficulties from school entry into adulthood: Literacy, mental health and employment outcomes. *Journal of Speech, Language & Hearing Research*, *52*(6), 1401-1416.

Law, J., Rush, R., Clegg, J., Peters, T., & Roulstone, S. (2015). The role of pragmatics in mediating the relationship between social disadvantage and adolescent behavior. *Journal of Developmental & Behavioral Pediatrics*, *36*(5), 389-398.

Millennium Cohort Study. www.cls.ioe.ac.uk

Mueller, K.L. & Tomblin, J.B. (2012). Examining the co-morbidity of language disorder and ADHD. *Topics in Language Disorders, 32*(3), 228-246.

Norbury, C.F. (2014). Practitioner review: Social (pragmatic) communication disorder; conceptualisation, evidence and clinical implications. *Journal of Child Psychology & Psychiatry, 55*(3), 204-216.

Oerbeck, B., Stein, M.B., Wentzel-Larsen, T., Langsrud, O., & Kristensen, H. (2014). A randomized controlled trial of a home and school-based intervention for selective mutism-defocused communication and behavioural techniques. *Child and Adolescent Mental Health, 19*(3), 192-198.

Oerbeck, B., Stein, M.B., Pripp, A.H., & Kristensen, H. (2015). Selective mutism follow-up study 1 year after end of treatment. *European Child & Adolescent Psychiatry, 24*(7), 757-766.

Ozonoff, S. (2012). Editorial perspective; Autism Spectrum Disorders in DSM-5 - An historical perspective and the need for change. *Journal of Child Psychology & Psychiatry, 53*(10), 1092-1094.

Pan, B.A., Rowe, M.L., Singer, J.D., & Snow, C.E. (2005). Maternal correlates of growth in toddler vocabulary development production in low-income families. *Child Development, 76*(4), 763-782.

Paulson, J.F., Keefe, H.A., & Leiferman, J.A. (2009). Early parental depression and child language development. *Journal of Child Psychology & Psychiatry, 50*(3), 254-262.

Petersen, I., Bates, J., D'Onofrio, B., Coyne, C., Lansford, J., Dodge, K., Petit, G., & Van Hulle, C. (2013). Language ability predicts the development of behavioural problems in children. *Journal of Abnormal Psychology, 122*(2), 542-557.

Piotrowska, P.J., Stride, C.B., Croft, S.E., & Rowe, R. (2015). Socioeconomic status and antisocial behaviour among children and adolescents: A systematic review and meta-analysis. *Clinical Psychology Review, 35*, 47-55.

Prizant, B., Audet, L., Burke, G., Hummel, L., Maher, S., & Theadore, G. (1990). Communication disorders and emotional/behavioural disorders in children and adolescents. *Journal of Speech and Hearing Research, 55*(2), 179-192.

Redmond, S.M., Thompson, H.L., & Goldstein, S. (2011). Psycholinguistic profiling differentiates language impairment from typical development and from Attention-Deficit/ Hyperactivity Disorder. *Journal of Speech, Language and Hearing Research, 54*(1), 99-117.

Rescorla, L. (1989). The Language Development Survey: A screening tool for delayed language in toddlers. *Journal of Speech & Hearing Disorders, 54*(4), 587-599.

Rescorla, L., Ross, G.S., & McClure, S. (2007). Language delay and behavioural/emotional problems in toddlers: Findings from two developmental clinics. *Journal of Speech, Language & Hearing Research, 50*(4), 1063-1078.

Ripley, K. & Yuill, N. (2005). Patterns of language impairment and behavior in boys excluded from school. *British Journal of Educational Psychology, 75*(1), 37-50.

Sadiq, F., Slator, L., Law, J., Skuse, D., Gillberg, C., & Minnis, H. (2012). A comparison of the pragmatic skills of children with reactive attachment disorder and high functioning autism. *European Child and Adolescent Psychiatry, 21*, 267-276.

Sharkey, L. & McNicholas, F. (2014). Selective mutism: A prevalence study of primary school children in the Republic of Ireland. *Irish Journal of Psychological Medicine, 29*(1), 36-40.

Snow, P.C. & Powell, M.B. (2011). Oral language competence in incarcerated young offenders: Links with offending severity. *International Journal of Speech-Language Pathology, 13*(6), 480-489.

Snowling, M., Bishop, D.V.M., Stothard, S., Chipchase, B., & Kaplan, C. (2006). Psychosocial outcomes at 15 years of children with a preschool history of speech-language impairment. *Journal of Child Psychology & Psychiatry, 47*(8), 759-765.

Steinhausen, H. & Juzi, C. (1996). Elective mutism: An analysis of 100 cases. *Journal of the American Academy of Child & Adolescent Psychiatry, 35*(5), 606-614.

Sylvestre, A. & Merette, C. (2010). Language delay in severely neglected children: A cumulative or specific effect of risk factors. *Child Abuse and Neglect, 34*(6), 414-428.

The Communication Trust. www.communicationtrust.org.uk

Van Dahl, J., Verhoven, L., & van Balkom, H. (2007). Behaviour problems in children with language impairment. *Journal of Child Psychology & Psychiatry, 48*(11), 1139-1147.

Walsh, I.P., Scullion, M., Burns, S., & Mac Evilly, D. (2014). Identifying demographic and language profiles of children with a primary diagnosis of attention deficit hyperactivity disorder. *Emotional and Behavioural Difficulties, 19*(1), 59-70.

Whitehouse, A.J., Robinson, M., & Zubrick, S.R. (2011). Late talking and the risk for psychosocial problems during childhood and adolescence. *Paediatrics, 128*(2), e324-332.

Yew, S.G. & O'Kearney, R. (2013). Emotional and behavioural outcomes in later childhood and adolescence for children with specific language impairments: Meta-analyses of controlled prospective studies. *Journal of Child Psychology & Psychiatry, 54*(5), 516-524.

Zeanah, C.H. & Gleason, M.M. (2015). Annual research review: Attachment disorders in early childhood – clinical presentation, causes, correlates and treatment. *Journal of Child Psychology & Psychiatry, 56*(3), 207-222.

3 Language and communication in adults with mental health disorders: Considerations for understanding speech and language therapy process and practice

I.P. Walsh, C. Jagoe and J. Brophy

Introduction

Unlike the area of language and communication impairment as associated with childhood mental health disorders, language and communication functioning in adults with psychiatric presentations has received considerably less attention in the literature. This lack of attention is particularly in relation to the potential and the need for the discipline of speech and language therapy to be part of multidisciplinary input and to work alongside colleagues in psychiatry, psychology, social work, nursing and occupational therapy, for example. This multidisciplinary input is relevant to all stages of the therapeutic process for those individuals who have language and communication difficulties as intrinsic to, or associated with, their diagnosis.

Despite reports of associations between communication impairment and mental (ill)health in adults (Palmer et al., 2019; Whitehouse, 2009), specific studies addressing the incidence and prevalence of speech and language problems in adult mental health populations are few, aside from a few key studies (Bryan & Roach, 2001; Emerson & Enderby, 1996; Walsh, Regan, Sowman, Parsons, & McKay, 2007). Often dismissed as 'just being part of' or 'integral to' the psychiatric diagnosis and therefore, by some implication, not easily amenable to intervention, language and communication issues are not always considered as being within the remit of the Speech and Language Therapist (SLT). Notwithstanding Gravell and France's assertion in the early 1990s of the "centrality of language and communication to diagnosis" to psychiatry (Gravell & France, 1991, p.3), the awareness of language and communication issues as pivotal to the processes (i.e., diagnostic assessment and therapeutic intervention) and profiles (i.e., clinical presentations within diagnoses, such as schizophrenia) in adult psychiatry, has been limited. Consequently, language and communication difficulties may be missed, overlooked and/or not considered in planning supports for people accessing or attending services. Coupled with the fact that many of the diagnostic and therapeutic processes in mental health services are mediated through spoken language (e.g., psychotherapy, cognitive behavioural therapy (CBT), social skills training), a lack of consideration of language impairment can impact upon how service users with communication difficulties (and their families) gain access to tailored support and services. Reduced or constrained access to services prevents the individual from actively participating in their own recovery in practical and meaningful ways.

However, in the almost 30 years since Gravell and France's (1991) original assertion of the need to consider language as central to psychiatry, there have been some significant moves to consider language and communication within the context of therapeutic *practice* and *processes*, along with moves to enhance the overall understanding of clinical presentations in psychiatry. Some of these are illustrated here by examples from within service development in Ireland.

Firstly, in terms of *practice*, Walsh et al. (2007) screened for the presence of impairments in language, communication and swallowing among a randomly chosen sample of adults (n=60). This sample of adults, who were attending inpatient and community psychiatric services, presented with a variety of mental health disorder diagnoses. Findings indicated that over 80% of individuals screened showed previously undetected impairments in one or more of the tests of receptive and expressive language administered by SLTs, with over 60% of the individuals rated as having impairment in communication and discourse skills. Additionally, over 30% of the sample showed some impairment in swallowing (dysphagia). The findings contributed to: (i) an increased knowledge of the nature of speech, language and communication disorders often associated with, or intrinsic to, many psychiatric presentations; (ii) an identified marked prevalence of these disorders in this clinical group; and

(iii) (further) proof of the need for speech and language therapy input with such individuals. The findings of this study led to the appointment of the first clinical specialist in speech and language therapy for this client population in Ireland in 2006. Many of the approaches to intervention discussed later in this chapter have developed from this focus on practice since that appointment over a decade ago.

Another more recent development in terms of *process* in the Irish context was the publication of the Irish Association of Speech and Language Therapists' (IASLT) *Speech and Language Therapy in Mental Health Services: A Guidance Document* (IASLT, 2015). This document serves as a guide to both therapists and other professionals who work with people with mental health disorders, whether providing services to a dedicated psychiatric caseload or as part of a more general client group presenting with other primary conditions (e.g., adults with intellectual disabilities). The *Guidance Document* is referenced in this chapter to help inform the reader of current understanding and *processes* within adult mental health contexts, using Ireland as an example.

Some of the main clinical presentations in adult psychiatry will also be presented in this chapter (i.e., schizophrenia, mood disorders, and anxiety), with attention paid to both the language and communication clinical features, complemented by first-person and family-member experiences of communication and conversational interactions. Such accounts illustrate the need to hear the voice of the person with the mental health disorder and accounts of communication barriers, in the interests of both attempting to better understand and respect the experiences whilst also ensuring that such needs are considered in planning person-centred support and services (Kovarsky & Curran, 2007). Paying attention to the voice of the person with communication difficulties and that of their family (i.e., their communication partners) can help inform both the process and practice of speech and language therapy with this clinical population.

People with schizophrenia

A common psychiatric diagnosis in adulthood is schizophrenia and although not as common as other mental health conditions, the symptoms can be significantly disabling and debilitating, most especially if early in onset (young adulthood) and persisting to its chronic form (Lavretsky, 2008). Affecting 21 million people worldwide (World Health Organisation (WHO), 2018a), or one in every 100 people (Moller, 2013), schizophrenia may manifest first in adolescence or early adulthood, although it can also occur later in life. Moller (2013) states that in three-quarters of all cases schizophrenia manifests between the ages of 15 and 34 years. Though prevalence is considered equal across men and women, onset of schizophrenia occurs earlier in males but with better outcomes reported in females (Sadock, Sadock, & Ruiz, 2015). Hospital admission rates are relatively high for people with schizophrenia when compared to other psychiatric presentations. For example, in a recent Health Research Board (HRB) report, schizophrenia accounted for 20% of all admissions to psychiatric units and hospitals in Ireland in 2017, second only to depressive disorders (Daly & Craig, 2018).

Core to a diagnosis of schizophrenia are disturbances of thinking, feeling and behaviour. *The Diagnostic and Statistical Manual of Diseases*, 5th Edition (DSM-5) (American Psychiatric Association, 2013) includes six criteria for consideration in making a diagnosis of schizophrenia, including characteristic symptoms of, for example, delusions, hallucinations, disorganized speech and negative symptoms, degrees of social occupational dysfunction, and relationship to global developmental delay or Autism Spectrum Disorder (ASD). The latter criterion references the close relationship the core symptoms of schizophrenia may have to neurodevelopmental correlates, including developmental language or communication disorders – something that SLTs must consider in this context. This is a point that was discussed in the past by Murray and Lewis (1987), Weinberger (1987) and Walsh (1997), and also via a follow-up study by Isohanni and colleagues (2004) which investigated the persistence of developmental markers in childhood and adolescence and risk for schizophrenia in adult life. Similar arguments have been more recently proposed by Arango, Fraguas and Parellada (2014), specifically in relationship to the commonalities in neurodevelopmental trajectories in early onset bipolar and schizophrenia disorders.

Positive and negative symptoms of schizophrenia and language and communication

The symptoms of schizophrenia can be considered under two headings: *positive* and *negative* symptoms. A person may present with predominantly positive symptom presentation or predominantly negative symptom presentation, or a mix of both symptom profiles depending on stage of the illness, with negative symptoms tending to be longer lasting or persistent than positive symptoms (Shine, n.d). However, Lunn (2011) warns that such symptoms as described below may not always be indicative of a schizophrenia diagnosis, but can also occur in other clinical presentations, such as mood disorders, or as associated with recreational substance abuse.

The categorization into *positive* and *negative* groups is a classification system that is attributed to Crow (1980) and Andreasen and Olson (1982), among others. Positive symptoms are those that reflect "an exaggeration or distortion of normal brain function" while negative features represent "a diminution or loss of normal brain function" (Moller, 2013, p.347). Frith (1992, p.10) explains positive symptoms as "abnormal by their presence" while negative symptoms are "abnormal by their absence". More recently, the groups of symptoms have been referenced as 'active' and 'passive' symptoms, respectively (Shine, n.d.). Positive or active symptoms include: hallucinations (e.g., auditory, visual, tactile and olfactory, though auditory are the most common in schizophrenia), delusions, disorganized behaviour and inappropriate affect, including what is often referred to as positive formal thought disorder (i.e., a characteristic of which is incoherent speech where unexpected shifts of topic occur without logical connections between utterances). A person exhibiting positive symptoms may be disorganized in their conversations, characterized by being overly talkative, persisting on certain topics or themes of interest to them, or jumping across topics without warning, while not taking account of a listener's confusion or disinterest. Hinzen and Rossello (2015) discuss thought disorder in schizophrenia as "language pathology across positive symptoms", hypothesizing that the main features of positive symptoms can:

> ...fall into place as failures in language-mediated forms of meaning, manifest either as a disorder of speech perception (Auditory Verbal Hallucinations), abnormal speech production running without feedback control (Formal Thought Disorder), or production of abnormal linguistic content (Delusions) (p.1)

Negative or 'passive' symptoms may appear gradually and may be more characteristic of the chronic stage of the illness (Kirkpatrick, Buchanan, Ross, & Carpenter, 2001). Negative symptoms include poverty of speech and poverty of content of speech (i.e., reduction in amount and content of spontaneous speech) and flattening of affect (e.g., poor facial expression to express emotion) or emotional blunting, in addition to social withdrawal (Foussias, Agid, Fervaha, & Remington, 2014; Kirkpatrick, Fenton, Carpenter, & Marder, 2006; Lunn, 2011). A person with predominantly a negative symptom presentation of schizophrenia can appear withdrawn, quiet and difficult to engage in communication or, if engaged, responses can be minimal with the listener having to work hard to keep the conversation going.

Positive and negative symptoms of schizophrenia can therefore affect language and communication in a variety of ways. It is not surprising then that the clinical presentation of schizophrenia is associated with a variety of speech, language and communication difficulties (Clegg, Brumfitt, Parks, & Woodruff, 2007; France & Muir, 1997; Frith, 1997; Mc Kenna & Oh, 2005). There have been numerous attempts to describe and interpret the language features of schizophrenia at different linguistic levels (Covington et al., 2005; Thomas, 1997) including phonetic and phonological (Cutting, 1985; Chaika, 1974), syntactic (Condray, Steinhauer, Kammen, & Kasperak, 2002; Thomas, King, Fraser, & Kendell, 1990), semantic (Marvel, Schwartz, & Isaacs, 2004; Woods, Weinborn, Posada, & O' Grady, 2007), pragmatic (Meilijson, Kasher, & Elizur, 2004; Jagoe, 2013), and with regard to (referential) discourse and conversation skills (Docherty, Cohen, Nienow, Dinzeo, & Dangelmaier, 2003; Walsh-Brennan, 2001).

Personal accounts of experience of communication in schizophrenia

Depending on an individual's symptom and linguistic profile, language difficulties can negatively impact the communicative competence of the person, making it difficult to sustain verbal interaction or for others to obtain an accurate 'reading' of how the person with schizophrenia is feeling.

Communication breakdown and/or miscommunication, therefore, is common in interactions with people with schizophrenia (Brophy, 2009; Jagoe, 2015; Walsh-Brennan, 2001; Walsh, 2008), affecting not only the person themselves impacting on their social interactions and involvement, but also on those around them who struggle to respond to (perhaps) odd or confusing communicative intent. However, it is important to avoid automatically attributing the cause of the breakdown to the person with the diagnosis but rather consider it as a (joint) product of the interaction with the communication partner (Jagoe, 2013, 2015; Walsh-Brennan, 2001; Walsh, 2008). Hearing first person and family members' accounts of troubled communication can help elucidate the nature of communication breakdowns further.

From such accounts, the frustration and upset at not being able to think or communicate clearly is all too obvious to both the person affected and those around them, as illustrated in the following quotes. For example, a person with schizophrenia refers to the struggle to communicate as agonizing, with "the darkness growing" with each experience of failed communication (Ruocchio, 1991), as follows:

> There is agony in not being able to communicate one's mind. The destined target is there, within physical touch, but a thousand miles away if he cannot be touched with words, cannot hear what is in my head. With each uncommunicated experience, the darkness grows (p.358).

Similarly, Smith and Sweeney (1997) cite a poetic description by a person with schizophrenia of the frustration and confusion as a result of not being able to communicate effectively:

> Inside my head; Slivers of wood are lodged; They prevent messages passing; From one part of my brain; To another (...); I attempt to dislodge these wooden pieces; Yet the more I try; The more firmly they become wedged; Confusion reigns. They are hurting my head; They are hurting my thoughts; They are hurting my feelings; They are hurting ME [sic]. (p.66).

Frustration at not being able to express oneself is obvious in these quotes, as is the added frustration of some who report difficulties in understanding what others are saying to them (Cutting, 1985):

> I used to get the sudden thing that I couldn't understand what people said. Like it was a foreign language. My mind went blank. (p.252).

Furthermore, the following series of quotes from Brophy's (2009) interviews with people with schizophrenia illustrate sentiments of being 'lonely', staying 'quiet' and feeling 'mad':

> It's very lonely...all this reality going on in my head and I can't talk to anybody about it.

> I used to be very chatty and quite bubbly...now I'm very quiet and I listen a lot.

> I can't think of things to say cause what's going on in my
> head are things I don't want to say because I feel mad (p.48).

Below, a mother of a person with schizophrenia reflects on the struggles to communicate with her son, referring to the impact of a 'blunted affect' (or lack of facial expression) on communicative interactions (Mueser & Gingerich, 1994):

> I don't know where Ed stands on so many things. Sometimes
> he says one thing, but then his facial expression suggests
> something different. At other times he hardly wants to
> talk at all. I want to help him, but I don't know what he
> wants (p.125).

It is not difficult to see from these personal accounts that communication can be challenging when interacting with people with schizophrenia. Communication interactions can exact a particular burden on both speaker and listener in these contexts.

Language and communication difficulties in schizophrenia and speech and language therapy

Attempting to understand the symptoms of schizophrenia in language or linguistic terms is not new. The more recently stated hypothesis that "schizophrenia is a breakdown of how language configures thought in the normal brain" (Hinzen & Rossello, 2015, p.2) is a welcome addition to this consideration, especially when considering the key role of speech and language therapy with this clinical group. In a recent systematic review, Joyal, Bonneau and Fecteau (2016) found that 14 out of the 18 studies reviewed yielded positive effects of language therapy (or 'training') on language and/or speech skills in 433 adults with a diagnosis of schizophrenia, with most studies focusing on discourse or expressive language skills. The authors conclude that "pragmatics and discourse skills are skills that can be trained in patients with schizophrenia and that this training can be retained over time" (Joyal et al., 2016, p.92). Moreover, the review demonstrated that individual therapy was preferred over group interventions, but with improvements reported in both contexts. However, such a conclusion must take into account that duration of therapy in the studies reviewed was hugely variable, ranging from 15 days to two years. The authors, like others before them (Walsh et al., 2007), call for increased involvement of SLTs in working with this clinical group, with increased attention paid to developing standardized assessments to evaluate speech and language skills and more effective ways to measure the impact of improved communication skills on symptom reduction and quality of life. Moreover, the issue of 'training' versus 'therapy' and generalization of improved skills remains contentious. Likewise, the optimum way of working with – or alongside – this client group, that is, avoiding apportioning 'blame' for communication breakdown on the person with the diagnosis, is important. Communication success or failure is a product of both or all of the interlocutors in a conversational interaction, a dynamic of communication in any context. However, understanding communication dynamics and taking shared responsibility for communication breakdown with people with schizophrenia can go some way to alleviate the communicative distress caused in daily, moment-by-moment conversations.

People with mood disorders

Depression

Prevalence rates of mood disorders in general can only be interpreted as rough estimates, given that depression may often go undiagnosed and/or untreated, coupled with the fact that depression, co-morbid with physical illness, is often missed (Fenton, Lodge, & Henderson, 2016). However, it is estimated by the World Health Organisation that there are more than 300 million people of all ages living with depression worldwide (WHO, 2018b). The diagnostic criteria for major depressive disorder in DSM – 5 (APA, 2013) include symptoms such as depressed mood, loss of interest and pleasure, feelings of worthlessness, and diminished ability to think or concentrate which demonstrate a change from typical functioning over a specific period of time. Impairment in social, occupational and other areas of functioning is also a feature.

Speech, language and communication changes as associated with depression has been reported in the literature. An early study of speech changes in people with depression (Darby, Simmons, & Berger, 1984) demonstrated that changes to speech dimensions on a 'depressed voice scale' were most consistently altered in depression yet showed improvement after treatment of depressive symptoms. There may be perceptual and acoustic changes in speech, with slow speech rate, low vocal volume and changes in prosodic features affecting intonation (Alpert, Pouget, & Silva, 2001; Cannizzaro, Harel, Reilly, Chappell, & Snyder, 2004; Garcia-Toro, Talavera, Saiz-Ruiz, & Gonzalez, 2000; Moore, Clements, Peifer, & Weisser, 2004; Scherer, 1987; Uekermann, Abdel-Hamid,

Lehmkamoer, Vollmoeller, & Daum, 2008). France (2001a, p.76) describes the overall effect as a "'dead', 'listless' voice with reduced volume, stress and rhythm".

Sadock et al. (2015, p.366) state that a person who is clinically depressed may "respond to questions with single words and exhibit delayed responses to questions. The examiner may literally have to wait 2 or 3 minutes for a response to a question". Language expression can be limited, conveying minimal information (France, 2001a). According to Sadock et al. (2015), about 10% of people with this diagnosis may have features of thought disorder (e.g., thought blocking) in addition to poverty of content of speech. Additionally, language features which may also affect the (written) discourse of people with depression include an increase in the use of negative words and use of pronoun 'I' (Rude, Gortner, & Pennebaker, 2004), with an increased use of absolutist terms (i.e., words or phrases that denote totality, e.g., 'completely', 'everyone', 'all') as reported by Al-Mosaiwi and Johnstone (2018). From a social interaction and communication perspective, a person with a clinical diagnosis of depression will experience withdrawal and/or avoidance of social contact (e.g., Schelde, 1998), along with changes in social skills (Joiner & Timmons, 2008; Sergin, 2001).

Once again, some excerpts from first-person interviews with people experiencing depression illustrate the depth of despair often felt by people with depression in social communication interactions. One person explained how feelings of poor self-esteem impact on his ability to interact socially: "I always feel so badly about myself. I never thought that anyone would want to be my friend" (Brophy, 2009, p.60). Another person talked of the need to be left alone: "you just don't want to interact you just want to be left alone" (Brophy, 2009, p.44).

Bipolar and related disorders

Bipolar affective disorder is one of the leading causes of disability worldwide (Krahn, 2011), with concomitant social and occupational dysfunction in affected individuals to varying extents. Bipolar and related disorders are a range of conditions that are characterized by an oscillation in moods, from depression to mania. Eagles (2011, p.62) describes bipolar affective disorder as being "characterised by separate episodes of mood disturbance at the two 'poles' of depression and mania".

'Bipolar I' was formerly known as, and is synonymous with, the term 'bipolar disorder' and "is defined as having a clinical course of one or more manic episodes and, sometimes, major depressive episodes"; 'Bipolar II' is characterised by "episodes of major depression and hypomania rather than mania" (Sadock et al., 2015, p.348) with the term 'hypomania' being used to refer to milder occurrences of mania. Sadock et al. (2015, p.348) further describe both mania and hypomania as "associated with inflated self-esteem, a decreased need for sleep, distractibility, great physical and mental activity, and overinvolvement in pleasurable behaviour". In addition, during a manic phase people may feel very creative and experience feelings of grandiosity, which may include "ideas of self-importance" (Fenton et al., 2016, p.116). Cyclothymia, a related mood disorder, is characterized by episodes of hypomania which do not reach the threshold for diagnosis of bipolar disorder, along with periods of mild-to-moderate depression (Robillard & Hickie, 2015).

Mood disorders and communication

In comparison to schizophrenia, there is relatively little research specifically focused on the speech, language and communication symptoms in bipolar disorders, even though symptoms such as 'pressure of speech' and 'tangentiality' typically feature in descriptions. However, Perlini et al. (2012, p.364) report that there are some studies on language processing in patients with bipolar disorder which have shown a general poverty of speech and content (not unlike that found in negative symptom schizophrenia), along with circumstantiality and self-reference. Apart from circumstantiality, which may be typically seen in manic phases, these symptoms are usually found in people during the depressive phases. Therefore, the effects of bipolar affective disorder on speech, language and communication can depend on whether the person is experiencing depression (in which case the effects will be as described in the previous section) or mania/hypomania. In periods of mania, the individual may display a faster rate of speech, flight of ideas, and distractibility in their interactions with others. North and Yutzy (2010, p.23) describe such speech as "a push of speech, that is, speech in which a great deal is said in a short amount of time". Sadock et al. (2015) give an account of what the disturbed speech of a person experiencing mania may sound like, as their mania increases:

> As the mania gets more intense, speech becomes louder, more rapid, and difficult to interpret. As the activated state increases, their speech is filled with puns, jokes, rhymes, plays on words, and irrelevancies. At a still greater

> activity level, associations become loosened, the ability to concentrate fades and fight of ideas, clanging, and neologisms appear. In acute manic excitement, speech can be totally incoherent and indistinguishable from that of a person with schizophrenia (p.367).

Sadock et al. (2015, p.368) further describe other communication features of a person who may be experiencing mania, including that they may be "easily distracted and their cognitive functioning in the manic state is characterized by an unrestrained and accelerated flow of ideas".

While specific impact on pragmatic abilities is not well documented, there are several lines of research which suggest that people with bipolar disorder may experience disturbances in this domain. Firstly, in terms of theory of mind and executive function – cognitive abilities considered to underlie pragmatic function (Cummings, 2009, 2017) – there is some evidence that impairments in theory of mind are present even when symptoms of depression and mania are controlled (Samamé, Martino, & Strejilevich, 2012), as well as impairments in executive functioning and verbal memory (Martínez-Arán et al., 2004). The processing of speech may also be affected in specific ways in people with bipolar disorder. Research has demonstrated that people with bipolar disorder have disturbances in how they process the vocal signals of emotion (emotional prosody) (Hoertnagl et al., 2015). These features of the speech signal may not be extracted as features of importance and further processing of the utterance will be affected (Paris, Mahajan, Kim, & Meade, 2018). Social functioning may be disproportionately affected in people with this diagnosis, in comparison to functioning on individual tasks. The reasons for this discrepancy are not yet clear, but may involve stigma and self-stigmatization (Tığlı Filizer, Cerit, Tuzun, & Aker, 2016), but the impact of specific communication factors has yet to be systematically explored.

Once again, a first-person account gives some insight into the nature of the struggles with communication when experiencing a mood disorder. The impact of a depressive phase and its impact on communication is described by an anonymous author below (Anonymous, 2006):

> My brain slows right down. I become stuck, unable to answer a simple question, unable to establish eye contact and unable to comprehend what is being asked of me (p.727).

Aside from the effort to engage conversationally, many people with a mood disorder may find it difficult, or be unable, to talk about their feelings and thoughts. O'Callaghan (2003, p.108) states "it's often the untold story of depression, the failure to reach out for help, the inability or reluctance to tell that story". Being unable to express oneself and talk about the experiences of depression can stymie progression to personal recovery. However, O'Callaghan (2003) explains how communication helped him clarify his thoughts and set him on the path towards recovery from his depression:

> My ongoing recovery was a difficult journey, but talking
> eased the toughness of it all. Recovery became easier because
> I chose to speak out, to spew out twisted feelings that were
> no longer scary once they had been brought out into the
> open. Because my mind was no longer cluttered and shut
> off, my thinking started to become more productive and
> my feelings calmer and more beneficial to me (p.103).

The role of the SLT in working with people with mood disorders is under-researched. However, as part of their remit with this client population SLTs have to facilitate language expression and effective communication (whether language or communication skills are impaired or 'dumbed down' by the illness process), in order to at least assist a person to engage in their own recovery.

Anxiety disorders

Anxiety disorders are the most common group of mental health disorders in the general population, with one-third of the population affected during their lifetime (Bandelow & Michaelis, 2015). Anxiety disorders can be difficult to diagnose accurately as they can occur co-morbidly with other mental illnesses (Fenton et al., 2016). Prevalence of anxiety disorders is greater in women than men, and prevalence decreases with higher socioeconomic status (Sadock et al., 2015). Fenton et al. (2016, p.147) state that the greater prevalence in women could be explained by "a cultural expectation that women will feel more anxiety and an acceptance that they will seek help".

Anxiety disorders result in constant and unsubstantiated worry that causes significant distress and interferes with daily life. The sub-types of anxiety disorders recognized in the DSM-5, and relevant to the discussion about mental health disorders in adults, include: panic disorder, agoraphobia, social anxiety disorder (social phobia), specific phobia, generalized anxiety disorder (GAD). While post-traumatic stress disorder and obsessive-compulsive disorder have a close relationship to anxiety disorders, the current DSM-5 classifies them elsewhere (Starcevic & Castle, 2016).

Anxiety can occur co-morbidly with other psychiatric presentations. For example, co-morbid anxiety disorders are reported in over 50% of people with schizophrenia (Pallanti, Quercioli, & Hollander, 2004). The presence of anxiety disorders in schizophrenia has been associated with poor social functioning and greater risk of relapse (Blanchard, Mueser, & Bellack, 1998). Of particular significance is the prevalence of social anxiety disorders which has been found to be in excess of 36% in outpatients with schizophrenia (Pallanti et al., 2004). In addition, it is reported that 25% of people presenting with first episode psychosis have social anxiety disorder (Michail & Birchwood, 2009). Co-morbid anxiety also predicts poorer treatment outcomes for people with bipolar affective disorder and major depressive disorder (Fava et al., 2008; Simon et al., 2004) though the relevance of this to clinical practice needs to be further researched.

Anxiety and communication

The nature of the relationship between anxiety disorders and speech, language and communication is complex. France (2001b) explains the complexity as follows:

> Communication and speech problems associated with anxiety and other stress-related disorders encompass every aspect of speech, language and communication. There are those speech disorders which accompany anxiety disorders and those which result from them, and there are communication problems that result from social inadequacy and perhaps exacerbate an anxiety disorder. The dividing line between these three categories is difficult to define... (p.37).

The relationship between anxiety and speech has been researched in the past (Pope, Blass, Siegman, & Raher, 1970), particularly with regard to the consideration of speech rate or speech disturbance as a possible indicator of anxiety (Cook, 1969). People with anxiety disorders can present with a variety of speech, language and communication problems during anxiety-provoking encounters. Increased proportions of pausing and changes in fundamental frequency have been associated with high states of anxiety, and higher perceived nervousness from listeners (Laukka et al., 2008).

The prevalence of anxiety in children with communication disorders has also been investigated (Cantwell & Baker, 1987), with research showing that children with early language impairment are more likely to have higher rates of anxiety disorders in early adulthood (19 years old) (Beitchman et al., 2001). A more recent longitudinal study of almost 10,000 children from the Avon Longitudinal Study of Parents and Children (who were followed up to 13 years of age), found that communication and social difficulties may constitute a significant risk factor for developing social anxiety (Pickard, Rijsdijk, Happé, & Mandy, 2017). Such findings further reinforce the complex relationship between communication disorders and anxiety extending into adulthood.

The association between stuttering and anxiety has probably received more attention in research than other areas of co-morbidity. Stuttering has been associated with a heightened risk of anxiety disorders (Iverach et al., 2009). Craig and Tran (2014) conducted a meta-analysis of research studies in the area of anxiety and stuttering (involving almost 1300 adults in total). Craig and Tran's (2014, p.35) results confirmed that "adults with chronic stuttering do have elevated trait and social anxiety", thereby underscoring the need for the treatment of stuttering to include programmes to manage such anxiety disorders. Likewise, Iverach and Rapee (2014, p.69) have called for increased collaboration between psychologists and SLTs "to develop and implement comprehensive assessment and treatment programmes for social anxiety among people who stutter".

In terms of interventions, while some people may experience an improvement in their anxiety-related speech features following pharmacological treatment, this is not the case for all (Laukka et al., 2008). However, other interventions, for example, Cognitive Behaviour Therapy, have shown to have positive effects (see Chapter 12 this volume) and, if adapted accordingly, may have greater potential in general to be used with people whose speech, language, communication skills or cognition may be impaired (Brown, Duff, Karatzias, & Horsburgh, 2011). However, further work is needed in this area of practice to establish effectiveness with particular clinical populations (e.g., people with ASD) (Weston, Hodgekins, & Langdon, 2016).

As for other mental health disorder presentations, looking to first-person accounts of anxiety and communication can give some insight into the challenges faced by individuals. Finding communication too stressful to engage in is illustrated by an interviewee in Brophy's (2009, p.50) study, as follows: "you have to be able to converse with people and I find that terribly stressful". Likewise, an adult with a diagnosis of anxiety and Asperger's Syndrome talks of the crippling anxiety associated with communication, as opposed to that associated with the diagnosis directly, as in "it's not the Asperger's that causes the anxiety it's the communication" and "I'm afraid of myself not understanding people—people can use words to trip me up" (Walsh, Delmar, & Jagoe, 2018, p.117). The relationship between anxiety and social skills deficits in people with ASD is intricate and could be considered bi-directional in nature. For example, Bridge (2016), a young adult with ASD and social anxiety, vividly describes the anxiety aroused to respond to a simple "how are you?":

> I didn't want to say I am fine because I am not. I am tired and I have a headache and being outside the house was stressing me out. So I just kind of looked at the person blankly. Then they looked back at me for a while and it was really quiet. I hate the quiet because it gives me too much time to think. If I think too much, then I give myself more stuff to worry about. The list can be endless if it goes on too long. On the other hand, if neither of us are talking, then neither of us are saying the wrong thing and I like that. I finally told them I was tired and then left it at that...They then looked back at me expectantly. I could not for the life of me work out what they wanted. It turns out they wanted me to ask "How are you?" back (pp.58-59).

It seems that anxiety can be exacerbated for some individuals when the added load of social communication is added to the equation, while Wood and Gadow (2010) discuss the fact that social skills deficits in people with ASD may be further impaired by feelings of anxiety. As with France's (2001b) explanation referred to above, it is often the case for many individuals with language or communication impairments that anxiety can prevent a person from engaging, yet not engaging socially can in turn cause further anxiety. This vicious circle of despair for some is one that is not easily broken without help and support.

The role of the SLT in adult mental health: Levels of intervention

Given the central role of communication to mental health (and disorder), and the range of communication disturbances experienced by people with mental health disorders, it is not difficult to appreciate the unique contribution a SLT can bring to multidisciplinary management of this clinical group (France, 2001c). The role of the SLT can be operationalized across different 'levels' of services. The nature of this role is described here using the multi-level model from the IASLT's (2015) *Speech and Language Therapy in Mental Health Services: A Guidance Document* (IASLT, 2015, p.27).

The multi-level model outlines three levels or domains in which services are provided: at the level of the *person*, the level of the *environment* and that of the wider *community*. These levels are not mutually exclusive and, more often than not, an SLT will be providing different types of services across these levels.

At the level of the *person*, working directly with the individual and their immediate environment is the focus. Examples of the types of activities which SLTs might undertake at this level, include: (i) assessment of speech, language and communication needs; (ii) input into differential diagnosis; (iii) individual 1:1 or group therapy and/or family education or support regarding communication (and swallowing); and (iv) monitoring communication in the context of medication. The input of the SLT at this level should lead to outcomes which impact on the wellbeing of the service user, with associated risks if these services are not available (e.g., failure to have needs met due to difficulty in communicating effectively, misdiagnosis resulting in mismanagement, and/ or reduced sense of agency and related reduction in opportunities to direct the courses of the service user's own treatment and choice making) (IASLT, 2015, p.29).

At the level of the *environment*, the role of the SLT includes interventions to facilitate related health services to provide care that recognizes the communication needs of the service user. The SLT may be involved, therefore, in a number of activities at the level of environmental intervention. These activities may include: (i) sharing information about an individual's communication support needs and training people in the environment in communication strategies to support successful interactions; (ii) scaffolding specific clinical interactions between a service user and a member of the multidisciplinary team and acting as a resource for other members of the team; (iii) advising on modification of the communication environment; and finally, (iv) contributing to policy development. At this level, the role of the SLT is primarily related to issues of equal access and inclusion. It follows then that an adult with mental health difficulties and communication needs has a right to be able to easily access mainstream (and other) healthcare services as required, in addition to all aspects of the specialist mental health services which they may be already in receipt of in a way that respects their individual communication needs. Some of the expected outcomes of intervention at this level include a services user's increased access to services, and support to allow the service user to reach their potential, including access to a quality communication environment, with multidisciplinary team members having the skills to support the service user in communication. Like other levels of intervention, there are risks too if this type of intervention is not available at the level of their environment. For example, a reduced access to, or standard of, service delivery may culminate in an increase in vulnerability for the individual and the family as they struggle to access optimal services in their environment. The risks of not engaging at the level of the environment are many, not least that services may fail to meet the national quality standards, with inadequate or incomplete provision of specialist mental health care plans (IASLT, 2015, p.31).

Finally, the SLT has a role to play within the wider *community*. At this level, the interventions are aimed at the general population and the focus is on improved communicative wellbeing and social inclusion of people with mental health difficulties and communication needs. Some of the expected outcomes for intervention at this level include a reduction in stigmatization, with increased opportunity for participation due to reduced interactional and attitudinal barriers. The concomitant risks of no consideration at the level of the community are increased isolation and exclusion from society, with an increased dependency on social welfare systems (IASLT, 2015, p.35).

Considering intervention at the nexus of these levels (i.e., the *person*, the *environment* and the *community*) might help to more meaningfully navigate the way to prevent experiences of communication breakdown in this context from being "misunderstood, misinterpreted and mismanaged" (France, 2001c, p.16).

Conclusion

Adults with mental health disorders can present with a diverse range of language and communication challenges, as considered intrinsic to their psychiatric diagnosis or as associated with it. Some of the language and communication challenges associated with a diagnosis of schizophrenia, bipolar and related disorders, and anxiety have been outlined in this chapter, including reference to first/other person accounts. Regardless of the origin of the language and communication difficulties experienced, people with mental health disorders (and their communication partners, be they family or healthcare professionals) can benefit from the specialist skills of the SLT, whose remit is to support all aspects of communication at all levels of interaction with the person, the environment and the community. However, despite a long-overdue but growing awareness and recognition of the need for speech and language therapy input for adults in this domain of practice, progress is slow in terms of development of services. What is required now is a more systematic mapping of clinical care pathways in speech and language therapy in mental health domains. Mapping therapeutic trajectories is needed to demonstrate the effectiveness of input, not only for the individual and their communication partner, but wherever communication is pivotal to successful interactions and individuals' wellbeing and recovery.

Finally, in the account of his journey to recovery – entitled *A Day called Hope* – O'Callaghan (2003, p.xii) calls on professionals to improve their practices, to keep up their part of the conversation by finding (in a metaphorical sense) a "way of speaking louder and in a language that people don't find threatening" if they are to proactively and meaningfully assist in an individual's recovery from a mental health disorder. Acknowledging the communication difficulties that exist for many adults with mental health disorders is a necessary first step in responding to this plea.

Acknowledgement

This chapter was informed, in part, by the authors' previous work as part of a writing team to compile *Speech and Language Therapy in Mental Health Services: A Guidance Document* (IASLT, 2015).

References

Al-Mosaiwi, M. & Johnstone, T. (2018). In an absolute state: Elevated use of absolutist words is a marker specific to anxiety, depression, and suicidal ideation. *Clinical Psychological Science*, 6(4) 529–542.

Alpert, M., Pouget, E.R., & Silva, R.R. (2001). Reflections of depression in acoustic measures of the patient's speech. *Journal of Affective Disorders*, 66(1), 59–69.

American Psychiatric Association (2013). *Diagnostic and Statistical Manual of Mental Disorders – 5*. 5th ed. Arlington, VA: American Psychiatric Publishing.

Andreasen, N. & Olson, S. (1982). Negative versus positive schizophrenia: Definition and validation. *Archives of General Psychiatry, 39*(7), 789–794.

Anonymous (2006). On madness: A personal account of rapid cycling bipolar disorder. *British Journal of General Practice, 56,* 726–728.

Arango, C., Fraguas, D., & Parellada, M. (2014). Differential neurodevelopmental trajectories in patients with early-onset bipolar and schizophrenia disorders. *Schizophrenia Bulletin, 40*(Suppl2), S138–S146.

Bandelow, B. & Michaelis, S. (2015). Epidemiology of anxiety disorders in the 21st century. *Dialogues in Clinical Neuroscience, 17*(3), 327–335.

Beitchman, J.H., Wilson, B., Johnson, C.J., Atkinson, L., Young, A., Adlaf, E., Escobar, M., & Douglas, L. (2001). Fourteen-year follow-up of speech/language-impaired and control children: Psychiatric outcome. *Journal of the American Academy of Child & Adolescent Psychiatry, 40*(1), 75–82.

Blanchard, J.J., Mueser, K.T., & Bellack, A.S. (1998) Anhedonia, positive and negative affect and social functioning in schizophrenia. *Schizophrenia Bulletin, 24,* 413–424.

Bridge, E.L. (2016). *Autism, Anxiety and Me: A Diary in Even Numbers.* London: Jessica Kingsley.

Brophy, J. (2009). Working alongside people with schizophrenia: Directions for speech and language therapy practice. Unpublished Master's Thesis, Trinity College Dublin, Ireland.

Brown, M., Duff, H., Karatzias, T., & Horsburgh, D. (2011). A review of the literature relating to psychological interventions and people with intellectual disabilities: Issues for research, policy, education and clinical practice. *Journal of Intellectual Disabilities, 15*(1), 31–45.

Bryan K. & Roach J. (2001). Assessment of speech and language in mental health. In J. France & S. Kramer (Eds), *Communication and Mental Illness* (pp.110-122). London: Jessica Kingsley.

Cannizzaro, M., Harel, B., Reilly, N., Chappell, P., & Snyder, P.J. (2004). Voice acoustical measurement of the severity of major depression. *Brain and Cognition, 56*(1), 30–35.

Cantwell, D.P. & Baker, L. (1987). The prevalence of anxiety in children with communication disorders. *Journal of Anxiety Disorders, 1*(3), 239–248.

Chaika, E. (1974). A linguist looks at "schizophrenic" language. *Brain and Language, 1*(3), 257–276.

Clegg, J., Brumfitt, S., Parks, R.W., & Woodruff, P.W.R. (2007). Speech and language therapy intervention in schizophrenia: A case study. *International Journal of Language and Communication Disorders, 42*(S1), 81–101.

Condray, R., Steinhauer, S.R., van Kammen, D.P., & Kasparek, A. (2002). The language system in schizophrenia: Effects of capacity and linguistic structure. *Schizophrenia Bulletin, 28*(3), 475–490.

Cook, M. (1969). Anxiety, speech disturbances and speech rate. *British Journal of Social and Clinical Psychology, 8*(1), 13–21.

Covington, M.A., He, C., Brown, C., Naci, L. McClain, J.T., Fjordbak, B.S., Semple, J., & Brown, J. (2005). Schizophrenia and the structure of language: The linguist's view. *Schizophrenia Research, 77*(1), 85–98.

Craig, A. & Tran, Y. (2014). Trait and social anxiety in adults with chronic stuttering: Conclusions following metanalysis. *Journal of Anxiety Disorders, 40*, 35–43.

Crow, T.L. (1980). Molecular pathology of schizophrenia: More than one disease process? *British Medical Journal, 12*(280), (6207), 66–68.

Cummings, L. (2009). *Clinical Pragmatics*. Cambridge: Cambridge University Press.

Cummings, L. (2017). Cognitive aspects of pragmatic disorders. In L. Cummings (Ed.), *Research in Clinical Pragmatics. Perspectives in Pragmatics, Philosophy & Psychology*, Volume 11. Switzerland: Springer.

Cutting, J. (1985). *The Psychology of Schizophrenia*. London: Churchill Livingstone.

Daly, A. & Craig, S. (2018). *Activities of Irish Psychiatric Hospitals 2017: Main Findings*. Dublin, Ireland: Health Research Board.

Darby, J.K., Simmons, N., & Berger, P.A. (1984). Speech and voice parameters of depression: A pilot study. *Journal of Communication Disorders, 17*(2), 75–85.

Docherty, N.M., Cohen, A.S., Nienow, T.M., Dinzeo, T.J., & Dangelmaier, R.E. (2003). Stability of formal thought disorder and referential communication disturbances in schizophrenia. *Journal of Abnormal Psychology, 112*(3), 469–475.

Eagles, J. (2011). Mood disorders. In N. Dogra, B. Lunn & S. Cooper (Eds), *Psychiatry by Ten Teachers* (pp.53–70). London: Hodder & Stoughton.

Emerson, J. & Enderby, P. (1996). Prevalence of speech and language disorders in a mental illness unit. *European Journal of Disorders of Communication, 31*, 221–236.

Fava, M., Rush, A.J, Alpert J.E., Balasubramani G.K., Wisniewski, S.R., Carmin, C.N., Biggs, M.M., Zisook, S., Leuchter, A., Howland, R., Warden, D., & Trivedi, M.H. (2008). Difference in treatment outcome in outpatients with anxious versus nonanxious depression: A STAR*D report. *The American Journal of Psychiatry, 165*(3), 342–351.

Fenton, C., Lodge, K-M., & Henderson, J. (2016). *Psychiatry*. London: JP Medical Ltd.

Foussias G., Agid O., Fervaha G., & Remington, G. (2014). Negative symptoms of schizophrenia: Clinical features, relevance to real world functioning and specificity versus other CNS disorders. *European Neuropsychopharmacology, 24*(5),693–709.

France, J. (2001a). Depression and other mood disorders. In J. France & S. Kramer (Eds), *Communication and Mental Illness: Theoretical and Practical Approaches* (pp.65–80). London: Jessica Kingsley.

France, J. (2001b). Anxiety disorders. In J. France & S. Kramer (Eds), *Communication and Mental Illness: Theoretical and Practical Approaches* (pp.26–41). London: Jessica Kingsley.

France, J. (2001c). Disorders of communication and mental illness. In J. France & S. Kramer (Eds), *Communication and Mental Illness: Theoretical and Practical Approaches* (pp.15–25). London: Jessica Kingsley.

France, J. & Muir, N. (1997). Introduction: About communication and the mentally ill patient. In J. France & N. Muir (Eds), *Communication and the Mentally-ill Patient* (pp.1–9). London: Jessica Kingsley.

Frith, C. (1992). *The Cognitive Neuropsychology of Schizophrenia*. East Sussex: Lawrence Erlbaum.

Frith, C. (1997). Language and communication in schizophrenia. In J. France & N. Muir (Eds), *Communication and the Mentally-ill Patient* (pp.10–17). London: Jessica Kingsley.

Garcia-Toro, M., Talavera, J.A., Saiz-Ruiz, J., & Gonzalez, A. (2000). Prosody impairment in depression measured through acoustic analysis. *The Journal of Nervous and Mental Disease, 188*(12), 824–829.

Gravell, R. & France, J. (1991). Mental disorders and speech therapy: An introduction. In R. Gravell & J. France (Eds), *Speech and Communication Problems in Psychiatry* (pp.1–21). London: Chapman & Hall.

Hinzen, W. & Rossello, J. (2015). The linguistics of schizophrenia: Thought disturbance as language pathology across positive symptoms. *Frontiers in Psychology, 6*(971), 1–17.

Hoertnagl, C.M., Biedermann, F., Yalcin-Siedentopf, N., Muehlbacher, M., Rauch, A.S., Baumgartner, S., Kaufmann, A., Kemmler, G., Deisenhammer, E., Hausmann, A., & Hofer, A. (2015). Prosodic and semantic affect perception in remitted patients with bipolar I disorder. *The Journal of Clinical Psychiatry, 76*(6), e779–86.

Irish Association of Speech & Language Therapists (IASLT). (2015). *Speech and Language Therapy in Mental Health Services: A Guidance Document*. Dublin: IASLT.

Isohanni, M., Murray, G.K., Jokelainen, J., Croudace, T., & Jones, P.B. (2004). The persistence of developmental markers in childhood and adolescence and risk for schizophrenic psychoses in adult life. A 34-year follow-up of the Northern Finland 1966 birth cohort. *Schizophrenia Research, 71*(2–3), 213–25.

Iverach, L. & Rapee, R.M. (2014). Social anxiety disorder and stuttering: Current status and future directions. *Journal of Fluency Disorders, 40*, 69-82.

Iverach, L., O'Brian, S., Jones, M., Block, S., Lincoln, M., Harrison, E., Hewat, S., Menzies, R.G., Packman, A., & Onslow, M. (2009). Prevalence of anxiety disorders among adults seeking speech therapy for stuttering. *Journal of Anxiety Disorders, 23*(7), 928–934.

Jagoe, C. (2013). Schizophrenia and metarepresentational abilities in conversation: A preliminary analysis of question interpretation. In E.Walaszewska & A. Piskorska (Eds), *Relevance Theory: More than Understanding* (pp.261-278). Cambridge: Cambridge Scholars Publishing.

Jagoe, C. (2015). Collaborative meaning-making in delusional talk as a search for mutual manifestness: A relevance theory approach. *Journal of Interactional Research in Communication Disorders, 6*(1), 53–71.

Joiner, T.E. & Timmons, K.A. (2008). Depression in its interpersonal context. In I.H. Gotlib & C.L. Hammen (Eds), *Handbook of Depression*, 2nd ed. (pp.322–339). New York: Guilford Press.

Joyal, M., Bonneau, A., & Fecteau, S. (2016). Speech and language therapies to improve pragmatics and discourse skills in patients with schizophrenia. *Psychiatry Research, 30*(240), 88-95.

Kirkpatrick, B., Buchanan, R.W., Ross, D.E., & Carpenter, W.T. (2001). A separate disease within the syndrome of schizophrenia. *Archives of General Psychiatry, 58*(2), 165-171.

Kirkpatrick, B., Fenton, W.S., Carpenter W.T., & Marder, S.R. (2006). The NIMH-MATRICS consensus statement on negative symptoms. *Schizophrenia Bulletin, 32*(2), 214-219.

Kovarsky, D. & Curran, M. (2007). A missing voice in the discourse of evidence-based practice. *Topics in Language Disorders, 27*(1), 50-61.

Krahn, G.L. (2011). WHO World Report on Disability: A review. *Disability and Health Journal, 4*(3), 141-142.

Laukka, P., Linnman, C., Åhs, F., Pissiota, A., Frans, Ö., Faria, V., Michelgård, A., Appel, L., Fredrikson, M., & Furmark, T. (2008). In a nervous voice: Acoustic analysis and perception of anxiety in social phobics' speech. *Journal of Nonverbal Behavior, 32*(4), 195-214.

Lavretsky, H. (2008). History of schizophrenia as a psychiatric disorder. In K.T. Mueser & D.V. Jeste (Eds), *Clinical Handbook of Schizophrenia* (pp.3-12). New York: Guilford Press.

Lunn, B. (2011). Schizophrenia. In N. Dogra, B. Lunn & S. Cooper (Eds), *Psychiatry by Ten Teachers* (pp.95-103). London: Hodder & Stoughton.

Martínez-Arán, A., Vieta, E., Colom, F., Torrent, C., Sánchez-Moreno, J., Reinares, M., Benabarre, A., Goikolea, J.M., Brugué, E., Daban, C., & Salamero, M. (2004). Cognitive impairment in euthymic bipolar patients: Implications for clinical and functional outcome. *Bipolar Disorders, 6*(3), 224-232.

Marvel, C.L., Schwartz, B.L., & Isaacs, K.L. (2004). Word production deficits in schizophrenia. *Brain and Language, 89*(1), 182-191.

McKenna, P. & Oh, T. (2015). *Schizophrenic Speech: Making Sense of Bathroots and Ponds that Fall in Doorways*. Cambridge: Cambridge University Press.

Meilijson, S., Kasher, A., & Elizur, A. (2004). Language performance in chronic schizophrenia: A pragmatic approach. *Journal of Speech, Language and Hearing Research, 47*, 695-713.

Michail, M. & Birchwood, M. (2009). Social anxiety disorder in first-episode psychosis: Incidence, phenomenology and relationship with paranoia. *British Journal of Psychiatry, 195*(3), 234-241.

Moller, M.D. (2013). Neurobiological responses and schizophrenia and psychotic disorders. In G.W. Stuart (Ed.), *Principles and Practice of Psychiatric Nursing* (pp.344-381). St Louis, MI: Elsevier.

Moore, E., Clements, M., Peifer, J., & Weisser, L. (2004). Comparing objective feature statistics of speech for classifying clinical depression. In *Conference Proceedings of the 26th Annual International Conference of the IEEE Engineering in Medicine and Biology Society, 1* (pp.17-20).

Mueser, K.T. & Gingerich, S. (1994). *Coping with Schizophrenia: A Guide for Families*. Oakland, CA: New Harbinger Publications.

Murray, R.M., & Lewis, S.W. (1987). Is schizophrenia a neurodevelopmental disorder? *British Medical Journal* (Clinical Research Edition), *295*(6600), 681-682.

North, C.S. & Yutzy, S.H. (2010). *Goodwin and Guze's Psychiatric Diagnosis*. New York: Oxford University Press.

O'Callaghan, G. (2003). *A Day called Hope: A Personal Journey Beyond Depression*. London: Hodder & Stoughton.

Pallanti, S., Quercioli, L., & Hollander, E. (2004). Social anxiety in outpatients with schizophrenia: A relevant cause of disability. *American Journal of Psychiatry*, *161*(1), 53-58.

Palmer, A.D., Carder, P.C., White, D.L., Saunders, G., Woo, H., Graville, D.J., & Newsom, J.T. (2019). The impact of communication impairments on the social relationships of older adults: Pathways to psychological well-being. *Journal of Speech, Language and Hearing Research*, *62*, 1-21.

Paris, M., Mahajan, Y., Kim, J., & Meade, T. (2018). Emotional speech processing deficits in bipolar disorder: The role of mismatch negativity and P3a. *Journal of Affective Disorders*, *234*, 261-269.

Perlini, C., Marini, A., Garzitto, M., Isola, M., Cerruti, S., Marinelli, V., Rambaldelli, G., Ferro, A., Tomelleri, L., Dusi, N., Bellani, M., Tansella, M., Fabbro, F., & Brambilla, P. (2012). Linguistic production and syntactic comprehension in schizophrenia and bipolar disorder. *Acta Psychiatrica Scandinavia*, *126*(5), 363-376.

Pickard, H., Rijsdijk, F., Happé, F., & Mandy, W. (2017). Are social and communication difficulties a risk factor for the development of social anxiety? *Journal of the American Academy of Child and Adolescent Psychiatry*, *56*(4), 344-351 e3.

Pope, B., Blass, T., Siegman, A.W., & Raher, J. (1970). Anxiety and depression in speech. *Journal of Consulting and Clinical Psychology*, *35*(1, Pt.1), 128-133.

Robillard, R. & Hickie, I.B. (2015). Sleep and biological rhythms in mania. In K.A. Babson & M.T. Feldner (Eds), *Sleep and Affect* (pp.293-319). San Diego, CA: Academic Press.

Rude, S.S., Gortner, E-M., & Pennebaker, J. (2004). Language use of depressed and depression-vulnerable college students. *Cognition and Emotion*, *18*(8), 1121-1133.

Ruocchio, P.J. (1991). First person account: The schizophrenic inside. *Schizophrenia Bulletin*, *17*(2), 357-360.

Sadock, B.J., Sadock, V.A., & Ruiz, P. (2015). *Kaplan & Sadock's Synopsis of Psychiatry*, 11th ed. London: Wolters Kluwer.

Samamé, C., Martino, D.J., & Strejilevich, S.A. (2012). Social cognition in euthymic bipolar disorder: Systematic review and meta-analytic approach. *Acta Psychiatrica Scandinavia*, *125*(4), 266-280.

Sergin, C. (2001). *Interpersonal Processes in Psychological Problems*. New York: Guilford Press.

Schelde, J.T.M. (1998). Major depression: Behavioural markers of depression and recovery. *Journal of Nervous and Mental Disease*, *186*(3), 133-140.

Scherer, K.R. (1987). Vocal assessment of affective disorders. In J.D. Maser (Ed.), *Depression and Expressive Behavior* (pp.57-82). Hillsdale. NJ: Lawrence Erlbaum Associates Inc.

Shine (n.d.) Schizophrenia and psychosis. Retrieved from https://www.shine.ie/information-on-mental-health/schizophrenia-and-psychosis/

Simon, N.M., Otto, M.W., Wisniewski, S.R., Fossey, M., Sagduyu, K., Frank, E., Sachs, G.S., Nierenberg, A.A., Thase, M.E., & Pollack, M.H. (2004) Anxiety disorder comorbidity in bipolar disorder patients: Data from the first 500 participants in the Systematic Treatment Enhancement Program for Bipolar Disorder (STEP-BD). *The American Journal of Psychiatry, 161*(12), 2222–2229.

Smith, K. & Sweeney, M. (1997). *Beyond Bedlam: Poems Written out of Mental Distress.* London: Anvil Press.

Starcevic, V. & Castle, D.J. (2016). Anxiety disorders. In G. Fink (Ed.), *Stress: Concepts, Cognition, Emotion, and Behavior* (pp.203–211). San Diego, CA: Academic Press.

Thomas, P. (1997). What can linguistics tell us about thought disorder? In J. France & N. Muir (Eds), *Communication and the Mentally-ill Patient* (pp.30–42). London: Jessica Kingsley.

Thomas, P., King, K., Fraser, W.I., & Kendell, R.E. (1990). Linguistic performance in schizophrenia: A comparison of acute and chronic patients. *British Journal of Psychiatry, 156,* 204–210.

Tığlı Filizer, A., Cerit, C., Tuzun, B., & Aker, A.T. (2016). Social aspect of functioning deteriorates more than individual aspect in patients with remitted bipolar disorder. *Noro Psikiyatri Arsivi, 53*(2), 158–162.

Uekermann, J., Abdel-Hamid, M., Lehmkamoer, C., Vollmoeller, W., & Daum, I. (2008). Perception of affective prosody in major depression: A link to executive function? *Journal of the International Neuropsychological Society, 14*(4), 552–561.

Walsh-Brennan, I.P. (2001). 'Speak to me...speak to me please': Conversational sociability amidst perceived disability in chronic schizophrenia. Unpublished doctoral thesis, Trinity College Dublin, Ireland.

Walsh, I.P. (1997). Conversational skills and schizophrenia: An exploration. In J. France & N. Muir (Eds), *Communication and the Mentally-ill Patient* (pp.98–116). London: Jessica Kingsley.

Walsh, I.P. (2008). Whose voice is it anyway? Hushing and hearing 'voices' in speech and language therapy interactions with people with chronic schizophrenia. *International Journal of Language & Communication Disorders, 43*(1), 81–95.

Walsh, I.P., Delmar, P., & Jagoe, C. (2018). "It's not the Asperger's that causes the anxiety, it's the communication": Person-centred outcomes of hope and recovery in a cultural–clinical borderland. *Topics in Language Disorders, 38*(2), 108–125.

Walsh, I., Regan, J., Sowman, R., Parsons, B., & McKay, P. (2007). A needs analysis for the provision of a speech and language therapy service to adults with mental health disorders. *Irish Journal of Psychological Medicine, 24*(3), 89–93.

Weinberger, D.R. (1987). Implications of normal brain development for the pathogenesis of schizophrenia. *Archives of General Psychiatry, 44,* 660–669.

Weston, L., Hodgekins, J., & Langdon, P.E. (2016). Effectiveness of cognitive behavioural therapy with people who have autistic spectrum disorders: A systematic review and meta-analysis. *Clinical Psychology Review, 49*, 41-54.

Whitehouse, A. (2009). Differentiating between childhood communication disorders. *Acquiring Knowledge in Speech, Language and Hearing, 11*(3), 149-151.

Wood, J.J. & Gadow, K.D. (2010). Exploring the nature and function of anxiety in youth with autism spectrum disorders. *Clinical Psychology Science & Practice, 17*(4), 281-292.

Woods, S.P., Weinborn, M., Posada, C., & O'Grady, J. (2007). Preliminary evidence for impaired rapid verb generation in schizophrenia. *Brain and Language, 102*(1), 46-51.

World Health Organisation (WHO) (2018a). Schizophrenia (Factsheet). Retrieved 23rd July, 2018 from http://www.who.int/news-room/fact-sheets/detail/schizophrenia

World Health Organisation (WHO) (2018b). Depression (Factsheet). Retrieved 14th February, 2019 from https://www.who.int/news-room/fact-sheets/detail/depression

4 Language and communication in psychiatry of old age: The perspective of a UK psychiatrist

Ramin Nilforooshan

Introduction

The number of older people in the world is growing proportionately faster than other groups. The United Nations reports that in 1980 there were around 382 million older people worldwide, more than doubling to 962 million in 2017, with a projection that this figure will in turn be doubled by 2050 when nearly 2.1 billion people will be aged 60 years or over (United Nations, 2017). Additionally, by 2030, the population aged 60 years or over in Europe is projected to increase by 23%, and by 41% in Northern America, with even greater increases elsewhere in the world (e.g., Asia and Africa) (United Nations, 2015). Furthermore, in the even older age bracket, there are projections of a three-fold increase in people age 80 years or over worldwide, rising from 137 million in 2017 to 425 million in 2050 (United Nations, 2017). The rise in numbers is highly significant, therefore, not least for the appropriate planning and implementation of healthcare services, both locally and on a worldwide scale. The mental health of older persons is a consideration within this context of the increasing population within this age cohort, both in terms of dementia as well as other mental health disorders.

Mental health problems increase with age. The recent European-wide study MentDis_ICF65+ reported that almost a quarter of the sample of older adults displayed a mental health disorder, with the most prevalent being anxiety disorders at 11% and affective disorders at 8%. The study specifically set out to explore mental disorders other than dementia and found that one in three older adults reported a mental health disorder within the last year and one in four had a current mental health disorder (Andreas et al., 2017).

This chapter briefly explores some of the language/communication considerations in psychiatry of older adults against the backdrop of service provision in the UK context. Case examples are provided in which language and communication breakdown presents as part of the clinical picture in the context of psychiatry of old age.

Older adult mental health care

Older People's Mental Health Services are concerned with the care and treatment of people with complex mixtures of psychological, cognitive, functional, behavioural, physical and social problems relating to ageing. Old age psychiatry evolved as a distinct specialty in the UK over the second half of the last century. In the 1940s, some of the most influential psychiatrists of the day, such as David Kay Henderson and Audrey Lewis, took an active interest in the wellbeing of older people. There are approximately 700 posts for consultant psychiatrists in Mental Health Services for Older Adults in the UK; however, the vacancy rate is high with around 12% of these posts unfilled (Royal College of Psychiatrists, 2017).

Older Adult Mental Health Services operate in many different settings to meet the needs of people with mental health problems: in primary care; their own home; by community-based services and inpatient facilities; acute general hospitals; inpatient units; residential care homes; hospices and prisons.

All these services should function within a philosophy of person-centred care, and this care should be accessible and culturally appropriate. Older adult mental health in the UK includes the care of people with dementia, but encompasses any psychiatric disorder occurring in older age, such as depression, anxiety, late-onset schizophrenia, personality disorder and substance misuse. While older adults may have experienced the onset of mental health disorders in their younger years, some may present for the first time in old age. Mental Health Services should therefore be alert to this possibility in order to appropriately identify, diagnose and treat older people who present for the first time with mental illness.

Psychiatric units for older adults

The number of psychiatric beds has been significantly reduced over the last decade in the UK. Nowadays, only patients with severe psychiatric needs who present with a serious risk to themselves or others can be admitted to a psychiatric unit in the National Health Service in the UK. There are two types of psychiatric units for older adults in England and this distinction provides a useful context in which to discuss the two main groups of patients seen by psychiatry of old age.

Functional units are for patients with functional psychiatric illnesses such as affective disorder, psychotic disorder and personality disorder. The majority of these patients are on antipsychotics, antidepressants or mood stabilizers, and many of them suffer from a variety of physical illnesses (such as diabetes, hypertension, stroke, Parkinson's Disease, etc.). One of the major challenges for clinicians who work in an inpatient unit is looking after patients with severe depression or psychosis, who present with severe self-neglect, including refusing to eat or drink. Although poor appetite and losing weight is a common presentation of depression, it is very important to identify the nature and severity of any eating, drinking and swallowing difficulties in this group of patients in order to provide holistic assessment and management. At present, SLTs are not typically a part of the multidisciplinary team, either in a community psychiatric team or in an inpatient psychiatric unit. Therefore, identifying specific communication needs and swallowing difficulties in this group of patients depends entirely on the skills of individual clinicians. This means that if a patient does not complain of any swallowing problems, or the disturbances in communication are not recognized as potentially addressed by speech and language therapy, he or she will hardly ever be referred to a specialist for assessment. Consequently, there will be no support for carers regarding communication adjustments or future swallowing difficulties.

Dementia units comprise the other type of unit for older adults. Many of the patients in these units present with language/communication and/or swallowing difficulties. We already know that they have difficulty with their communication, language and cognition and therefore they may face barriers in expressing their needs or their difficulties to clinicians. Dementia units admit patients from care homes or from their own home to assess their dementia needs, or for managing their behaviour and psychological symptoms of dementia. These symptoms include irritability, agitation, aggression, depression, apathy, hallucinations, delusions and disturbance in eating and sleeping. A multidisciplinary approach to eating, drinking and swallowing needs is a necessary aspect of a comprehensive end-of-life approach (Royal College of Speech and Language Therapists (RCSLT), 2014). Failure to assess and manage communication in this group of patients may result in frustration and behavioural challenges. Training staff and family carers to recognize how people in such units communicate their anxiety, pain and distress will result in providing better care and preventing a person with dementia from harming themselves or others. Also, well-trained staff and family carers are able to recognize signs of abuse and neglect and how to initiate safeguarding procedures.

Dementia

Dementia falls within the remit of psychiatry of old age in the UK. It is beyond the scope of this chapter to explore the details of the growing evidence related to the extensive and nuanced communication changes associated with different types of dementia. Speech and Language Therapists (SLTs) are already very active within this domain of practice and the reader is referred to Bayles, McCullough and Tomoeda (2020).

Dementia affects 7.1% of those aged over 65 years in the UK (Prince et al., 2014), with estimates putting the total number of people living with dementia in England and Wales at 767,000, and projections suggesting that 1,205,000 in the same geographic area will be living with dementia by 2040 (Ahmadi-Abhari et al., 2017). The national cost of dementia in the UK is estimated to be £26 billion per year (Lewis, Karlsberg Schaffer, Sussex, O'Neill, & Cockcroft, 2014) and projected to rise to £55 billion by 2040 (Prince et al., 2014).

In the 5th edition of the *Diagnostic and Statistical Manual of Mental Disorders* (DSM-5) (American Psychiatric Association, 2013) dementia is defined as a syndrome characterized by deficits in multiple cognitive domains, including memory, which represent a decline from a previously higher level of functioning and cause significant impairment in social or occupational functioning. It is similarly defined in the International Classification of Diseases-11 (ICD-11) (WHO, 2018) as a:

> ... decline from a previous level of cognitive functioning with impairment in two or more cognitive domains (such as memory, executive functions, attention, language, social cognition and judgment, psychomotor speed, visuoperceptual or visuospatial abilities).

There are many different types of dementia. Some of the most common types of dementia and their estimated distribution in the UK are as follows (Prince et al., 2014): Alzheimer's disease 62%; vascular dementia 17%; mixed dementia 10%; dementia with Lewy bodies 4%; frontotemporal dementia 2%; Parkinson's dementia 2%; other 3%.

One of the most important parts of a cognitive assessment is assessing speech and language. Communication difficulties happen in all types of dementia in the latter stages, and these difficulties become increasingly challenging for the person with dementia and their carers (Bourgeois, 1991; Bourgeois & Hickey, 2009). Historically, it was thought that as dementia progressed to a severe stage (this includes most types of dementia including those associated with Huntington's disease, Parkinson's disease, Alzheimer's disease), psychiatric needs of this group reduce, but it is obvious that the behaviour and psychological symptoms of dementia in many of those people persist through the end of life and require a multidisciplinary approach. Collaboration between old age psychiatrists, palliative care specialists and other members of the team, including SLTs, is very important at all stages, from diagnostic processes onwards. Different patterns of communication changes are seen with different types of dementia, and therefore it is very important to consider comprehensive assessment of communication difficulties to provide detailed differential diagnosis. Research has demonstrated the diagnostic relevance of comprehensive communication profiles for many of the different types of dementia. Indeed, the diagnosis of the primary progressive aphasias (a subtype of frontotemporal dementia) is dependent on clear, comprehensive and accurate assessment of language and communication (Gorno-Tempimi et al., 2011). The SLT is best placed to provide a detailed profile of language and communication abilities.

Early identification of, and intervention with, people with dementia is very important. Identification of communication needs is crucial as difficulties communicating affect in their relationships can cause major distress for people with dementia (Bryan & Maxim, 2003). NICE clinical guideline 97 (National Institute for Health and Care Excellence (NICE), 2018) recognizes the importance of communication (and swallowing) in working with people with dementia. The guidance, for example, advocates for training of family carers and staff in relation to adapting communication to optimize interactions with the person with dementia (section 1.11 and 1.13). Clearly, however, considerations of language and communication in this population extend to diagnosis and comprehensive management plans, as well as supporting successful communication with staff and family carers.

Mental health disorders in older adults

Mental disorders other than dementia are also relevant in the care of older adults. The communication disturbances associated with these disorders have been addressed in Chapter 3 (Walsh, Brophy & Jagoe, this volume), and these features may present similarly, or alongside other disorders associated with ageing. High rates of depression and anxiety disorders occur in the older adult population (Andreas et al., 2017). The risk of neurological disorders also increases with age, and many of the disorders may co-occur with mental health disorders. For example, in Parkinson's Disease systematic reviews have found an average point prevalence of anxiety of 31% (Broen, Narayen, Kuijf, Dissanayaka, & Leentjens, 2016), with clinically significant depressive symptoms present in 35% of this population (Reijnders, Ehrt, Weber, Aarsland, & Leentjens, 2008). Psychological distress is common following stroke at 50% and even higher in those with post-stroke aphasia at 93% (Hilari, 2011). Mental health disorders in older adults are not only associated with neurological conditions, but physical health conditions too. For example, up to 42% of those with chronic lung disease have been found to present with depression (Sirey, Raue, & Alexopoulos, 2007). Language and communication disturbances in these groups are likely to be complex with features of the primary neurological disorder occurring, along with communication changes associated with the mental health disorder (such as depression).

Psychiatry in this context of older adults is concerned with gathering clinical information objectively and by history taking, examination of mental state, and categorizing this information to come to a conclusion, formulation and diagnosis. There are a very limited number of investigations with high sensitivity and specificity available for psychiatrists to use to help them confirm a diagnosis or monitor response to medication. Therefore, a psychiatrist has to gather a very detailed history and carefully examine the mental state of a patient to be able to offer a comprehensive care plan. Detailed profiles of language and communication abilities add very valuable information available for diagnosis. Addressing communication and swallowing needs may allow for hospital admissions to be avoided or minimized, and reduced unnecessary treatment, including artificial feeding and pain management. Clear communication between members of the multidisciplinary team, the person themselves and family members about difficult treatment decisions and options is essential to be able to provide optimum care for these groups of patients, particularly where communication is affected.

Case examples

To illustrate the integral nature of communication in older adult mental health care, three cases that are routinely seen by old age psychiatrists are presented below. A fourth case in which swallowing difficulties are considered is also presented.

Case example 1

John is an 80-year-old gentleman with a diagnosis of severe Alzheimer's disease, who has been living in a nursing home for one year. Staff at the nursing home asked the GP to refer John to an old age psychiatrist, as he had become increasingly irritable, agitated, verbally and physically aggressive towards staff and other residents to the point that he had made it difficult for everyone to live and work with him. John requires help for most of his activities of daily living, and his speech is limited to a few words; he has also been losing weight.

There are clearly a number of challenges that an old age psychiatrist faces when dealing with this type of case, therefore it is very important that a multidisciplinary team, including a SLT, is involved. In this particular case, John had significant receptive aphasia, and therefore had difficulty understanding why people were asking him to do things, leading to frustration, and affecting his mood and his behaviour. With his limited verbal output, John probably showed his frustration with aggression. Staff in the residential setting lacked the communication techniques to successfully facilitate interactions with John. Another key consideration in John's profile (as referred to above), was the fact that he was losing weight, and a detailed history gathering showed that recently he had been choking and coughing more often. It has been found that 68% of people with dementia in care homes have dysphagia (Steele et al., 1997). Assessment and analysis of eating and swallowing difficulties in those with advanced dementia, as carried out by SLTs, is very important, and is considered part of a comprehensive multidisciplinary assessment (Logemann et al., 2008; Robbins et al., 2008).

Case example 2

Elisabeth is a 60-year-old woman who has been recently diagnosed with frontotemporal dementia (specifically semantic dementia/semantic variant of primary progressive aphasia), and is coming back to the outpatient clinic for a six-month review at her husband's request. Elisabeth had been working as an Information Technology (IT) manager, and she had been keen to continue working, but had recently been very frustrated with word-finding difficulties at work. Her husband is also very frustrated as he thinks that any conversation with his wife takes much longer than it previously did. On many occasions he has to finish the sentences for her, which often results in his wife becoming irritable and agitated.

One aspect of dementia care provided by old age psychiatrists and their team is to improve the communication skills for someone with dementia and their carer, and therefore any care plan should be individualized and look at the pattern of language breakdown in different forms of dementia. In this particular case, old age psychiatrists could refer this woman to be seen by an SLT, with a view to offering some advice on the following:

1. Help Elisabeth to produce a personal vocabulary book, including some names that she uses at home and specific words that she is required to use more often at work.

2. Encourage Elisabeth to carry a card explaining that she has some communication difficulties to show to people who do not know her.

3. Enable her to use a written script for answering the phone at home and at work.

4. Finally, organize a carer's assessment for Elisabeth's husband to help him understand and better manage her communication difficulties.

Case example 3

Robert is a 76-year-old man with a history of vascular dementia and has recently been admitted to hospital after he had another stroke. His wife has contacted Social Services and requested some help to look after Robert at home, as she does not want to place him in a nursing home. Robert was in a Stroke Unit for three days. His CT scan showed a massive stroke, and it has seriously affected his speech, his swallowing, and the right side of his body. He requires help to go to the toilet and most of his other activities of daily living. He has become very emotional and cries as he tries to speak, and therefore he has been referred to a Liaison Old Age Psychiatrist to assess his mood, and also to help the Stroke Physician assess his capacity for making a decision about his future placement. Robert did not sign any Lasting Power of Attorney, and he always hated the idea of going to a care home.

In this case, an old age psychiatrist will assess Robert's mental state, but obviously, considering that Robert has severe difficulty with his speech and language, assessing his mental state and capacity, and deciding about his future placement, is very challenging. There are four parts in the Mental Capacity Act (Department of Health, 2005) which need to be considered when assessing someone's capacity. In this particular case, it is very important to be satisfied that Robert can (i) understand the provided information about making a decision regarding his future placement; (ii) retain the information long enough to make a decision; (iii) weigh up the information and consider the risk of benefits of each option; and in the end (iv) can communicate his wishes. Within this context, then, Robert requires extensive support, which can be provided by a SLT alongside an old age psychiatrist, to facilitate and help him in each part of this capacity assessment, and to provide the information in a way that it is easy for Robert to understand and optimize the communication level for him to make a decision. Without a comprehensive and detailed assessment, Robert can be seen as a person who lacks capacity to make a decision about his future care, which may affect the nature of that care and his relationship with his wife. The importance of appropriate communication support and the role of the SLT is comprehensively addressed in Jones and Volkmer (2018).

All of the above cases are where a patient with dementia presented in different settings with varying speech, language and communication, and swallowing difficulties. As discussed earlier, older adult mental health services are not just about dementia. The life expectancy of a patient with schizophrenia and other chronic mental illnesses has improved over the last couple of decades, and now there are many patients with a diagnosis of chronic schizophrenia or bipolar affective disorder in the care of these services. The ways in which these disorders impact on communication has been described in Chapter 3. A common problem among the elderly is with eating, drinking, coughing and choking. Dysphagia is a common cuase of mortality and morbidity in adults with schizophrenia (Kulkarni, Kamath, & Stewart, 2017) and an increased risk of dysphagia has been associated with antipsychotic medication (Cicala, Barbieri, Spina, & de Leon, 2019; Ruschena et al., 2003). Assessment and management of eating, drinking and swallowing difficulties and measuring the impact of these difficulties on an individual is a very important aspect of a holistic approach in older adult psychiatric services.

Case example 4

Elvira is a 73-year-old woman with a history of severe depression and was recently admitted to a psychiatric unit under Section 2 of Mental Health Act (under detention). Elvira was first diagnosed with depression after the birth of her second child when she was 31 years old. She had four admissions to psychiatric units and her last admission was three years ago. She presents with low mood, anhedonia (i.e., reduced motivation and ability to experience pleasure), low energy, hopelessness and suicidal thoughts. She has always been an anxious person and overtly concerned about her physical health. A few months before the current episode of depression, she presented with signs and symptoms of oesophagitis and was started on Omperazole for her heartburn. Since been admitted to a psychiatric unit, she claims that she is not able to swallow food and her medication. She stopped eating and drinking and she started to lose weight. She was prescribed a high dosage of antipsychotic and antidepressant medication. Finally, she underwent electroconvulsive therapy (ECT) as she became dehydrated and at risk of acute kidney failure. Elvira developed delusions about her swallowing difficulties and her condition deteriorated rapidly. A referral to a SLT could help facilitate a better understanding of Elvira's clinical presentation and concerns (for both herself and her family) and provide a comprehensive care plan for her.

Conclusion

It is vital for all staff working in health or social care organizations with older people to have the necessary skills in recognizing and caring for the mental health needs of these groups. Therefore, it is important for commissioners to look at a range of available local services to be able to commission the best service to these patients and their carers. The service must be commissioned on the basis of need and not merely age, and older people are entitled, like other groups, to high-quality age-appropriate services. This type of service should be delivered by professionals who have had training, qualifications and a range of knowledge and expertise to look after older adults. Services should have the same standard of care as services for younger people and should follow national guidelines, including waiting times and offering choices for older adults and their families. A good service will provide comprehensive psychiatric, psychological, physical and social input for older people including access to speech and language therapy.

References

Ahmadi-Abhari, S., Guzman-Castillo, M., Bandosz, P., Shipley, M.J., Muniz-Terrera, G., Singh-Manoux, A., ... & Brunner, E.J. (2017). Temporal trend in dementia incidence since 2002 and projections for prevalence in England and Wales to 2040: Modelling study. *British Medical Journal, 358,* j2856.

American Psychiatric Association. (2013). *Diagnostic and Statistical Manual of Mental Disorders (DSM-5),* 5th ed. Arlington, VA: American Psychiatric Publishing.

Andreas, S., Schulz, H., Volkert, J., Dehoust, M., Sehner, S., Suling, A., ... & Grassi, L. (2017). Prevalence of mental disorders in elderly people: The European MentDis_ICF65+ study. *The British Journal of Psychiatry, 210*(2), 125-131.

Bayles, K., McCullough, K., & Tomoeda, C.K. (2020). *Cognitive-communication Disorders of MCI and Dementia: Definition, Assessment, and Clinical Management,* 3rd ed. San Diego, CA: Plural Publishing.

Bourgeois, M.S. (1991). Communication treatment for adults with dementia. *Journal of Speech and Hearing Research, 34*(4), 831-844.

Bourgeois, M.S. & Hickey, E.M. (2009). *Dementia: From Diagnosis to Management. A Functional Approach.* New York, NY: Taylor and Francis.

Broen, M.P., Narayen, N.E., Kuijf, M.L., Dissanayaka, N.N., & Leentjens, A.F. (2016). Prevalence of anxiety in Parkinson's disease: A systematic review and meta-analysis. *Movement Disorders, 31*(8), 1125-1133.

Bryan, K. & Maxim, J. (2003). Managing language and communication difficulties in Alzheimer's dementia: The link to behaviour. In T. Adams & J. Manthorpe (Eds), Dementia Care (pp.69-85). London: Arnold.

Cicala, G., Barbieri, M.A., Spina, E., & de Leon, J. (2019). A comprehensive review of swallowing difficulties and dysphagia associated with antipsychotics in adults. *Expert Review of Clinical Pharmacology, 12*(3), 219-234.

Department of Health. (2005). Mental Capacity Act. London: HMSO.

Gorno-Tempini, M.L., Hillis, A.E., Weintraub, S., Kertesz, A., Mendez, M., Cappa, S.F., ... & Grossman, M. (2011). Classification of primary progressive aphasia and its variants. *Neurology, 76*(11), 1006-1014.

Hilari, K. (2011). The impact of stroke: Are people with aphasia different to those without? *Disability and Rehabilitation, 33*(3), 211-218.

Jones, I. & Volkmer, A. (2018). *Speech and Language Therapists and Mental Capacity: A training resource for adult services.* Guildford: J&R Press.

Kulkarni, D.P., Kamath, V.D., & Stewart, J.T. (2017). Swallowing disorders in schizophrenia. *Dysphagia, 32*(4), 467-471.

Lewis, F., Karlsberg Schaffer, S., Sussex, J., O'Neill, P., & Cockcroft, L. (2014). *The Trajectory of Dementia in the UK - Making a Difference.* Report for Alzheimer's Research UK: OHE Consulting.

Logemann, J.A., Gensler, G., Robbins, J., Lindblad, A.S., Brandt, D., Hind, J.A., Kosek, S., ... & Miller Garnder, P.J. (2008). A randomized study of three interventions for aspiration of thin liquids in patients with dementia or Parkinson's disease. *Journal of Speech, Language and Hearing Research*, 51(1), 173-183.

National Institute for Health and Care Excellence. (2018). Dementia: Assessment, management and support for people living with dementia and their carers. UK: NICE. Retrieved from https://www.nice.org.uk/guidance/ng97

Prince, M., Knapp, M., Guerchet, M., McCrone, P., Prina, M., Comas-Herrera, A., ... & Rehill, A. (2014). *Dementia UK: Update*. UK: Alzheimer's Society.

Reijnders, J.S., Ehrt, U., Weber, W.E., Aarsland, D., & Leentjens, A.F. (2008). A systematic review of prevalence studies of depression in Parkinson's disease. *Movement Disorders*, 23(2), 183-189.

Robbins, J., Gensler, G., Hind, J., Logemann, J.A., Lindblad, A.S., Brandt, D., Baum, H., Lilienfeld, D., ... & Miller Gardner, P.J. (2008). Comparison of 2 interventions for liquid aspiration on pneumonia incidence: A randomized trial. *Annals of Internal Medicine*, 148(7), 509-518.

Royal College of Psychiatrists (2017). *Census 2017: Workforce Figures for Consultant and Specialty Doctor Psychiatrists*. London: RCPsych.

Royal College of Speech and Language Therapy. (2014). *Speech and Language Therapy Provision for People with Dementia*. London: RCSLT.

Ruschena, D., Mullen, P.E., Palmer, S., Burgess, P., Cordner, S.M., Drummer, O.H., Wallace, C., & Barry-Walsh, J. (2003). Choking deaths: The role of antipsychotic medication. *The British Journal of Psychiatry*, 183, 446-450.

Sirey, J.A., Raue, P.J., & Alexpoulos, G.S. (2007). An intervention to improve depression care in older adults with COPD. *International Journal of Geriatric Psychiatry*, 22(2), 154-159.

Steele, C.M., Greenwood, C., Ens, I., Robertson, C., & Seidman-Carlson, R. (1997). Mealtime difficulties in a home for the aged: Not just dysphagia. *Dysphagia*, 12(1), 43-50.

United Nations, Department of Economic and Social Affairs, Population Division (2015). *World Population Ageing 2015* (ST/ESA/SER.A/390).

United Nations, Department of Economic and Social Affairs, Population Division (2017). *World Population Ageing 2017 - Highlights* (ST/ESA/SER.A/397).

World Health Organisation. (2018). *International Statistical Classification of Diseases and Related Health Problems*, 11th Revision. Retrieved from https://icd.who.int/browse11/l-m/en

Section 2

Communication and mental health: Developing theory

5 Pragmatic language and social conversational skills intervention for children with mental health disorders

Sinéad Kellaghan

Introduction

Although once neglected by the speech and language therapy community, pragmatic theory has come to have some influence on speech and language therapy practice. Attending to pragmatics is now considered to be a "standard part of the assessment and intervention protocols" used by clinicians (Cummings, 2007a, p.99). As noted by many authors (including Novak & Kapolnek, 2001; Spence, 2003), pragmatic language and social skills interventions are often part of the suite of clinical supports offered to both children and adults with mental health disorders (MHDs).

Since its relatively recent emergence, the field of pragmatics has grown considerably but remains orientated towards its original purpose, namely, the study of meaning-making and "human inferential behaviour" within a philosophical-linguistic context (Horn & Ward, 2004, p.xii). As such, pragmatics provides much in the way of frameworks, concepts, constructs as well as debates that are relevant to communication. It is perhaps unsurprising that clinicians and researchers who are interested in communication have been drawn to the rich resource pool that is pragmatic theory to guide their work.

In order to understand how pragmatic theory might be usefully drawn on when providing intervention, this chapter begins with a brief overview of the emergence of the broad field of pragmatics. Following this, the practice area of clinical pragmatics is discussed. Finally, themes emergent from the clinical pragmatics literature environment are considered in relation to social skills and pragmatic language interventions for children who experience MHDs.

Why is pragmatics important when working with children who experience mental health disorders?

Strong links between mental health and language and communication skills are broadly acknowledged in the literature, leading Snow (2009, p.95) to state that "language competence…cannot be separated out from mental health across the lifespan". Despite this, the impact of pragmatic difficulties and differences on wellbeing and achieving educationally, socially and vocationally has had little discussion until recently (Cummings, 2014). The importance of developing capacity in language and communication to enable children with MHDs to access both mainstream and specific mental health services that are language dependent (such as talking therapies, advocacy services, as well as educational, employment and vocational supports, etc.) is worth considering in this context.

The presence of language and communication impairments among children who experience MHDs is also well recognized in the literature (see Clegg, Chapter 2, this volume, for overview). Although there remains much to be learned about the relationship between these phenomena, it has been suggested that there may be at least a bi-directional if not symbiotic relationship between mental health, language and communication. Law, Reilly and Snow (2013, p.491) described this close connection between mental health and language and communication when they note "communicative competence occupies a unique place in the lives of children, as it is of interest both as a *predictor* variable and an *outcome* variable with respect to mental health".

The well-established, but poorly understood, relationship between mental health and language and communication points to an obvious role for Speech and Language Therapists (SLTs) in this context. SLTs holistically support children and adolescents who experience MHDs to identify strengths and needs as well as supporting these young people to maximize their potential in relation to speech, language and communication. The importance of accurately identifying language and communication strengths and needs, alongside the provision of appropriate language and communication supports, is sharpened by recognizing the 'central role' of language and communication in the interventions that are commonly offered to children with MHDs (such as counselling/talking therapies, Cognitive Behavioural Therapy, social skills training, etc.) as noted by Im-Bolter and Cohen (2007, p.532).

The 'pragmatic turn' and speech and language therapy

It is generally agreed that the field of pragmatics developed from the study of the semiotic (Morris, 1938), the philosophy of language (Austin, 1962; Grice, 1975; Searle, 1969, 1976) and disquiet with the study of language as a purely abstract, structural entity (Lakoff, 1971; Lakoff & Ross, 1976). Many of the key topics in pragmatics today (including deixis, presupposition, implicature and speech acts) emerged at this time. The important role that was played by thinkers such as John Dewey, George Herbert Mead and William James in shaping modern-day pragmatics has also been noted (Duchan, 1995; Formigari, 2004).

Charles Morris's (1938, p.6) tripartite split of linguistic theory into the areas of 'syntactics', 'semantics' and 'pragmatics' is widely recognized as a defining moment for pragmatics (e.g., Levinson, 1983). Morris's (1938, p.6) oft-cited definition of pragmatics as "the study of the relation of signs to interpreters" has had a lasting impact on linguistic theory. Consequently, pragmatics is often defined as the study of language as it is used and interpreted in everyday life.

In or around the 1970s, the growing regard for pragmatic theory in linguistics became known as the 'pragmatic turn' (Mey, 2006, p.17). At around this time, the priority accorded to syntax in linguistic theory was questioned and fresh theoretical foundations for exploring language as a contextualized and dynamic process continued to develop. This shift in linguistic thinking, or 'pragmatics revolution', has increasingly influenced those who draw on linguistic theory in their work, including SLTs (Kamhi, 2000, p.182).

In the 1970s and 1980s, increasing evidence emerged (e.g., Bates 1976a, 1976b; Bruner, 1974; Bruner & Watson, 1983; Dore, 1974; Halliday, 1975) which posited that children acquired and developed language in an interactionally-based manner. This interactional understanding of language acquisition contrasted with the then dominant idea that children acquired language primarily through biological and/or operant conditioning processes. Language learning became increasingly envisaged as a highly contextualized process which was socially and culturally as well as biologically, behaviourally and linguistically mediated (Bruner, 1974; Bruner & Watson, 1983). Subsequently, certain authors highlighted a discomfort regarding the strong influence that behaviourist and structuralist paradigms had on speech and language therapy practices (e.g., Craig, 1984). The notion of language as a dynamic process, used for relating and acting in the world, as espoused by pragmatic theory, provided an alternative paradigm to the previous conceptualization of language as a static linguistic code through which meaning was transmitted. Accordingly, SLTs were legitimized by the 'pragmatic turn' to look beyond linguistic structure (and units such as phonemes, words and sentences) within their assessments and interventions (Duchan, 2000).

However, it has long been suggested that changes in linguistic thinking are not always completely mirrored in clinical practice (McTear & Conti-Ramsden, 1990). Despite Bates' (1976b, p.420) assertion that "all of language is pragmatic to begin with", a trend of treating pragmatics as an isolated linguistic module, ripe for assessment, by comparing a list of 'pragmatic' behaviours and skills with static developmental norms continues to this day as evidenced by many of the pragmatics checklists that are available. Work which charted the development of pragmatic skills and behaviours in various populations of children began in the 1980s. Interest in developmental milestones reflecting the acquisition of pragmatic skills and behaviours proliferated (e.g., Conti-Ramsden & Gunn, 1986; Wetherby & Prutting, 1984). Deviations from norms were used to identify impairments which in turn became the primary focus of intervention, as has often been the case historically in speech and language therapy practice (Duchan, 2005).

Pragmatics has, then, at times become superficially interpreted as yet another list of norms and skills that act as a site for the construction of impairment, rather than a holistic way to evaluate communicative events and problems therein. In this vein, the intervention that follows is likely to focus on the didactic teaching of isolated linguistic structures utilizing methods that rely, in part, on behaviourist traditions (such as positive reinforcement and the provision of rewards for each 'correct' or 'right' elicitation). This approach to intervention would seem to be incongruous with the dynamic, context-sensitive nature of communication suggested by much of pragmatic theory (Duchan, 2000).

It would also appear that, as Perkins (2000) notes, in certain corners of the literature concepts from pragmatic theory have been introduced directly into clinical practice and research without alteration. It is not surprising, then, that the unmodified use of abstract pragmatic theory in real-life clinical settings has led to charges of a descriptive and superficial understanding of pragmatics (Cummings, 2007b, 2009; Perkins, 2005a). Additionally, in its short existence, the area of clinical pragmatics has been marred by a history of nosological confusions and unresolved debates (e.g., Bishop, 2014; Bishop, Snowling, Thompson, Greenhalgh, & CATALISE Consortium, 2016, 2017; Norbury, 2014)[1].

Using norms as the sole way of identifying communication difficulties and intervention outcomes has been questioned, particularly following the recognition of a dissociation between structural, formal linguistic skills and communication skill in some instances. For example, seminal research from Sarno (1969), Holland (1979, 1982) and later from other authors (such as Beeke, Wilkinson, & Maxim, 2007; Simmons-Mackie & Damico, 1995) highlighted the communicative competence exhibited by some people with aphasia despite significant linguistic difficulties. This trend of decoupling purely structural linguistic skills and overall communication skill continues in studies of aphasia, intellectual disability and beyond where the use of sparse linguistic resources to achieve effective interactional results has at times been demonstrated (e.g., Antaki, Finlay, Walton, & Pate, 2008; Beeke et al., 2007; Finlay & Antaki, 2012; Ulatowska & Olness, 2007; Williams, 2011).

The converse is also evident. Some studies of people with strong structural language skills proposed that sometimes these same individuals, despite their adequate structural linguistic skills, may lack functional communication skills (e.g., Philofsky, Fidler, & Hepburn, 2007; Wetherby & Prutting, 1984). The conversational behaviour and the lack of functional communication skill observed in particular clinical populations may be regarded as being disproportionately challenged in light of the simultaneously strong, structural linguistic abilities (e.g., the ability to produce grammatically well-formed sentences). It has been suggested that a clearer demarcation between pragmatic language skills and communication skills is required to clarify this discrepancy (Norbury, 2014).

Pragmatic theory offers a wealth of resources which enable communication to be analyzed at both a macro, societal level as well as a micro, individual level. This theoretical breadth complements a profession such as speech and language therapy which aims to effect change at both societal and individual

---

1 The exact nature of the interaction between language impairment and social and cognitive differences and/or difficulties remains an unresolved and highly complex issue (Norbury, 2014). However, recent changes to terminology have facilitated clearer description of presenting conditions and their relationship to language impairment. Bishop and colleagues (2016, 2017) describe Developmental Language Disorder (DLD) as a persistent language disorder which impacts on a child's everyday activities (including educational attainments and social interactions) that presents without another differentiating condition, although it is important to note that DLD can co-occur alongside other challenges and diagnoses such as poor motor skills or ADHD (Hill, 2001; Mueller & Tomblin, 2012).

levels and, indeed, levels in between (e.g., Irish Association of Speech and Language Therapists (IASLT), 2015; Law et al., 2013; Royal College of Speech and Language Therapists (RCSLT), 2009; Snow, 2009). SLTs working in the area of mental health have been specifically charged with attending to pragmatics and social communication in their work with children by their professional bodies (IASLT, 2006, 2015; RCSLT, 2009). All in all, SLTs now find themselves in a compromise position of being required to provide assessment and intervention in the area of pragmatics but, in doing so, have an incomplete body of knowledge and a contentious literature environment to guide their practice (Adams, 2008; Gerber, Brice, Capone, Fujiki, & Timler, 2012; Norbury, 2014).

Doing clinical pragmatics

Assessment

The practice area of clinical pragmatics remains relatively unspecified and uncharted. Despite this, the assessment of pragmatics is now a 'routine' part of speech and language therapy practice (Hewitt, 2000a, p.258). The reader is referred to Adams (2002), Cummings (2009, 2014) and Norbury (2014) for a more thorough discussion of the practice area of clinical pragmatics. The discussion below serves mainly to offer the reader a brief overview of clinical practice in the area of pragmatics.

The resources and tools used when working with pragmatics in clinical settings have generally been discussed under the three categories, following both Adams (2002) and Cummings (2009), as (i) formal and standardized tests; (ii) interview and observational schedules/checklists/profiles; and (iii) systems for analyzing discourse. These categories are not mutually exclusive. It also can be difficult to isolate pragmatic assessments from other language and communication assessments as noted by Manochiopinig, Sheard and Reed (1992) and Norbury (2014.)

Formal and standardized tests

Very few available published, formal and standardized tests exclusively focus on pragmatics. The term 'formal and standardized' is being used with reference to assessments which are administered in a standard manner and which quantitatively compare an individual's performance against a cohort of peers (as in *The Test of Pragmatic Language 2*; Phelps-Terasaki & Phelps-Gunn, 2007).

These types of assessment typically ask a child to generate responses to prompts such as verbal questions, pictures and/or hypothetical scenarios in controlled settings. Some formal language and communication assessments also have a pragmatic component or content that could be deemed pragmatic. For example, the *Assessment of Comprehension and Expression* (Adams, Coke, Crutchley, Hesketh, & Reeves, 2001) explores inferential comprehension, nonliteral language and retell of narrative. Some formal, standardized assessments of narrative are also available including *Bus Story* (Renfrew, 2010), the *Strong Narrative Assessment Procedure* (Strong, 1998) and the *Expression, Reception, and Recall of Narrative Instrument* (Bishop, 2003a).

It has been suggested that while formal assessments capture important information about a child's competence, they do not always reflect how a child uses their language and communication skills outside of structured assessment settings (Norbury, 2014). The dynamic contextual influences on communication highlighted by much of pragmatic theory may not be readily replicated or controlled for in a standardized testing situation making a "test of pragmatics almost a contradiction in terms" (Paul, 2007, p.364). Perhaps an acceptance of this fact accounts for the lack of formal and standardized assessments in the area of clinical pragmatics as suggested by Fujiki and Brinton (2009):

> Unfortunately, pragmatic skills do not lend themselves to standardized assessment formats. Pragmatic behaviors, by definition, are influenced by contextual and social variables. Formal tests attempt to neutralize these factors by standardizing context to allow reliable comparison of performance to a normative standard (p.412).

Interview and observational schedules/checklists/profiles

In comparison to the availability of standardized formal assessments, the interview and observational schedules, checklists and profiles discussed in this section are more plentiful in number. Included in this category of assessments are checklists and profiles which clinicians use to gather and organize information about pragmatics and/or communication via interview or observation (e.g., Bishop, 2003b; Dewart & Summers, 1995; Prutting & Kirchner, 1987; Semel, Wiig, & Secord, 2003). These assessment tools do not always provide standardized scores and many but not all are criterion-referenced or qualitatively analyzed[2]. The use of individual profiling tools in addition to standardized, formal assessment has been advocated in speech and language therapy practice in general (Joffe, Cruice, & Chiat, 2008), and in the practice area of pragmatics in particular (Norbury, 2014).

Non-standardized assessments have been praised as methods which enable clinicians to explore language and communication in contextualized, dynamic and ecologically valid ways, in that they allow for "describing performance in the context of real-world settings and activities and exploring the effects of systematic changes in communication and cognitive demands and partner supports" (Coelho, Ylvisaker, & Torstar, 2005, p.223). However, authors such as Perkins (2005a, 2007) and Hyter (2007) have voiced concerns regarding the grouping of skills and behaviours as targeted in pragmatics assessments. Often there appears be little theoretical rationale for grouping certain language and communication skills and/or behaviours together during assessment except that they are related to nonverbal or paralinguistic aspects of communication (and thus have been historically viewed as 'pragmatic' in nature). Additionally, analyzing and interpreting assessment results outside of robust theoretical frameworks can be problematic in terms of accurate identification of difficulties and consequent intervention planning with descriptive rather than explanatory conclusions being reached during assessment (Perkins, 2005a, 2007).

Checklists, schedules and profiling tools often rely on information from significant conversational partners or other people who know a child well (such as parents, teachers, healthcare or educational professionals). Additionally, some self-rating checklists also exist. Examples of self-rating checklists can be found in *Talkabout* (Kelly, 2001), *Social Use of Language Programme* (Rinaldi, 1992), and *Socially Speaking* (Schroeder, 1996).

Assessments taking the form of schedules, checklists and profiles can be completed live or from recordings of interaction. The informant is often asked to evaluate a variety of phenomena relevant to specific linguistic or nonverbal behaviours or overall communicative efficacy. As noted by Manochiopinig et al. (1992), the focus of these assessment tools ranges from exploring discrete 'pragmatic' behaviours or certain 'pragmatic' skills to making a judgement about a child's overall communicative efficiency or functionality.

Systems for analyzing discourse

Discourse has a broad frame of reference relating to both the process and

---

2 However, one notable exception is Bishop's (2003b) *Children's Communication Checklist-2* which provides normative data for children between the ages of 4 and 16 years.

product of language use "above and beyond the sentence" (Schiffrin, Tannen, & Hamilton, 2013, p.1). The clinical analysis of discourse appears to draw predominantly on frameworks from the areas of Conversation Analysis (CA) and Discourse Analysis (DA). Conversation, narrative, descriptive and procedural discourse appear to be among the most commonly cited genres of discourse which are examined in clinical settings (Cummings, 2009).

DA explores discourse at various levels or units of analysis. Discourse can be explored at a microlinguistic (i.e., within sentence level), microstructural (i.e., the analysis of phenomena across sentences) and/or at a macrostructural and/or superstructural level (Coelho, 2007). Broadly speaking, macrostructural analysis explores the overall 'global semantic content' or the overarching topic of a piece of discourse (van Dijk & Kintsch, 1983, p.194). Superstructural level analysis focuses on exploring the organization of content or information within the discourse (e.g., narrative schema or argumentative schema as pointed out by Cummings, 2009).

A variety of concepts have been used to analyze different levels of discourse clinically. For example, Halliday and Hasan's (1976, pp.333-339) cohesive ties (namely *reference, conjunction, substitution, lexical relations, ellipsis* and *repetition*) have been used as methods of evaluating cohesion at the microstructural level of discourse (as in Craig & Evans, 1993). A further example is the analysis of narrative superstructure using Labov's (1972) high point analysis (as in Rollins, 2000). Despite the wide variety of personal and cultural variation recognized in narrative skills (as stressed by Bliss & McCabe, 2008; Norbury & Bishop, 2010; Rollins, 2000), particular patterns of narrative production have been associated with particular diagnoses (Botting, 2002; Boudreau & Chapman, 2000; Miranda, McCabe, & Bliss, 1998). Narrative skills have also become a platform from which particular patterns of impairment are identified. For example, the presence of tense-marking errors, shorter story length and a lack of story organization in narratives have been tentatively suggested as useful in distinguishing children with and without language impairment (Botting, 2002). As noted above, standardized narrative assessments also exist.

CA is another particularly salient framework in which clinical approaches to discourse have been embedded. The CA approach emerged from anthropological and sociological explorations into language use. CA principally developed from the work of Harvey Sacks and his colleagues (Sacks, Schegloff, & Jefferson, 1974; Schegloff, 2007). CA specifically explores how talk is managed collaboratively and locally by all participants in an interaction. The structural and sequential management of talk in interaction[3], rather than the identification of pre-specified linguistic impairments, is the focus of CA. Thus, when applied to the clinical setting, CA does not automatically presume that the use of unconventional discourse or disordered linguistic skills are problematic or a source of conversational trouble. There are now examples of commercially-available assessments for use with certain clinical populations which draw primarily on CA as their analytic framework (e.g., Lock, Wilkinson, & Bryan, 2001; Whitworth, Perkins, & Lesser, 1997).

The analysis of discourse is a widely endorsed method of assessment in the context of pragmatics across a wide variety of clinical populations (e.g., Bloch & Beeke, 2008; Boles, 1998; Brinton & Fujiki, 2003; Green, Johnson, & Bretherton, 2014; Rumpf, Kamp-Becker, Becker, & Kauschke, 2012). Analysis of talk in interaction has been put forward as a revealing and useful clinical tool which often augments findings from other forms of assessment, such as more formal standardized tests (Beeke, Wilkinson, & Maxim, 2003; Body & Perkins, 2004; Ulatowska & Olness, 2007). Outside of the speech and language therapy community, both CA and DA have also been used across disciplines, specifically to develop increased knowledge about children's mental health (Fasulo, 2015; Kiyimba, 2015).

Intervention

As intervention in the area of pragmatics is lacking in terms of a firm theoretical grounding, superficial and sometimes overlapping topics have been used, as below, to group and discuss intervention in this area, namely: *social skills, conversational skills, discourse and narrative* and *higher-level language*. In this chapter, the practice of using such unsatisfactory terminology continues for the sake of simplicity and clarity.

Social skills

Social skills and its cognates are umbrella terms that pertain to a wide variety of phenomena. While pragmatics is often used interchangeably with terms such as 'social communication skills' or 'social skills', there remains a lack of consensus about the exact nature of the relationship between these phenomena (Cummings, 2009).

3　The terms 'talk in interaction' and 'discourse' will be used synonymously for the sake of simplicity, although both terms can evoke different theoretical affiliations and traditions.

There is currently a significant interest in social skills as is reflected in their inclusion as part of the clinical and educational programmes offered in many different settings (Adams, 2008). The popularity of social skills training is also, perhaps, suggested by the broad array of disciplines that attend to social skills in their work, including, for example, those who work in educational settings (Gulchak & Lopes, 2007; Maddern, Franey, McLaughlin, & Cox, 2004) and also those professionals working in the areas of psychiatry (Wallace, 1998), occupational therapy (Gol & Jarus, 2005; Tsang & Pearson, 2001) and social work (De Mey, Coussee, Vandenbroeck, & Bouverne-De Bie, 2009). The sometimes precarious evidence of effectiveness and methodological issues in the social skills research has troubled some authors (Koenig, De Los Reyes, Cicchetti, Scahill, & Klin, 2009; Law & Garrett, 2004; Law, Garret, & Nye, 2003; Reichow, Steiner, & Volkmar, 2013; Storebø et al., 2011; Walsh, 2008a). The role that SLTs have come to assume in social skills interventions has also been questioned considering the paucity of research in this area (Adams, 2008; Gerber et al., 2012).

In order to provide an example, one intervention approach that focuses on social skills is discussed below. Although this is just one intervention approach, this example has been used to provide a flavour of the content of language and communication interventions during which social skills are focused on. Importantly, the intervention approach chosen as an example is one which has had considerable research attention (Adams et al., 2012a; Adams, Gaile, Lockton, & Freed, 2015; Adams, Lockton, Gaile, Earl, & Freed, 2012b). The *Social Communication Intervention Programme* (SCIP as developed by Adams & Gaile, 2015) presents a model of social communication intervention that involves working on "social understanding, pragmatics, and language processing" (Adams et al., 2015, p.295).

This intervention approach identifies different priorities for each individual based on a child's strengths and weaknesses, as observed and assessed in their everyday context, so that a specific schedule of intervention is generated for each child. The 'language processing' aspects of the intervention programme consists of work with the children aimed at 'remediation of impairments in semantics and high-level language skills' while the 'pragmatics' section of the programme primarily involves the use of 'metapragmatic therapy' (Adams et al., 2012b, p.249). Finally, the 'social understanding and interaction' aspect of the programme focuses on "addressing limitations of social interaction and social cue interpretation" (Adams et al., 2012b, p.249).

Environmental opportunities and barriers to social communication are also considered in this approach. Indeed, school staff and parents/carer(s) are expected to work collaboratively in the delivery of the SCIP. In an earlier case study, Adams, Baxendale, Lloyd and Aldred (2005, p.233) had stressed that social communication intervention should focus in part on 'communication adaptation' which would involve working to modify environmental variables such as conversational styles of interaction partners. Providing environmental and transactional supports complements the reality that language and communication difficulties and/or differences may be a long-term challenge for some children, in that "ultimately, some aspects of language impairment are impervious to intervention and that compensation and support may be a meaningful long-term approach" (Adams et al., 2015, p.304).

Conversational skills

Conversational skills training has been discussed as a characteristic part of 'pragmatic' intervention in that "remediation of conversation skills is typically part of most pragmatic language interventions" (Cummings, 2009, p.197). Conversational skills and social skills or social communication skills are often positioned as skills which are associated in a super- or sub-ordinate relationship. For example, in Kelly (2001) conversational skills are positioned as a subset of social communication skills. Intervention focusing on social and conversational skills often co-occurs.

Broadly speaking, two theoretical approaches appear to underpin intervention focusing on conversational skills, namely those which lean towards behavioural theory and those which are more closely aligned with the study of discourse or talk in interaction (such as CA).

Conversational skills interventions that draw on the behaviourist tradition appear to treat language use like any other behaviour. As such, intervention techniques are based on the assumption that "learning takes place when associations between stimuli and responses are built up via conditioning" (Hewitt, 2000b, p.189). In order to provide intervention, conversation is often deconstructed into constituent skills that can be objectively learned about and then reinforced through conditioning and repetition. For example, Kelly (2001, p.103) suggests discrete conversational or communicative topics are focused on and taught during intervention including "listening... turn taking... asking questions... be relevant". Breaking down conversations into component parts assumes that an individual will learn to pair superficial linguistic, conversational constructions with the settings and situations in which they are appropriate for use.

Repetition appears to be an important facet of behavioural approaches to conversational skills. The old adage of 'practice makes perfect' alongside a meta-communicative educational approach appears in many of the activities advocated in some conversational skills programmes (e.g., Schroeder, 1996). During intervention, clients are often exposed repeatedly to situations in which particular behaviours and skills are discussed meta-linguistically, then these conversational skills are elicited and practised until they can be performed to certain specifications. However, some authors have suggested that improved awareness of social and conversational rules alone may not impact change. For example, Lockton, Adams and Collins (2016) suggested that clinicians also support children to reflect on the impact of inappropriate and ineffective language use and thus improve their motivation for appropriate and effective language use

Certain conversational skills may also be elicited and practised in mock situations in which the clinician and client assume pretend roles. A child may be asked to perform particular skills as if they are in certain hypothetical situations (e.g., a child might be asked to pretend to be in 'the post office' or 'asking for directions' in role play with the therapist, as in Rinaldi, 1992, p.55). Alternatively, the clinician may use props (such as a table, real or pretend food) to create a more natural atmosphere, or may carry out intervention with the client in natural settings within a client's local community (such as the local café) in order to facilitate the generalisation of skills learned during intervention to everyday settings (Schroeder, 1996, pp.140–142). Interventions for language in general and pragmatics in particular, which are based on behaviourist theories, have been critiqued as being somewhat superficial by both Cummings (2009) and Hewitt (2000b). They both have noted how behaviourist techniques may lead to the acquisition of the target skill but in a restricted and superficial way.

As well as underpinning some commercially-available assessment tools[4], CA has also been drawn on to inform intervention programmes in the area of pragmatics, particularly in the context of working with adults who experience communication difficulties. Examples of programmes which draw on the CA approach include *Supporting Partners of People with Aphasia in Relationships and Conversation* (Lock et al., 2001) and an approach named *Supported Conversation for Adults with Aphasia* (Kagan, Black, Duchan, Simmons-Mackie, & Square, 2001). CA assumes a mutual responsibility for the progression of

---

4 For example, *Conversation Analysis Profile for People with Aphasia* by Whitworth, Perkins, & Lesser, (1997).

a conversation. Changing ineffective conversational patterns in order that communication breakdown is avoided is the focus, in that "CA intervention begins with the premise that changing the conversational behaviour of either partner ... may provide an opportunity for change in the conversational behaviour of the other speaker" (Beeke, Maxim, & Wilkinson, 2007, p.141). Typically, conversational partners are trained by clinicians following a CA analysis to cease using strategies which impede the conversation while the use of supportive conversational strategies may also be suggested by the SLT during this type of intervention.

Discourse and narrative

Intervention in the realm of discourse has increased in salience in the clinical literature environment. Intervention focusing on discourse ranges from approaches characterized by the didactic teaching of discrete linguistic structures in a piecemeal fashion (as discussed in Duchan, 1995), to more naturalistic approaches which focus on generating a meaningful context for language learning as an integrated whole (e.g., Hoffman & Norris, 1994; Ingersoll, Meyer, & Jelinek, 2012). Additionally, frameworks of intervention are also evident which reflect an intermediate position between the above atomistic and whole-language approaches (e.g., Ingersoll et al., 2012).

As with assessment, intervention in the area of discourse might focus on one discourse level or a number of levels at the same time (as in Rogalski & Edmonds, 2008). Intervention focusing on micro-linguistic or within-sentence level could, for example, aim to facilitate increased grammatical complexity and productivity (as discussed by Coelho, 2007). Micro-structural level intervention may focus on phenomena (such as cohesion) that are relevant to the achievement of local coherence between sentences. Intervention at macro-structural and super-structural levels of discourse could focus on facilitating the development of overall thematic/global coherence or narrative structure, respectively. For example, intervention at the macro-structural level focusing on narrative often explicitly teaches story grammars (e.g., Davies, Shanks, & Davies, 2004; Swanson, Fey, Mills, & Hood, 2005). Using peers, parents and other professionals to foster narrative skills (McGregor, 2000; Peterson, Jesso, & McCabe, 1999; Swanson et al., 2005) has also been shown to have some positive impacts on children's narrative development.

Higher level language

The terms 'high' or 'higher' level language have been used interchangeably (e.g., Freed et al., 2015). These terms have been used in the speech and language therapy context and beyond to refer to language that is ostensibly non-literal or 'figurative' (Im-Bolter & Cohen, 2007, p.529). As such, the term 'higher level language' captures a wide range of skills and competencies with which pragmatics is particularly affiliated (e.g., understanding and use of inference, sarcasm and idioms, etc.). Higher level language is often assumed to be related to many of the cognitive, linguistic and social skills which continue to develop in early adulthood (Nippold, 2007). For example, Adams and Lloyd (2007, p.230) describe 'work on the child's social understanding' as including phenomena which might be deemed 'higher level':

> ... directly teaching an understanding of emotional language
> ... encouraging flexibility in thinking ... working directly
> on an [sic] understanding social and verbal inferences,
> metaphors and hidden meaning in language.

There often seems to be little or no overt theoretical motivation for grouping together the skills described as 'higher level language'. However, higher level language skills have come to be linked with critical reasoning, emotional state vocabulary, navigating increasingly complex social situations and the use of language in increasingly more sophisticated ways (e.g., to complain, persuade or negotiate). Additionally, the term 'higher order language' has been used to refer to certain language and linguistic skills which are thought to be particularly reliant on an interface between language and cognition (Coelho, 2007, pp.128-129). Thus, higher level language has come to be associated with the language used in adolescence and early adulthood where interactions have a tendency to become more sophisticated and nuanced. Language development and use in the adolescent and young adult years has traditionally received far less research and clinical attention than language development in younger populations (Malcom & Myers, 2001; McCartney, 2000; Norbury, 2004).

In summary, a limited and sometimes disparate range of assessment and intervention tools are available for the practitioner of clinical pragmatics. The lack of theoretical development in the area of clinical pragmatics presents a challenge for clinicians and researchers when it comes to devising intervention. Interventions appear to have been developed from the ground up, in a practice-led manner, in that interventions in clinical pragmatics tend to be "resource rather than principle driven, due to the research vacuum" (Adams et al., 2005, p.229). The resources available to clinicians are limited and although 'practical' they lack a robust evidence base in that: "fundamental questions regarding effectiveness and theoretical models underlying the potential mechanisms of intervention remain" (Adams et al., 2015, p.295). Thus, speech and language therapy intervention in the area of clinical pragmatics has been described as being 'eclectic' and guided by a clinician's experience and exposure to available resources and intervention methods (Cummings, 2009, p.177).

It appears that, at times, a reductionist and modular view of pragmatics is evident in the clinical literature environment related to assessment and intervention methods. When pragmatics is treated as a subset of superficial skills that can be taught via simple conditioning the complex and emergent nature of the communicative process, suggested by much of pragmatic theory, is neglected. Perhaps the theoretical infancy of clinical pragmatics and the lack of high-quality research evidence for guiding clinicians on how to apply pragmatic theory can account for the disparate perspectives and unresolved debates which remain in the area.

Considering (a) the historical emergence and context of clinical pragmatics, (b) the ongoing debates within the field, and finally, (c) the yet to be fully specified and validated nature of many clinical interpretations of pragmatic theory, how then might pragmatic theory be applied in practice? These questions form a point of departure for the remainder of this chapter.

Drawing on pragmatic theory when supporting language and communication and children with MHDs: Context, collaboration and functional communication

Pragmatic theory proposes that clinicians move beyond treating pragmatics as a discrete and superficial module of skills and behaviours to be remediated (Duchan, 1984, 2000; Perkins, 2005a, 2005b). Additionally, I would like to suggest that pragmatic theory has encouraged those working with communication to acknowledge context, practise collaboratively and to take a functional stance. The final section of this chapter draws on these themes to tentatively propose avenues for exploring how pragmatic theory might inform the intervention process when striving to support language and communication for children who experience MHDs. It is important to note that, like much theory from the area of pragmatics, the frameworks and concepts discussed below have yet to be fully validated, from a research perspective, for clinical use.

Context

Much of pragmatic theory challenges clinicians and researchers to look beyond communication as a product of discrete, intrinsic and individually located skills and in its place proposes a view of communication as an emergent, contextualized and interactional process (Perkins, 2005b). The important role of context in communication is one of the most prominent themes across the vast body of knowledge that is pragmatic theory.

Context is an elusive concept and can be difficult to specify. The amorphous nature of context has long been problematized and debated within the scientific community in general and also within the area of pragmatics (e.g., Mishler, 1979; Prutting, 1982). Context can be defined in multiple ways and at a variety of levels (as noted by Kasher, 1998). Context can be defined in a narrow way, as for example Norbury (2005) has done, when context was operationalized as grammatical information (in this case in the linguistic environs of an ambiguous word). Alternatively, context can be defined in a slightly broader way as in, for example, López and Leekam (2003, p.286), where context is defined both in verbal and visual terms. Wider still definitions of context are also evident. A seminal example of a broad definition of context was proposed by Hymes (1972). The SPEAKING mnemonic identifies the contextual components of an interaction which guide ethnographic considerations of language use. These contextual components of interaction were grouped together as *Setting and Scene, Participants, Ends, Act sequence, Key, Instrumentalities, Norms* and *Genres* (Hymes, 1977, pp.51-62). In addition to the factors considered during more traditional assessment procedures, considering a child's language and communication skills alongside and within these broader, contextual parameters may help identify external as well as internal influences on communicative breakdown and success.

Understanding contextual influences is key if a practitioner is trying to support a child in managing both intrinsic and extrinsic communication barriers. The situated view of communication espoused by pragmatic theory behoves SLTs to look beyond communication breakdown as an issue which is solely the responsibility of one individual because of the fact that communication is viewed as a process that occurs in an interpersonal context, that is, "in relationship with another (or others)" as Hyter (2007, p.131) noted.

Interpreting the notion of context in a broad way enables the researcher and clinician to look beyond a child's intrinsic skills and behaviours when working in the area of language, communication and MHDs. Paying clinical attention to contextual phenomena, however, suggests that factors which were once deemed extraneous may become important during assessment and intervention (Prutting, 1982). For example, the language and communication skills of friends and family of individuals with communication difficulties may now be focused on during intervention (e.g., Byng & Duchan, 2004; Kagan et al., 2001). Correspondingly, goals for intervention may not necessarily be at the level of impairment and may potentially include targets such as "participation in life's activities, relationships, and personal self-esteem" (Worrall, 2006, p.320). Law and Garrett (2004) highlighted the importance of attending to extrinsic contextual factors when they discussed outcome measurement in relation to the provision of language and communication supports to children and adolescents. Here, they discuss a broad range of outcomes (including behaviour, school exclusion rates, parental stress levels and socialisation) as 'secondary effects' of speech and language therapy supports (Law & Garret, 2004, p.52). However, members of the speech and language therapy community must be cognisant of their role and scope of professional practice and recognize when onward referral and/or MDT consultation is required.

Pragmatic theory recognizes that a communicative event, whether it be a psychotherapy session or a fight in school, is shaped and influenced by everyone in that interaction as well as the broader context in which that interaction is framed (Walsh, 2007). As interventions to support language, communication and mental health are often mediated through language, the interactional context of the therapeutic encounter also requires consideration (Ferguson, 2009). Pragmatic theory has been drawn on to explore and highlight the importance of the interaction itself during the provision of clinical services (with reference to those both providing and accessing speech and language therapy services; for examples see Ferguson & Armstrong, 2004; Kovarsky & Duchan, 1997; Walsh, 2007, 2008b). Thus, pragmatic theory reminds us that the communication skills of all involved in the therapeutic encounter (not just the children and adolescents accessing speech and language therapy services) as well as the context in which language is used and communication occurs should be considered during intervention.

Collaboration

As noted above, pragmatic theory encourages an understanding of communication (and communication breakdown) as a highly contextualized and, as such, individualized and situated process. The use of objective measurements alone may fail to capture some the relevant information during assessment and outcome measurement. Consequently, qualitative and subjective evidence coupled with objective quantitative evidence may be required in order that an individual's experiences of communication difficulty and success are accurately specified (Brinton & Fujiki, 2003; Kovarsky, 2008; Kovarsky & Curran, 2007). Identification of language and communication strengths, weaknesses, barriers and opportunities can be achieved by not only gathering evidence through the use of more traditional assessments, but also by collaboratively generating evidence based on the perspective of the child and his[5] significant communication partners. The necessity of drawing on the opinions and support of family, peers and other significant conversational partners during intervention is a thread that runs through much of the literature informed by pragmatic theory (e.g., Duchan, 1997; Duchan, Hewitt, & Sonnenmerier, 1994; Lock et al., 2001).

It would seem that the emphasis on personal development and growth, espoused by the recovery model (Anthony, 1993, 2000) (which is also discussed in Chapters 7 and 9 in this book), strongly dovetails with the practice of drawing on qualitative data and subjective evidence from the people who access services. Evoking such evidence helps to ensure that personally meaningful therapy goals are generated and then evaluated. Anthony (1993, p.13) describes recovery as a deeply personal process that is not focused solely on the remission of clinical symptoms. Drawing on the recovery model also points to collaborative identification of indicators for wellbeing and recovery with an individual as they access mental health support services to support them in their journey to recovery. This collaborative process contrasts sharply with an expert-led model that prioritizes a clinician's perspective and focuses on impairment-based phenomena during assessment and outcome measurement.

Operationalizing the recovery model during intervention guides the clinician to support a child to maximize their communicative potential in the context of successfully coping with MHDs. Historically, SLT practice has been guided by the expert model. In order to apply the recovery model to SLT practice some rebalancing of power may be necessary. Listening to the unique experiences that each individual brings to therapy places a value on the perspectives of the child and their significant communication partners and thus

---

5 For the sake of simplicity and clarity, allusions to children accessing SLT support will be referred to in the male gender.

enables the generation of a more balanced and collaborative understanding of language and communication issues (Duchan & Black, 2001). However, the use of subjective evidence during assessment and outcome measurement is a contentious issue that is embedded within much larger epistemological debates about the nature of quality evidence in clinical practice. There appears to be a growing acknowledgement that subjective and qualitative forms of evidence may be important in assessment and outcome measurement, particularly for complex behavioural interventions such as speech and language therapy (e.g., Kovarsky, 2008; Morse, 2006).

With the recovery model firmly in mind, it seems apparent that input from the child and their significant others is a prerequisite for identifying language and communication outcomes that are personally relevant and meaningful. It may be wise to note here that the process of directly gathering information from children in clinical situations is more traditional and consequently more developed in certain clinical corners such as psychology and psychiatry (Whitcomb & Merrell, 2013). There may well be some learning for SLTs from other professions in this regard.

Other constructs evident in today's mental health discourse, such as *resilience*, may also be relevant to speech and language therapy. Factors that nurture resilience, such as describing feelings, regulating emotions, participating socially and achieving educational goals, have inherent 'communication dimensions' but the specifications of these factors may differ between individuals (Law et al., 2013, p.491). Again, the importance of collaboration between the clinician, child and his significant communication partners becomes relevant to both identify and fully specify factors which foster resilience for any given child.

In relation to the practice area of clinical pragmatics in particular, the lack of robust and explicit theoretical frameworks being employed in speech and language therapy practice has also contributed to concerns that evidence generated during assessment and outcome measurements may be swayed by practitioners' subjective opinions (Adams, 2002; Ball, 2000). For example, if a clinician rates how appropriate a particular communication skill is without robust theoretical guidance on what qualifies as appropriate, these appraisals may be open to multiple interpretations as noted by Adams (2002, p.983): "... the remaining problem with appropriacy judgements is that they are subjective and therefore influenced by the way in which the assessor construes the world". It is suggested here that pragmatic theory encourages SLTs to look to those accessing speech and language therapy services, and their significant others, to collaboratively generate subjective evidence about their experiences, perspectives and hopes regarding language and communication, communication difficulty and the therapeutic process. This seems especially applicable to the context of children with MHDs, where language and communication are central to mental health, resilience and wellbeing (Gravell & France, 1991; Law et al., 2013).

Furthermore, in the context of mental health, collaboratively working with colleagues from other disciplines brings additional skill sets necessary for holistically meeting the needs of children from this population. It is well recognized that providing intervention in the context of a multidisciplinary team is the most effective way of supporting both children and adults who experience MHDs (Cromptom, 2001; Mackie & Law, 2010a; Novak & Kapolnek, 2001).

Focusing on the functional nature of communication

As Kamhi (2000) notes, pragmatic theory has guided the speech and language therapy community to use more naturalistic settings for mediating therapy and to focus on the functional nature of communication during intervention:

> Consistent with pragmatic notions, it has been assumed that to achieve the goal of effective communication, specific syntactic, semantic and even phonological objectives must be taught in naturalistic, functional, communicative, and meaningful contexts. (p.182).

In relation to communication supports, the term 'functional' is used to describe interventions that are meaningful, ecologically valid and carried out in naturalistic settings (Penn, 1999). However, often the term 'functional communication' is used as cognate with pragmatic language or pragmatic skills (e.g., Mackie & Law, 2010b). Intervention guided by pragmatic theory has shifted the emphasis from the didactic teaching of superficial sets of linguistic structures to functional therapy targets.

Pragmatic theory highlights the purposeful nature of communication alongside the active role that children play during language use, as noted by Smith and Leinonen (1991, p.252) when they state: "The essential point about pragmatics-based therapy is that the client is not cast in a passive role, but is helped to use communicative behaviour for his or her own purposes". Thus, a pragmatic perspective has enabled practitioners to infuse communication intervention with a purposeful focus and to move away from providing therapy which facilitates linguistic or communicative changes that are of no functional use to those accessing speech and language therapy services (Crystal, 1995).

Everyday conversations and tasks thus provide obvious sites in which the practitioner can explore the functional use of communication skills and identify opportunities and barriers in a child's natural communicative environment. Adopting naturalistic approaches may involve the practitioner assessing communication in real-life situations and activities in which it naturally occurs. Additionally, mediating intervention via meaningful tasks orientated towards purposeful objectives would also reflect a naturalistic focus.

Tools which have evolved from pragmatic theory (such as those involving principles from DA and CA) may be applied for assessment of communication during everyday activities with no need to manufacture tasks and activities specifically for the sake of assessment. However, although these techniques are relatively unobtrusive (i.e., they do not require the child to participate in direct testing), they are only just beginning to become more widely used to explore language and communication across a variety of clinical populations (e.g., Antaki, 2013; Finlay & Antaki, 2012; Williams, 2011). It would seem DA and CA have not yet become widely applied as clinical tools during assessment and intervention in mental health contexts (yet some inroads have been made in this regard as related to adults with schizophrenia, for example; see Jagoe, Chapter 6, this volume).

A pragmatic perspective suggests that language and communication support in general (not just interventions which are focused on phenomena which have been traditionally considered 'pragmatic') should be located in natural and everyday interactive situations. Indeed, similarly, it has been suggested that embedding mental health interventions in everyday contexts in a sustained manner is an effective way of supporting wellbeing in children (Green, Howes, Waters, Maher, & Oberklaid, 2005; Weare & Nind, 2011).

Going forward: Directions for further research

The fact that clinical pragmatics is a field which is still, relatively speaking, in its infancy suggests that there are many exciting and timely opportunities for research. There is little known about practice in the area of clinical pragmatics, and intervention efficacy is yet to be clearly established. There remains much to be learned about the application of pragmatic theory when supporting people from different clinical populations and/or across different cultural and social backgrounds (Hyter, Rivers, & DeJarnette, 2015; Norbury, 2014). Listed below are some avenues of research yet to be fully explored.

Generating theoretical coherence in clinical pragmatics

In light of the divergent paradigms used to approach pragmatics and a lack of general consensus on appropriate methodologies within the area of pragmatics (Müller, 2000; Spencer-Oatey & Žegarac, 2002), it is perhaps unsurprising that clinical pragmatics is a field which is characterized by clashing perspectives and a lack of unification. There is no one theory of pragmatics on which all things pragmatic are hung in the speech and language therapy clinic and with which intervention is approached; as Adams (2001, p.301) notes: "...approaches to pragmatic therapy currently in use tend to be eclectic and a 'method' of intervention would currently be difficult to identify". This suggests a lack of consistency in speech and language therapy practice in the area of clinical pragmatics.

When looking to define the area of clinical pragmatics a cacophony of disparate versions of pragmatics appear in the literature. Some authors (such as Perkins, 2005b, p.363) argue for a broad-based view of pragmatics which views all 'communication disorders' as being indicative of the presence of 'pragmatic impairment' to some extent. Others within the speech and language therapy community have argued for a narrower definition of clinical pragmatics, which excludes non-linguistic phenomena. Thus, pragmatics would be seen as part of a speaker's linguistic competence (e.g., Ninio, Snow, Pan, & Rollins, 1994). In particular, Cummings (2007a, 2009) has continually called for a tightening-up of the definition of (and indeed approaches to) clinical pragmatics, and to focus clinical pragmatics on linguistic phenomena. Greater theoretical coherence and demarcation within the broader field of pragmatics as well as within the area of clinical pragmatics is wanting and may enable fruitful and progressive research avenues to be pursued.

Developing greater understanding of how pragmatic theory is used clinically

Other than anecdotal information, there is little published exploration of how pragmatic theory is being applied in clinical situations. Indeed, clinical decision making in general is not yet well researched in the context of speech and language therapy practice (McCurtin & Carter, 2015). Investigating clinical decision making within the practice area of clinical pragmatics may enable the development of greater understanding of how SLTs import and apply theory in their practice. Additionally, charting current practice patterns in the area of clinical pragmatics may lead to the development of increased clinical consensus in this practice area.

Specifying and validating pragmatic theory for clinical use

Pragmatic theory provides a rich resource pool yet to be fully tapped for clinical applications. The abstract and descriptive nature of many of the constructs from pragmatic theory means that they may not always be readily applied in clinical situations (i.e., they may not yet be fit for clinical purposes). A purely descriptive account of communication breakdown may not necessarily be of much use in terms of intervention planning; however, this may be what is provided by some of the assessments used in the practice area of pragmatics (Hyter, 2007). Perkins (2007, 2010) has repeatedly noted:

> ...although theories of pragmatics provide a means of *describing* pragmatic impairments, the level of *explanation* they afford is rarely adequate for clinicians, in that it does not translate easily into clinical intervention. For example ... the child might be *described* as breaking Grice's maxims ... but such descriptive labels do not get us very far when trying to design a remedial programme. One can hardly tell the child to 'stop breaking Grice's maxims'! (Perkins, 2005a, p.369)

In the era of evidence-based practice, practitioners, funders and service users now expect clinical applications of theory to be both fully specified and validated. It may be that clinicians who draw on pragmatic theory to inform their practice, such as SLTs, may play some role in this specification and validation process.

Speech and language therapy practice in the context of MHDs

The nature and extent of speech and language therapy involvement during the process of MHD diagnosis requires further exploration by the research community in light of both the central role that language and communication skills play during a child's diagnostic journey, and the overrepresentation of language difficulties and differences in this population (Ketelaars, Cuperus,

Jansonius, & Verhoeven, 2010; Law & Stringer, 2013; Mackie & Law, 2010b; Sullivan et al., 2016). The evaluation of communicative and social behaviours has become part and parcel of the diagnostic process for children with mental health difficulties (American Psychiatric Association, 2013) but a speech and language therapist is not necessarily consulted in this regard. There remains a pressing need for clinicians and researchers to develop a greater understanding of how language and communication differences and difficulties are considered during diagnosis within the mental health community. Also, as many of the interventions offered to children with MHDs are verbally mediated, there appears to be a role for SLTs (as part of a multidisciplinary team) in facilitating access to mental health services which has yet to be fully explored.

Conclusion

Despite the somewhat unsatisfactory picture painted in this chapter regarding the practice area of clinical pragmatics, the demand and necessity of attending to pragmatics is palpable in the clinical literature environment. Pragmatic theory has much to offer to those who support language and communication in the context of children with MHDs. There are obvious dovetails between approaching communication (and its breakdown) as a contextualized, collaborative and functional process with understanding mental health through the paradigm of the recovery model, where wellbeing is achieved through both personal and societal changes in a collaborative and meaningful way (Mental Health Commission, 2008).

Despite expectations regarding the provision of complex interventions (such as social skills and pragmatic language interventions) by SLTs, challenges remain in evaluating their efficacy and, indeed, probity. Broadly speaking, as McCurtin and Roddam (2012) have noted, the speech and language therapy community has much work to do to generate evidence that their interventions are efficacious, and the area of clinical pragmatics is no exception.

The promise offered by pragmatic theory for informing practice in the area of language and communication support for children with MHDs has yet to be fulfilled. However, further research in this area and a comprehensive appreciation of language and communication as a contextual, collaborative and functional process may well begin to facilitate the promise of pragmatic theory being fully realized.

References

Adams, C. (2001). Clinical diagnostic and intervention studies of children with semantic-pragmatic language disorder. *International Journal of Language and Communication Disorders, 36*(3), 289-305.

Adams, C. (2002). Practitioner review: The assessment of language pragmatics. *Journal of Child Psychology and Psychiatry, 43*(8), 973-987.

Adams, C. (2008). Intervention for children with pragmatic language impairments. In C.F. Norbury, J.B. Tomblin & D.V.M. Bishop (Eds), *Understanding Developmental Language Disorders: From Theory to Practice* (pp.189-204). Hove, UK: Psychology Press.

Adams, C. & Gaile, J. (2015). *The Social Communication Intervention Programme (SCIP): Manual, Rationale and Intervention Resource.* Cheshire, UK: Napier Hill Press.

Adams, C. & Lloyd, J. (2007). The effects of speech and language therapy intervention on children with pragmatic language impairments in mainstream school. *British Journal of Special Education, 34*(4), 226-233.

Adams, C., Baxendale, J., Lloyd, J., & Aldred, C. (2005). Pragmatic language impairment: Case studies of social and pragmatic language therapy. *Child Language Teaching and Therapy, 21*(3), 227-250.

Adams, C., Coke, R., Crutchley, A., Hesketh, A., & Reeves, D. (2001). *Assessment of Comprehension and Expression 6-11.* Windsor, UK: NFER-Nelson.

Adams, C., Gaile, J., Lockton, E., & Freed, J. (2015). Integrating language, pragmatics and social intervention in a single-subject case study of a child with a developmental social communication disorder. *Language, Speech, Hearing Services in Schools, 46*(4), 294-311.

Adams, C., Lockton, E., Freed, J., Gaile, J., Earl, G., McBean, K., Nash, M., Green, J., Vail, A., & Law, J. (2012a). The Social Communication Intervention Project: A randomised controlled trial of the effectiveness of speech and language therapy for school-age children who have pragmatic and social communication problems with or without autism spectrum disorder. *International Journal of Language & Communication Disorders, 47*(3), 233-244.

Adams, C., Lockton, E., Gaile, J., Earl, G., & Freed, J. (2012b). Implementation of a manualised communication intervention for school-aged children with pragmatic and social communication needs in a randomised controlled trial: The Social Communication Intervention Project. *International Journal of Language & Communication Disorders, 47*(3), 245-256.

American Psychiatric Association (2013). *Diagnostic and Statistical Manual of Mental Disorders*, 5th ed. Arlington, VA: American Psychiatric Publishing.

Antaki, C. (2013). Two conversational practices for encouraging adults with intellectual disabilities to reflect on their activities. *Journal of Intellectual Disability Research, 57*(6), 580-588.

Antaki, C., Finlay, W., Walton, C., & Pate, L. (2008). Offering choices to people with intellectual disabilities: An interactional study. *Journal of Intellectual Disability Research, 52*(12), 1165-1175.

Anthony, W.A. (1993) Recovery from mental illness: The guiding vision of the mental health service system in the 1990s. *Psychosocial Rehabilitation Journal, 16*(4), 11-23.

Anthony, W.A. (2000). A recovery-orientated service system: Setting some system standards. *Psychiatric Rehabilitation Journal, 24*(2), 159-168.

Austin, J.L. (1962). *How to Do Things with Words.* Oxford, UK: Clarendon Press.

Ball, M.J. (2000). Problems of pragmatic profiling. In N. Müller (Ed.), *Pragmatics in Speech and Language Pathology: Studies in Clinical Applications* (pp.89-106). Philadelphia, PA: John Benjamins.

Bates, E. (1976a). *Language and Context: The Acquisition of Pragmatics.* London, UK: Academic Press.

Bates, E. (1976b). Pragmatics and sociolinguistics in child language. In M. Morehead & A. Morehead (Eds), *Language Deficiency in Children: Selected Readings* (pp.411-463). Baltimore, MD: University Park.

Beeke, S., Maxim, J., & Wilkinson, R. (2007). Using conversation analysis to assess and treat people with aphasia. *Seminars in Speech and Language, 28*(2), 136-147.

Beeke, S., Wilkinson, R., & Maxim, J. (2003). Exploring aphasic grammar 2: Do language testing and conversation tell a similar story? *Clinical Linguistics and Phonetics, 17*(2), 109-134.

Beeke, S., Wilkinson, R., & Maxim, J. (2007). Grammar without sentence structure: A conversation analytic investigation of agrammatism. *Aphasiology, 21*(3-4), 256-282.

Bishop, D.V.M. (2003a). *Expression, Reception, and Recall of Narrative Instrument.* London, UK: Harcourt.

Bishop, D.V.M. (2003b). *The Children's Communication Checklist-CCC 2,* 2nd ed. London, UK: The Psychological Corporation.

Bishop, D.V.M., (2014). Ten questions about terminology for children with unexplained language problems. *International Journal of Language and Communication Disorders, 4*(4), 381-415.

Bishop, D.V.M., Snowling, M.J., Thompson, P.A., Greenhalgh, T., & CATALISE Consortium (2016). CATALISE: A multinational and multidisciplinary Delphi consensus study. Identifying language impairments in children. *PLoS One, 11*(12). doi: https://doi.org/10.1371/journal.pone.0168066

Bishop, D.V.M., Snowling, M.J., Thompson, P.A., Greenhalgh, T., & CATALISE Consortium (2017). Phase 2 of CATALISE: A multinational and multidisciplinary Delphi consensus study of problems with language development: Terminology. *Journal of Child Psychology and Psychiatry, 58*(10), 1068-1080.

Bliss, L.S. & McCabe, A. (2008). Personal narratives: Cultural differences and clinical implications. *Topics in Language Disorders, 28*(2), 162-177.

Bloch, S. & Beeke, S. (2008). Co-constructed talk in the conversations of people with dysarthria and aphasia. *Clinical Linguistics and Phonetics, 22*(12), 974-990.

Body, R. & Perkins, M.R. (2004). Validation of linguistic analyses in narrative discourse after traumatic brain injury. *Brain Injury*, *18*(7), 707-724.

Boles, L. (1998). Conversational discourse analysis as a method for evaluating progress in aphasia: A case report. *Journal of Communication Disorders*, *31*(3), 261-274.

Botting, N. (2002). Narrative as a clinical tool for the assessment of linguistic and pragmatic impairments. *Child Language Teaching and Therapy*, *18*(1), 1-21.

Boudreau, D.M. & Chapman, R.S. (2000). The relationship between event representation and linguistic skill in narratives of children and adolescents with Down Syndrome. *Journal of Speech, Language, and Hearing Research*, *43*(5), 1146.

Brinton, B. & Fujiki, M. (2003). Blending quantitative and qualitative methods in language research and intervention. *American Journal of Speech-Language Pathology*, *12*(2), 165.

Bruner, J.S. (1974). From communication to language: A psychological perspective. *Cognition*, *3*(3), 255-287.

Bruner, J.S. & Watson, R. (1983). *Child's Talk: Learning to Use Language*. Oxford, UK: Oxford University Press.

Byng, S. & Duchan, J.F. (2004). Challenging aphasia therapies. In *Challenging Aphasia Therapies: Broadening the Discourse and Extending the Boundaries* (pp.8-18). Hove, UK: Psychology Press.

Coelho, C.A. (2007). Management of discourse deficits following traumatic brain injury: Progress, caveats, and needs. *Seminars in Speech and Language*, *28*(2), 122-135.

Coelho, C.A., Ylvisaker, M., & Turkstra, L.S. (2005). Non-standardised assessment approaches for individuals with traumatic brain injuries. *Seminars in Speech and Language*, *26*(4), 223-241.

Conti-Ramsden, G. & Gunn, M. (1986). The development of conversational disability: A case study. *International Journal of Language and Communication Disorders*, *21*(3), 339-351.

Craig, H.K. (1984). Applications of pragmatic language models for intervention. In T. Gallagher & C.A. Prutting (Eds), *Pragmatic Assessment and Intervention Issues in Language* (pp.101-127). San Diego, CA: College Hill Press.

Craig, H.K. & Evans, J.L. (1993). Pragmatics and SLI: Within-group variations in discourse behaviors. *Journal of Speech and Hearing Research*, *36*(4), 777-789.

Cromptom, Y. (2001) The speech and language therapist as a member of the mental health multidisciplinary team. In J. France & S. Kramer (Eds), *Communication and Mental Illness: Theoretical and Practical Approaches* (pp.158-166). London, UK: Jessica Kingsley.

Crystal, D. (1995). Postilion sentences. *Child Language Teaching and Therapy*, *11*(1), 79-90.

Cummings, L. (2007a). Pragmatics and adult language disorders: Past achievements and future directions. *Seminars in Speech and Language*, *28*(2), 96-110.

Cummings, L. (2007b). Clinical pragmatics: A field in search of phenomena. *Language and Communication*, *27*(4), 396-432.

Cummings, L. (2009). *Clinical Pragmatics*. Cambridge, UK: Cambridge University Press.

Cummings, L. (2014). *Pragmatic Disorders*. London, UK: Springer.

Davies, P., Shanks, B., & Davies, K. (2004). Improving narrative skills in young children with delayed language development. *Educational Review, 56*(3), 271-286.

De Mey, W., Coussee, F., Vandenbroeck, M., & Bouverne-De Bie, M. (2009). Social work and parent support in reaction to children's antisocial behaviour: Constructions and effects. *International Journal of Social Welfare, 18*(3), 299-306.

Dewart, H. & Summers, S. (1995). *The Pragmatics Profile of Everyday Communication Skills in Children.* Windsor, UK: NFER-Nelson.

Dore, J. (1974). A pragmatic description of early language development. *Journal of Psycholinguistic Research, 3*(4), 343-350.

Duchan, J.F. (1984). Language processing and geodesic domes. In T.M. Gallagher & C.A. Prutting (Eds), *Pragmatic Assessment and Intervention: Issues in Language* (pp.83-100). San Diego, CA: College Hill Press.

Duchan, J.F. (1995). *Supporting Language Learning in Everyday Life.* San Diego, CA: Singular.

Duchan, J.F. (1997). A situated pragmatics approach for supporting children with severe communication disorders. *Topics in Language Disorders, 17*(2), 1-18.

Duchan, J.F. (2000). Assessing children's language: Present, past, and future. *Seminars in Speech and Language, 21*(3), 189-192.

Duchan, J.F. (2005). The diagnostic practices of speech-language pathologists. In J.F. Duchan & D. Kovarsky (Eds), *Diagnosis as Cultural Practice* (pp.201-222). New York, NY: Mouton de Gruyter.

Duchan, J.F. & Black, M. (2001). Progressing toward life goals: A person-centred approach to evaluating therapy. *Topics in Language Disorders, 22*(1), 37-49.

Duchan, J.F., Hewitt, L.E., & Sonnenmeier, R.M. (1994). Three themes: Stage two pragmatics, combating marginalisation, and the relation of theory and practice. In J.F. Duchan, L.E. Hewitt, & R.M. Sonnenmeier (Eds), *Pragmatics from Theory to Practice* (pp.1-9). London, UK: Prentice-Hall.

Fasulo, A. (2015). The value of conversation analysis for the study of children's mental health. In J.N. Lester & M. O'Reilly (Eds), *The Palgrave Handbook of Child Mental Health* (pp.3-24). New York, NY: Palgrave.

Ferguson, A. (2009). The discourse of speech-language pathology. *International Journal of Speech-Language Pathology, 11*(2), 104-112.

Ferguson, A. & Armstrong, E. (2004). Reflections on speech and language therapists' talk: Implications for clinical practice and education. *International Journal of Language and Communication Disorders, 39*(4), 469-477.

Finlay, W.M.L. & Antaki, C. (2012). How staff pursue questions to adults with intellectual disabilities. *Journal of Intellectual Disability Research, 56*(4), 361-370.

Formigari, L. (2004). *A History of Language Philosophies* (P. Gabriel, Trans.). Philadelphia, PA: John Benjamins.

Freed, J., McBean, K., Adams, C., Lockton, E., Nash, M., & Law, J. (2015). Performance of children with social communication disorder on the Happé Strange Stories: Physical and mental state responses and relationship to language ability. *Journal of Communication Disorders, 55*, 1-14.

Fujiki, M. & Brinton, B. (2009). Pragmatics and social communication in child language disorders. In R.G. Schwartz (Ed.), *Handbook of Child Language Disorders* (pp.407-423). New York, NY: Psychology Press.

Gerber, S., Brice, A., Capone, N., Fujiki, M., & Timler, G. (2012). Language use in social interaction of school-age children with language impairments: An evidence-based systematic review of treatment. *Language, Speech and Hearing Services in Schools, 43*(2), 235-249.

Gol, D. & Jarus, T. (2005). Effect of a social skills training group on everyday activities of children with attention-deficit–hyperactivity disorder. *Developmental Medicine and Child Neurology, 47*(8), 539-545.

Gravell, R. & France, J. (1991). *Speech and Communication Problems in Psychiatry.* London, UK: Chapman and Hall.

Green, B.C., Johnson, K.A., & Bretherton, L. (2014). Pragmatic language difficulties in children with hyperactivity and attention problems: An integrated review. *International Journal of Language & Communication Disorders, 49*(1), 15-29.

Green, J., Howes, F., Waters, E., Maher, E., & Oberklaid, F. (2005). Promoting the social and emotional health of primary school-aged children: Reviewing the evidence base for school-based interventions. *International Journal of Mental Health Promotion, 7*(3), 30-36.

Grice, H.P. (1975). Logic and conversation. In J.P. Kimball, P. Cole, & J.L. Morgan (Eds), *Syntax and Semantics 3: Speech Acts* (pp.41-58). New York, NY: Academic Press.

Gulchak, D.J. & Lopes, J.A. (2007). Interventions for students with behavioral disorders: An international literature review. *Behavioral Disorders, 32*(4), 267-281.

Halliday, M.A.K. (1975). *Learning How to Mean: Explorations in the Development of Language.* London, UK: Edward Arnold.

Halliday, M.A.K. & Hasan, R. (1976). *Cohesion in English.* London, UK: Longman.

Hewitt, L.E. (2000a). Assessing communicative intents: A situated pragmatics approach. *Seminars in Speech and Language, 21*(3), 257-266.

Hewitt, L.E. (2000b). Does it matter what your client thinks? The role of theory in intervention: Response to Kamhi. *Language, Speech, and Hearing Services in Schools, 31*(2), 186-193.

Hill, E.L. (2001). Non-specific nature of specific language impairment: A review of the literature with regard to concomitant motor impairments. *International Journal of Language and Communication Disorders, 36*(2), 149-171.

Hoffman, P.R. & Norris, J.A. (1994). Whole language and collaboration work: Evidence from at-risk kindergarteners. *Communication Disorders Quarterly, 16*(1), 41-48.

Holland, A.L. (1979). Some practical consideration in aphasia rehabilitation. In M. Sullivan & M. Kommers (Eds), *Rationale for Adult Aphasia Therapy.* Omaha, NE: University of Nebraska Medical Centre Print Shop.

Holland, A.L. (1982). Observing functional communication of aphasic adults. *Journal of Speech and Hearing Disorders, 47*(1), 50-56.

Horn, L.R. & Ward, G. (2004). Introduction. In L.R. Horn & G. Ward (Eds), *The Handbook of Pragmatics* (pp.xi-xix). Oxford, UK: Blackwell.

Hymes, D. (1977). *Foundations in Sociolinguistics: An Ethnographic Approach.* London, UK: Tavistock.

Hymes, D. (1972). On communicative competence. In J.B. Pride & J. Holmes (Eds), *Sociolinguistics* (pp.269-293). London, UK: Penguin.

Hyter, Y.D. (2007). Pragmatic language assessment: A pragmatics-as-social practice model. *Topics in Language Disorders, 27*(2), 128-145.

Hyter, Y.D., Rivers, K.O., & DeJarnette, G. (2015). Pragmatic language of African American children and adolescents: A systematic synthesis of the literature. *Topics in Language Disorders, 35*(1), 8-45.

Im-Bolter, N. & Cohen, N.J. (2007) Language impairment and psychiatric co-morbidities. *Pediatric Clinics of North America, 54*(3), 525-542.

Ingersoll, B., Meyer, K., & Jelinek, S. (2012). A comparison of developmental social-pragmatic and naturalistic behavioural interventions on language use and social engagement in children with autism. *Journal of Speech, Language, and Hearing Research, 55*(5), 1301-1313.

Irish Association for Speech and Language Therapists. (2006). *The Role of the Speech and Language Therapist in Mental Health Services.* Dublin: IASLT.

Irish Association for Speech and Language Therapists. (2015). *Speech and Language Therapy in Mental Health Services: A Guidance Document.* Dublin: IASLT.

Joffe, V., Cruice, M., & Chiat, S. (2008). Language disorders in children and adults: Current themes, issues and connections. In V. Joffe, M. Cruice, & S. Chiat (Eds), *Language Disorders in Children and Adults: New Issues in Research and Practice* (pp.xi-xxvii). Chichester, UK: Wiley-Blackwell.

Kagan, A., Black, S., Duchan, J.F., Simmons-Mackie, N.S., & Square, P. (2001). Training volunteers as conversation partners using 'Supported Conversation for Adults with Aphasia' (SCA): A controlled trial. *Journal of Speech, Language, and Hearing Research, 44*(3), 624-638.

Kamhi, A.G. (2000). Practice makes perfect: The incompatibility of practicing speech and meaningful communication. *Language, Speech, and Hearing Services in Schools, 31*(2), 182-185.

Kasher, A. (1998). Postscript. In *Pragmatics: Critical Concepts: Vol V, Communication, Interaction and Discourse* (pp.144-159). London, UK: Routledge.

Kelly, A. (2001). *Talkabout: A Social Communication Skills Package.* Bicester, UK: Speechmark.

Ketelaars, M.P., Cuperus, J., Jansonius, K., & Verhoeven, L. (2010). Pragmatic language impairment and associated behavioural problems. *International Journal of Language & Communication Disorders, 45*(2), 204-214.

Kiyimba, N. (2015). The value of discourse analysis: A clinical psychologist's view. In J.N. Lester & M. O'Reilly (Eds), *The Palgrave Handbook of Child Mental Health* (pp.42-58). New York, NY: Palgrave.

Koenig, K., De Los Reyes, A., Cicchetti, D., Scahill, L., & Klin, A. (2009). Group intervention to promote social skills in school-age children with pervasive developmental disorders: Reconsidering efficacy. *Journal of Autism and Developmental Disorders, 39*(8), 1163-1172.

Kovarsky, D. (2008). Representing voices from the life-world in evidence-based practice. *International Journal of Language and Communication Disorders, 43*(Suppl. 1), 47-57.

Kovarsky, D. & Curran, M. (2007). A missing voice in the discourse of evidence-based practice. *Topics in Language Disorders, 27*(1), 50-61.

Kovarsky, D. & Duchan, J.F. (1997). The interactional dimensions of language therapy. *Language, Speech, and Hearing Services in Schools, 28*(3), 297-307.

Labov, W. (1972). *Language in the Inner City: Studies in the Black English Vernacular.* Philadelphia, PA: University of Pennsylvania Press.

Lakoff, G. (1971). On generative semantics. In D.D. Steinberg & L.A. Jakobovits (Eds), *Semantics: An Interdisciplinary Reader in Philosophy, Linguistics and Psychology* (pp.232-296). Cambridge, UK: Cambridge University Press.

Lakoff, G. & Ross, J.R. (1976). Is deep structure necessary? In D.J. McCawley (Ed.), *Syntax and Semantics 7: Notes from the Linguistic Underground* (pp.159-164). New York, NY: Academic Press.

Law, J. & Garrett, Z. (2004). Speech and language therapy: Its potential role in CAMHS. *Child and Adolescent Mental Health, 9(2),* 50-55.

Law, J., Garrett, Z., & Nye, C. (2003). Speech and language therapy interventions for children with primary speech and language delay or disorder. *Cochrane Database of Systematic Reviews 2003*, Issue 3. Art. No.: CD004110. doi: 10.1002/14651858.CD004110.

Law, J., Reilly, S., & Snow, P.C. (2013) Child speech, language and communication needs re-examined in a public health context: A new direction for the speech and language therapy profession. *International Journal of Language and Communication Disorders, 48*(5), 486-496.

Law, J. & Stringer, H. (2013) The overlap between behaviour and communication and its implications for mental health in childhood: The elephant in the room. *Emotional and Behavioural Difficulties, 19*(1), 2-6.

Levinson, S.C. (1983). *Pragmatics.* Cambridge, UK: Cambridge University Press.

Lock, S., Wilkinson, R., & Bryan, K. (2001). *Supporting Partners of People with Aphasia in Relationships and Conversation (SPPARC).* Bicester, UK: Speechmark.

Lockton, E., Adams, C., & Collins, A. (2016). Do children with social communication disorder have explicit knowledge of pragmatic rules they break? A comparison of conversational pragmatic ability and metapragmatic awareness. *International Journal of Communication Disorders, 51*(5), 508-517.

López, B. & Leekam, S.R. (2003). Do children with autism fail to process information in context? *Journal of Child Psychology and Psychiatry and Allied Disciplines, 44*(2), 285-300.

Mackie, L. & Law, J. (2010a). Pragmatic language and the child with emotional/behavioural difficulties (EBD): A pilot study exploring the interaction between behaviour and communication disability. *International Journal of Language & Communication Disorders*, 45(4), 397–410.

Mackie, L. & Law, J. (2010b). The functional communication skills with externalizing behavior with and without co-occurring language difficulties. *Emotional and Behavioral Difficulties*, 19(10), 89–105.

Maddern, L., Franey, J., McLaughlin, V., & Cox, S. (2004). An evaluation of the impact of an inter-agency intervention programme to promote social skills in primary school children. *Educational Psychology in Practice*, 20(2), 135–155.

Malcolm, A. & Myers, L. (2001). Challenges and opportunities for speech and language therapists in secondary schools. *International Journal of Language and Communication Disorders*, 36(S1), 481–486.

Manochiopinig, S., Sheard, C., & Reed, V.A. (1992). Pragmatic assessment in adult aphasia: A clinical review. *Aphasiology*, 6(6), 519–533.

McCartney, E. (2000). Include us out? Speech and language therapists' prioritisation in mainstream schools. *Child Language Teaching and Therapy*, 16(2), 165–180.

McCurtin, A. & Carter, B. (2015). 'We don't have recipes; we just have loads of ingredients': Explanations of evidence and clinical decision making by speech and language therapists. *Journal of Evaluation in Clinical Practice*, 21(6), 1142–1150.

McCurtin, A. & Roddam, H. (2012). Evidence-based practice: SLTs under siege or opportunity for growth? The use and nature of research evidence in the profession. *International Journal of Language & Communication Disorders*, 47(1), 11–26.

McGregor, K.K. (2000). The development and enhancement of narrative skills in a preschool classroom: Towards a solution to clinician-client mismatch. *American Journal of Speech-Language Pathology*, 9(1), 55–71.

McTear, M.F. & Conti-Ramsden, G. (1990). *Pragmatic Disability in Children*. London, UK: Whurr.

Mental Health Commission. (2008). *A Recovery Approach Within the Irish Mental Health Services: A Framework for Development*. Dublin: Mental Health Commission.

Mey, J. (2006). Pragmatics: Seen through the prism of society. In A. Capone & J.L. Mey (Eds), *Interdisciplinary Studies in Pragmatics, Culture and Society, Perspectives in Pragmatics, Philosophy & Psychology*, Vol. 4 (pp.15–41). Switzerland: Springer.

Miranda, A.E., McCabe, A., & Bliss, L.S. (1998). Jumping around and leaving things out: A profile of the narrative abilities of children with specific language impairment. *Applied Psycholinguistics*, 19(4), 647–667.

Mishler, E.G. (1979). Meaning in context: Is there any other kind? *Harvard Educational Review*, 49(1), 1–19.

Morris, C.W. (1938). Foundation of the theory of signs. In O. Neurath, R. Carnap, & C.W. Morris (Eds), *International Encyclopedia of Unified Science: Vol. 2, No. 1.* (pp.1–59). Chicago, IL: University of Chicago Press.

Morse, J.M. (2006). The politics of evidence. *Qualitative Health Research*, *16*(3), 395–404.

Mueller, K.L. & Tomblin, J.B. (2012). Examining the comorbidity of language disorders and ADHD. *Topics in Language Disorders*, *32*(3), 228–246.

Müller, N. (2000). Pragmatics in speech and language pathology: Clinical pragmatics. In N. Müller (Ed.), *Pragmatics in Speech and Language Pathology: Studies in Clinical Applications* (pp.1–6). Amsterdam, The Netherlands; Philadelphia, PA: John Benjamins.

Ninio, A., Snow, C.E., Pan, B.A., & Rollins, P.R. (1994). Classifying communicative acts in children's interactions. *Journal of Communication Disorders*, *27*(2), 157–187.

Nippold, M.A. (2007). *Later Language Development: School-age Children, Adolescents and Young Adults*, 3rd ed. Austin, TX: Pro-Ed.

Norbury, C.F. (2004) Factors supporting idiom comprehension in children with communication disorders. *Journal of Speech, Language, Hearing Research*, *47*, 1179–1193.

Norbury, C.F. (2005). Barking up the wrong tree? Lexical ambiguity resolution in children with language impairments and autistic spectrum disorders. *Journal of Experimental Child Psychology*, *90*(2), 142–171.

Norbury, C.F. (2014). Practitioner review: Social (pragmatic) communication disorder conceptualization, evidence and clinical implications. *Journal of Child Psychology and Psychiatry*, *55*(3), 204–216.

Norbury, C.F. & Bishop, D.V.M. (2010). Narrative skills of children with communication impairments. *International Journal of Language and Communication Disorders*, *38*(3), 287–313.

Novak, J.M. & Kapolnek, K.M. (2001). Speech-language pathologists serving clients with mental illness: A collaborative treatment approach. *Contemporary Issues in Communication Science and Disorders*, *28*, 111–122.

Paul, R. (2007). *Language Disorders from Infancy Through Adolescence: Assessment and Intervention*, 3rd ed. Edinburgh, UK: Elsevier Mosby.

Penn, C. (1999). Pragmatic assessment and therapy for persons with brain damage: What have clinicians gleaned in two decades? *Brain and Language*, *68*(3), 535–552.

Perkins, M.R. (2000). The scope of pragmatic disability. In N. Müller (Ed.), *Pragmatics in Speech and Language Pathology: Studies in Clinical Applications* (pp.7–28). Philadelphia, PA: John Benjamins.

Perkins, M.R. (2005a). Pragmatic ability and disability as emergent phenomena. *Clinical Linguistics and Phonetics*, *19*(5), 367–377.

Perkins, M.R. (2005b). Clinical pragmatics: An emergentist perspective. *Clinical Linguistics and Phonetics*, *19*(5), 363–366.

Perkins, M.R. (2007). *Pragmatic Impairment*. Cambridge, UK: Cambridge University Press.

Perkins, M.R. (2010). Pragmatic language impairment. In J.S. Damico, N. Müller & M.J. Ball (Eds), *The Handbook of Language and Speech Disorders* (pp.227–246). Oxford, UK: Wiley-Blackwell.

Peterson, C., Jesso, B., & McCabe, A. (1999). Encouraging narratives in pre-schoolers: An intervention study. *Journal of Child Language, 26*(1), 49-67.

Phelps-Terasaki, D. & Phelps-Gunn, T. (2007). *Test of Pragmatic Language 2*, 2nd ed. San Antonio: The Psychological Corporation.

Philofsky, A., Fidler, D.J., & Hepburn, S. (2007). Pragmatic language profiles of school-age children with autism spectrum disorders and Williams syndrome. *American Journal of Speech-Language Pathology, 16*(4), 368-380.

Prutting, C.A. (1982). Pragmatics as social competence. *Journal of Speech and Hearing Disorders, 47*(2), 123-134.

Prutting, C.A. & Kirchner, D.M. (1987). A clinical appraisal of the pragmatic aspects of language. *Journal of Speech and Hearing Disorders, 52*(2), 105-119.

Reichow, B., Steiner, A.M., & Volkmar, F. (2013). Cochrane review: Social skills groups for people aged 6-21 with autism spectrum disorders (ASD). *Evidence-Based Child Health, 8*, 266-315.

Renfrew, C.E. (2010). *Bus Story Test: A Test of Narrative Speech*. Bicester, UK: Speechmark.

Rinaldi, W. (1992). *The Social Use of Language Programme: Enhancing the Social Communication of Children and Teenagers with Special Educational Needs*. Windsor, UK: NFER-Nelson.

Rogalski, Y. & Edmonds, L.A. (2008). Attentive Reading and Constrained Summarisation (ARCS) treatment in primary progressive aphasia: A case study. *Aphasiology, 22*(7), 763-775.

Rollins, P.R. (2000). Culturally sensitive assessment of narrative skills in children. *Seminars in Speech and Language, 21*(3), 223-234.

Royal College of Speech and Language Therapists (2009). *Resource Manual for Commissioning and Planning Services for Speech Language and Communication Needs* (SLCN) - *Mental Health*. London: RCSLT.

Rumpf, A.L., Kamp-Becker, I., Becker, K., & Kauschke, C. (2012). Narrative competence and internal state language of children with Asperger Syndrome and ADHD. *Research in Developmental Disabilities, 33*(5), 1395-1407.

Sacks, H., Schegloff, E.A., & Jefferson, G. (1974). A simplest systematics for the organisation of turn taking for conversation. *Language, 50*(4), 696-735.

Sarno, M.T. (1969). *The Functional Communication Profile*. New York, NY: Institute of Rehabilitation Medicine.

Schegloff, E.A. (2007). *Sequence Organization in Interaction: A Primer in Conversation Analysis 1*. Cambridge, UK: Cambridge University Press.

Schiffrin, D., Tannen, D., & Hamilton, H.E. (2013). Introduction. In D. Schiffrin, D. Tannen, & H.E. Hamilton (Eds), *The Handbook of Discourse Analysis* (pp.1-10). Oxford, UK: Blackwell.

Schroeder, A. (1996). *Socially Speaking: A Pragmatic Social Skills Programme for Pupils with Mild to Moderate Learning Disabilities*. Wisbech, UK: LDA.

Searle, J.R. (1969). *Speech Acts: An Essay in the Philosophy of Language*. London, UK: Cambridge University Press.

Searle, J.R. (1976). A classification of illocutionary acts. *Language in Society, 5*(1), 1-23.

Semel, E., Wiig, E., & Secord, W. (2003). *Clinical Evaluation of Language Fundamentals*, 4th ed. San Antonio, TX: The Psychological Company.

Simmons-Mackie, N.N. & Damico, J.S., (1995). Communicative competence in aphasia: Evidence from compensatory strategies. *Clinical Aphasiology, 23*, 95-105.

Smith, B.R. & Leinonen, E. (1991). *Clinical Pragmatics: Unravelling the Complexities of Communicative Failure*. London, UK: Chapman & Hall.

Snow, P.C. (2009). Child maltreatment, mental health and oral language competence: Inviting speech-language pathology to the prevention table. *International Journal of Speech-Language Pathology, 11*(2), 95-103.

Spence, S. (2003). Social skills training with children and young people: Theory, evidence and practice. *Child and Adolescent Mental Health, 8*(2), 84-96.

Spencer-Oatey, H. & Žegarac, V. (2002). An introduction to applied linguistics. In N. Schmitt (Ed.), *Introduction to Applied Linguistics* (pp.72-91). London, UK: Arnold.

Storebø, O.J., Skoog, M., Damm, D., Thomsen, P.H., Simonsen, E., & Gluud, C. (2011). Social skills training for Attention Deficit Hyperactivity Disorder (ADHD) in children aged 5 to 18 years. *Cochrane Database of Systematic Reviews 2011*, Issue 12. Art. No.: CD008223. doi: 10.1002/14651858.CD008223.pub2

Strong, C. (1998). *The Strong Narrative Assessment Procedure*. Eau Claire, WI: Thinking Publications.

Sullivan, S.A., Hollen, L., Wren, Y., Thompson, A.D., Lewis, G., & Zammit, S. (2016). A longitudinal investigation of childhood communication ability and adolescent psychotic experiences in a community sample. *Schizophrenia Research, 173*(1-2), 54-61.

Swanson, L.A., Fey, M.E., Mills, C.E., & Hood, L.S. (2005). Use of narrative-based language intervention with children who have specific language impairment. *American Journal of Speech-Language Pathology, 14*(2), 131-143.

Tsang, H.W.H. & Pearson, V. (2001). Work-related social skills training for people with schizophrenia in Hong Kong. *Schizophrenia Bulletin, 27*(1), 139-148.

Ulatowska, H.K. & Olness, G.S. (2007). Pragmatics in discourse performance: Insights from aphasiology. *Seminars in Speech and Language, 28*(2), 148-158.

van Dijk, T.A. & Kintsch, W. (1983). *Strategies of Discourse Comprehension*. New York, NY: Academic Press.

Wallace, C.J. (1998). Social skills training in psychiatric rehabilitation: Recent findings. *International Review of Psychiatry, 10*(1), 9-19.

Walsh, I.P. (2007). Small talk is "big talk" in clinical discourse: Appreciating the value of conversation in SLP clinical interactions. *Topics in Language Disorders, 27*(1), 24-36.

Walsh, I.P. (2008a) Language socialisation among people with mental health disorders. In P.A. Duff & N. Hornberger (Eds), *Encyclopedia of Language & Education*, 2nd ed., Vol 8 (pp.327-340). New York, NY: Springer.

Walsh, I.P. (2008b) Whose voice is it anyway? Hushing and hearing 'voices' in speech and language therapy interactions with people with chronic schizophrenia. *International Journal of Language & Communication Disorders*, 43(1), 81-95.

Weare, K. & Nind, M. (2011). Mental health promotion and problem prevention in schools: What does the evidence say? *Health Promotion International*, 26(S1), i29 Vol 8, i69.

Wetherby, A.M. & Prutting, C.A. (1984). Profiles of communicative and cognitive-social abilities in autistic children. *Journal of Speech and Hearing Research*, 27(3), 364-377.

Whitcomb, S. & Merrell, K.W. (2013). *Behavioral, Social, and Emotional Assessment of Children and Adolescents*, 4th ed. New York, NY: Routledge.

Whitworth, A., Perkins, L., & Lesser, R. (1997). *Conversation Analysis Profile for People with Aphasia*. London, UK: Whurr.

Williams, V. (2011). *Discourse and Disability*. Oxford, UK: Wiley-Blackwell.

Worrall, L. (2006). Professionalism and functional outcomes. *Journal of Communication Disorders*, 39(4), 320-327.

6 Developing theoretically grounded approaches to pragmatic intervention with people with schizophrenia

Caroline Jagoe

Introduction

Schizophrenia is a common and enduring mental health disorder which is associated with disturbances in communication (see Chapter 3 for an overview). The evidence of disturbances in language and communication, specifically within pragmatic abilities of people with schizophrenia is long recognized and well documented. While disturbances in many levels of language have been described in this population, it is the pragmatic disturbance which is often considered most pervasive (e.g., Frith, 1992; Haas et al., 2015; Langdon, Davies, & Coltheart, 2002; Meilijson, Kasher, & Elizur, 2004). The impact of pragmatic difficulties extends to both linguistic and nonverbal aspects of communication (Lavelle, Healey, & McCabe, 2013), affecting interpersonal rapport and social interaction.

While most research on language and communication in people with schizophrenia has focused on the difficulties observed, certain pragmatic abilities and strengths of people with schizophrenia have emerged (e.g., Jagoe, 2015; McCabe, Leudar, & Antaki, 2004; McCabe, Skelton, Heath, Burns, & Priebe, 2002; Walsh, 2008). Despite these abilities, the subtle but sometimes pervasive difficulties in social communication are a significant obstacle for many people with the disorder, as illustrated by various first-person accounts:

I feel quiet, too quiet like when people are sitting down talking, having conversations and things like that. I don't really say much and I feel like the odd one out (Brophy, 2007, p.53).

My own experience of paranoia can be succinctly described using language games. [...] What I found was that my perception of how people conversed became reduced to the simple rules of a language game, and I was an unwilling participant in this game (Anonymous, 2011).

It is your responsibility as medical professionals to communicate well with us. We have schizophrenia. We are mentally ill and we can't always manage our interactions with other people. You must teach us how to communicate well with you (Schneider et al., 2004, p.574).

Given these accounts we, as clinicians and researchers, must recognize that, despite the demonstration of 'ability' in some contexts, people with schizophrenia appear to live with daily struggles related to socialization and communication. It is argued that these accounts should compel us to seek out explanatory theories which are able to guide appropriate assessment and intervention where required. Despite the lack of clarity as to the underlying reasons for communication disturbances in people with schizophrenia, intervention for difficulties in socialization and conversation have emerged out of necessity to work with these features clinically.

Speech and language therapists (SLTs), with their grounding in linguistics, psychology and speech-language disorders, are uniquely placed to work within this domain (Muir, 2001) – a domain at the interface of complex and nuanced pragmatic *disability* and a common lack of social opportunity to use the *ability* that is present. While current approaches to communication difficulties in people with schizophrenia have shown benefit, specific interventions which account for the complexity and rapidly changing nature of naturalistic conversation may increase the success of interventions. Such interventions are likely to emerge from strong theoretically-grounded approaches which then offer the opportunity for empirical testing and application.

An overview of approaches to communication in people with schizophrenia

This section provides a brief overview of the range of approaches used to address the communication disturbances which are common in schizophrenia. This area of practice is vast and multidisciplinary in nature and it is beyond the scope of this chapter to survey it in any depth. Rather, the aim is to provide a context and backdrop against which approaches grounded in pragmatic theory with strong cognitive foundations will be presented.

Social skills training

'Social Skills' programmes are frequently designed and carried out by mental health professionals. Social Skills Training (SST) typically involves a range of skill areas and entails:

> ...the systematic teaching of interpersonal skills through the process of breaking complex behaviors into their constituent elements, demonstrating (modeling) those skills in role plays, engaging clients in role plays to practice those skills, providing positive and corrective feedback to improve performance, additional role play practice, and developing assignments to practice those skills in naturally occurring interactions in clients' lives (Mueser & Bellack, 2007, p.549).

Most social skills programmes, having developed from early programmes in assertiveness training, have a communication or conversation skills component (Walsh, 2008). There is evidence for SST and its impact on social functioning (e.g., Bellack, 2004; Kurtz & Mueser, 2009). The significance of these improvements continue to be debated (Mueser & Bellack, 2007), with generalization of the changes in social skills a continued area of challenge (Pilling et al., 2002).

A variant of SST is that of Conversation Skills Training where there is a more directed and explicit focus on conversation. Such programmes incorporate the didactic teaching common in SST but extend the nature of the learning, as described by Walsh (2008):

> As well as direct instruction or the demonstration of appropriate conversational skills through focused individuals and group sessions, the enhancement of metacommunicative

awareness has been found to complement and reinforce the didactic approach often adopted. Hence, role-playing of particular communication situations accompanied by discussion of these situations in metacommunication terms enhances learning and generalization (p.32).

A meta-analysis of social skills intervention (Pilling et al., 2002) revealed that of the nine studies that conformed to the inclusion criteria, five used a combination of instruction, modelling, role-play and feedback to train social skills. The other studies used variants of behavioural rehearsal, modelling and discussion, as well as video modelling. The element of behavioural rehearsal is unlikely to reflect the complexity and novelty of each instance of communication, perhaps explaining why such attempts have little generalization beyond the training situation (*ibid*). Although the area of social skills training and related approaches is vast, research is limited in relation to the impact of these approaches on the nature of pragmatic competence in real-time naturalistic conversation. It is argued that, although many of the approaches show promise in the general area of socialization, they lack the specificity to truly address the specific and complex nature of pragmatic disability.

'Experiential' programmes for social skill development

A different approach to social skills 'training' includes interventions which could be classified as 'experiential programmes' based on their emphasis of 'learning through doing in context'. Many of the difficulties in social engagement may be effectively dealt with by programmes designed to increase supported socialization opportunities for people with schizophrenia (Davidson et al., 2004). However, pragmatic language difficulties are a core feature of the disorder for many individuals and there appear to be those for whom opportunity may not be enough. This need for both opportunity and supportive training is addressed in some of the 'experiential' approaches. These models, such as 'supported socialization' (Davidson et al., 2004, p.455), are built on the understanding that training in different areas of functioning often has limited generalization in people with mental health disorders. Supported socialization extends the observations that in other domains (e.g., living skills) supported integration into 'real life' settings has resulted in improved outcomes compared to the less contextualized approaches to 'training' (*ibid*). Other 'experiential programmes' include the In Vivo Amplified Skills Training (IVAST) (Liberman, Glynn, Blair, Ross, & Marder, 2002). Both these programmes work through many of the components common to SST and have a strong focus on supported

In Vivo exercises and contextualized supported practice. Where 'experiential approaches' are used to provide opportunity for skills training or learning they may fare better than didactic approaches – being based on the notion that experiencing successful conversation and reflecting on success and breakdown offers opportunities for on-line processing and judgements which could then, in some instances, serve as material for therapeutic reflection.

While these types of approaches do seem to 'tick the box' in terms of on-line naturalistic experience, they may fail to target a specific cognitive-pragmatic area of breakdown or specific pragmatic ability. They risk entailing a hit-and-miss approach. It is possible that engaging in 'chat' is less likely to consistently provoke the skills or situations which are challenging to the individual and thus required to achieve therapeutic change. However, there is a clear role for such experiential intervention from a social perspective, that is, de-stigmatizing the disorder within the community and providing a sense of competence, success and ability for the individual. Indeed, with regards to the Supported Socialization approaches, they are defined as such:

> The provision of structured opportunities and supports that enable people with psychiatric disabilities to participate in the naturally occurring rhythms of community life within the context of caring, reciprocal relationships in which they experience themselves as having something of value to offer other (Davidson et al., 2004, p.459).

Such intervention is situated within the social paradigm of disability which has played an important role in the approach to other communication disorders, such as aphasia. It must, however, be recognized that for individuals who wish to pursue intervention for specific pragmatic skills, a different – and probably complementary – approach must be developed.

Towards pragmatically grounded approaches to communication intervention in schizophrenia

The approaches outlined above have demonstrated some benefit for the person with schizophrenia. However, theoretically-driven approaches to addressing communication difficulties in this population are lacking. Joyal, Bonneau and Fecteau (2016) have called for a unified conceptual model to guide speech and language therapy intervention in schizophrenia – a statement which suggests the need for theory-driven approaches to intervention. It is argued that the specific pragmatic component of the difficulties experienced by some people with schizophrenia cannot be effectively dealt with in a theoretical vacuum. Pragmatic theory is essential to develop explanatory accounts of the disorder in order to provide a comprehensive set of approaches for the communication difficulties encountered by these individuals, an intervention paradigm in which the SLT plays an important role. Theories which draw on cognitive constructs are the best candidates to explain and advance the domain of clinical pragmatics (Cummings, 2009, 2014) and are therefore those which are likely to have some relevance to the development of theory-driven approaches to intervention in this population.

Cognitively situated theories of pragmatics

Pragmatic theories which situate themselves within cognitive science are likely to have clear, and potentially testable, application to working with people with schizophrenia with regards to communication ability. Arguably the two most comprehensively articulated pragmatic theories which draw on cognitive explanations are that of Cognitive Pragmatics Theory (see Bara, 2010, for a full articulation of the theory) and Relevance Theory (Sperber & Wilson, 1986/1995). For this reason, the remainder of this chapter will focus on those two accounts of communication.

Cognitive Pragmatics Theory has a growing body of literature on specific clinical applications of the principles arising from the theory (e.g., Bosco et al., 2018; Gabbatore et al., 2015) and is thus more 'established' from a clinical perspective. Relevance Theory has had less clinical application but provides a fertile ground to examine how concepts from a pragmatic theory may have clinical implications that ultimately could lead to the development of specific approaches to assessment and intervention. A brief overview of the two theories is provided below, following which the terminology and perspectives on mental states, a core issue for cognitive accounts of pragmatics, will be discussed and compared across the two theories. The application and potential application of each, in relation to the assessment and intervention in people with schizophrenia, will then be considered. It is beyond the scope of this chapter to systematically present all of the tenets of these theories. Instead, those elements of direct clinical significance, or potential significance, will be considered.

Both Cognitive Pragmatics Theory and Relevance Theory can be conceptualized as Neo-Gricean, but differ slightly in the Gricean foundation they take as their focal point. Cognitive Pragmatics Theory takes, as its Gricean foundation, the notion that communication is a cooperative activity

(Bara, 2010). Cognitive Pragmatics Theory is an inferential pragmatic theory, recognizing that there is typically a gap between what is said literally and what is meant by a speaker. It considers communication as a cooperative and intentional process – a 'behaviour game' – which involves both linguistic and extralinguistic means. These communication modalities are used to convey a message which is inferentially interpreted, beginning with the literal meaning of the utterance (Airenti, Bara, & Colombetti, 1993; Bara, 2010). The notion that interpretation begins with the literal meaning of the utterance is arguably one of the most significant points of departure between Cognitive Pragmatics Theory and Relevance Theory (RT).

Relevance Theory is also an inferential pragmatic theory, grounded in cognitive science. Relevance Theory sees communication as reliant on an overarching principle – that of Relevance. According to RT, understanding an utterance entails recognizing the communicator's intentions, which itself involves recognizing how the utterance was intended to be relevant. An utterance is only 'relevant' when the effort required to process it yields a valuable cognitive gain, making a "worthwhile difference to the individual's representation of the world" (Wilson & Sperber, 2004, p.608). A hearer is entitled to expect that any utterance produced by a speaker is one which is the most relevant they are capable of and willing to produce. Hearers are thus entitled to follow a path of least effort in the interpretation process (Wilson & Sperber, 2004). In this way, RT argues that the hearer is guided towards the intended interpretation of an utterance by expectations of relevance, rather than automatically beginning with the literal meaning of the utterance.

The notion of mental states is prominent in cognitively-based accounts of pragmatic ability, and features prominently in the explanatory accounts of both Cognitive Pragmatics Theory and RT. In Cognitive Pragmatics Theory particular attention is given to the idea of 'shared belief'. The equivalent concept in RT could be considered to be the notion of 'mutual manifestness'. Cognitive Pragmatics Theory identifies three 'levels' of beliefs: individual beliefs held by the individual; mutual or common beliefs which are held by groups of individuals (generally shared knowledge of surroundings or opinions which are common to a group of people, for example); and, finally, shared beliefs which are held by participants in an interaction and "which each participant is aware is possessed by all the other participants" (Bara, 2010, p.72). It is this shared belief which enables successful communication. Interlocutors may take certain information or beliefs as shared but, according to Bara (2010), this is always a subjective assumption. The concept of 'shared knowledge' is approached slightly differently in RT, using the notion of the mutual cognitive environment. Individuals each have distinct cognitive environments and come to the communicative interaction with different world knowledge, different perceptions and different inferential abilities. Information is considered to be manifest if it is potentially perceptible, even if not in the immediate focus of attention. RT asserts that the cognitive environments of individuals overlap to varying degrees. Certain communities may hold specific beliefs, friends share more assumptions than strangers. A 'special case' of overlap of cognitive environments is that of a mutual cognitive environment (Sperber & Wilson, 1986/1995). A mutual cognitive environment is one in which assumptions are potentially available to both communicators and it is manifest to both parties that they share these assumptions. It is mutual manifestness and the existence of a mutual cognitive environment which allows the communicators to 'align' and engage in conversation and create the communicative environment in which further interaction may occur. Crucially, both of these theories identify the role of recognizing intentions. The recognition of intentions – as mental states – is dependent on some degree of mentalizing or Theory of Mind. A significant body of literature of schizophrenia has documented an impairment in Theory of Mind and identifying intentions in people with schizophrenia supported by meta-analyses (e.g., Bora, Yucel, & Pantelis, 2009; Sprong, Schothorst, Vos, Hox, & van Engeland, 2007), making both theories applicable to the field.

Operationalizing Cognitive Pragmatics Theory

Cognitive Pragmatics Theory and pragmatic assessment

Cognitive Pragmatics Theory has yielded a specific assessment tool stemming directly from the theoretical perspective discussed above: *The Assessment Battery for Communication* (ABaCO; Sacco et al., 2008). This is a unique position – an assessment which stems directly from a single unified pragmatic theory. Given the development and research on this assessment battery, the focus of this section will be on describing the battery and its application to this point.

The ABaCo battery assesses both comprehension and production of a range of communication acts, with scoring based on defined criteria, across five evaluation scales: linguistic, extralinguistic, paralinguistic, context, and conversational. The entire battery consists of 180 items, 72 of which are presented by the assessor and the remaining 108 based on video scenarios or prompts (Bosco, Angeleri, Zuffranieri, Bara, & Sacco, 2012). While most of the subscales rely on vignettes or prompts, the conversational scale requires that the clinician and patient engage in four conversations on set topics. These interactions are then analyzed from the perspective of turn-taking abilities and topic maintenance (Davis, Guendouzi, Savage, Blackburn, & Williams, 2015). There are two forms of the assessment which are considered equivalent: Form A is slightly shorter, requiring fewer prompts and video scenarios. The Italian language assessment battery has demonstrated good reliability and validity (Sacco et al., 2008) and normative data are available according to sex, age and education of people 15-75 years old (Angeleri, Bosco, Gabbatore, Bara, & Sacco, 2012). It has been used across a number of clinical populations, including adults with TBI (Angeleri et al., 2008) and Italian adults with schizophrenia (Colle et al., 2013). Davis and colleagues undertook a translation of the ABaCo battery into English, collecting normative data on politeness tokens used by American adults, in order to document general politeness forms in American English and identify regional differences (Davis et al., 2015). The authors stress the potential clinical utility of the translated tool, but also identify several cultural issues in adaptation of the battery. The obvious implication is that an English translation cannot be transported into other cultural contexts for clinical use without clear normative data being developed first, as well as development of appropriate materials, including appropriate video scenarios.

A norm-reference, standardized, and easily administered assessment is often attractive in clinical settings, and culturally relevant versions of this battery are likely to be welcomed by clinicians but require significant development to ensure contextual relevance and good psychometric properties.

Cognitive Pragmatics Theory and pragmatic intervention

A clinical protocol, called Cognitive Pragmatic Treatment (CPT), has been developed on the basis of Cognitive Pragmatics Theory. The authors describe it as "an integrated treatment, working on all aspects of communication" (Sacco et al., 2016, p.2). This treatment protocol has been reported in relation to its application with people with traumatic brain injury (TBI) (Bosco et al., 2018; Gabbatore et al., 2015) and schizophrenia (Bosco, Gabbatore, Gastaldo, & Sacco, 2016). This very recently developed protocol displays promise with efficacy demonstrated with regards to behavioural outcomes (Gabbatore et al., 2015, 2017) and cerebral activity (Gabbatore et al., 2017; Sacco et., 2016), despite the fact that the clinical development of the approach is in its infancy.

CPT comprises between 20 and 24 group therapy sessions which, in the studies reported, have been administered over a 12-week period. CPT training activities are described as being designed to improve inferential abilities, the ability to use extralinguistic cues, paralinguistic cues and the appropriateness of communication with regards to social context (Sacco et al., 2016, p.4). The component sessions of CPT highlight the cognitive nature of the theoretical foundation, with sessions targeting awareness, executive functions (specifically planning) and theory of mind. Several sessions are devoted to each of the expressive modalities conceptualized in this theory, linguistic ability, extralinguistic ability and paralinguistic ability. In addition, sessions addressing social appropriateness, conversational ability (turn taking and topic management), narrative ability, and telephonic conversations are included (Gabbatore et al., 2015). Each session has a consistent internal structure, comprising: (1) a review of the previous topic; (2) activities addressing 'comprehension' of the cognitive or pragmatic topic of the session, typically using video scenarios and discussion; (3) activities to encourage 'production' or use of the skills which are the focus of the particular session, typically through role-play; and (4) conclusion and homework components to encourage further practice of the skills addressed. The group setting of this treatment could be argued to provide an ecological or experiential setting in which the skills taught can be practised, feedback provided and self-monitoring developed.

The structured, theoretically-grounded nature of this approach makes it a potentially attractive intervention protocol for clinical settings. The group context is not only theoretically and clinically justified but also has the benefit of cost-effectiveness. This approach would require significant commitment to the development of materials for implementation in other settings, given its reliance on video scenarios which would need to be recreated in the relevant language and cultural contexts.

Operationalizing Relevance Theory constructs for assessment and intervention

The application of RT to clinical pragmatics has, thus far, been largely in analyzing and describing the pragmatic abilities in clinical populations; examining the meaning-making process in interaction between a clinician and individuals with communication disabilities; and hypothesis testing. In contrast to Cognitive Pragmatics Theory, RT has not yet benefited from extensive application to clinical populations. Despite the fact that clinical application is still growing, RT provides some foundational theoretical concepts which arguably have clear potential to be applied to working with people with schizophrenia and ultimately in designing theoretically-sound intervention approaches. There are significant gaps in the research, including only a limited exploration of the precise pragmatic nature of the difficulties observed in people with schizophrenia from a Relevance Theory perspective (e.g., Jagoe, 2013, 2015). However, some of the concepts from RT may prove to have worth when considering the assessment and intervention in this group of people. In the discussion which follows, some possibilities for clinical exploration are raised.

From a Relevance Theory perspective, all communication is driven by considerations of relevance which itself is bound up with context and real-time processing of information as it pertains to 'worthwhile' benefits to the communicator in that moment. Reflecting on tasks, even video-based tasks, to make pragmatic judgements in assessment or intervention is likely to involve fundamentally different processes. In other words, when we ask individuals to step outside of an interaction and interpret what was intended by an actor on a screen, or predict what they might say in response, we may very well be activating specific cognitive processes that are distinct from those used by that individual when in real-time interaction. For this reason, operationalizing RT for clinical application requires novel means of engaging the individual in actual interaction contexts, which are constrained only insofar as the performance can be evaluated, shaped or monitored in some way. This is clinically challenging, but perhaps more authentic (both in a cognitive and social sense) and may lead to better generalization than more contrived methods.

Recreating a context which challenges the representation of the mutual cognitive environment may necessitate the use of a degree of 'contrived' tasks. However, it is likely to be important to maintain the interactive component rather than relying on abstracted tasks. The novel use and adaptation of more traditional tasks (like barrier or referential tasks) may allow the clinician to approximate naturalness and aim towards generalization of skills. Barrier tasks have been widely used across clinical pragmatics and have implicit within their construction a 'uniqueness' in the perspective of each participant. This uniqueness is also mutually manifest by virtue of the barrier obscuring the view of the interlocutor's visual context. Manipulating such tasks, so that participants are aware of what information is available, and unavailable, to their communication partner is possible through the use of grid structures in which some boxes are closed and not visible to one party. Problems of generalization are likely to arise, however. The contrived nature of barrier tasks is unquestionable. Novel adaptations, to modernize and approximate naturalness, may be possible. Several tasks have been described in pragmatics research which rely on participants engaging in an initial interaction with a fellow participant over what they believe to be a common experience or common goal, followed by a conversation with the researcher in which they evaluate the original interaction. The video conversation task used by Barker and Givón (2005) is a possible candidate for such a novel adaptation.

In their research, Barker and Givón (2005) asked pairs of participants to talk about a video which they had watched simultaneously but independently of each other. The participants were told that they had watched videos which were almost identical and were told to find out as much as possible about the video that their partner had seen. This type of task requires participants (service users in clinical contexts) to engage in collaborative talk. The nature of the task demands not only engagement in 'real-time' communication (with the participant partner), but engagement designed to tap into the ability to seek another's perspective. The design of this task inherently taps into the mutual cognitive environment, and modifications of the instructions could further tax context selection abilities. For example, by showing two related but different clips with the same instructions the participants would almost inevitably presume mutual manifestness of certain assumptions and need to negotiate meaning to resolve the task. For example, a service user and a conversation partner could be individually shown news items taken from two different channels with slightly different detail reported. The task could be to summarize the news – a process which would entail considering different perspectives and sources of information. This type of task has potential as both an assessment and intervention task. As an assessment task it can be carried out by the clinician and an assistant (as the fellow conversationalist) or even another client. Although time consuming and resource dependent, the information would provide a rich source for analysis of pragmatic performance on a number of fronts, including negotiation of the mutual cognitive environment, the ability to infer meaning within conversation and the ability to convey meaning within considerations of optimal relevance. As a therapy task, feedback processes and reflection could be incorporated into the task, as could strategy training, for example, facilitating awareness of signals indicating conversational breakdown, which can then be applied in 'real-world' conversations.

Considering programme design

How might such intervention be delivered? One protocol which might be borrowed and extended to pragmatic ability in the emerging area of practice in mental health intervention is that of Metacognitive Training (MCT) (Moritz & Woodward, 2007). MCT targets areas such as 'Jumping to Conclusions' and Theory of Mind, using a combination of discussion, reflection and exercises aimed at tapping these skills:

> Exercises targeting each bias individually demonstrate the fallibility of human cognition in general, with an explicit focus on thinking biases that are important in schizophrenia. Personal examples of these biases expressed by MCT participants, and discussion of ways to counter them, serve to provide corrective experiences in a fun and supportive atmosphere, yielding obvious advantages over mere lecturing (Moritz & Woodward, 2007, p.621).

Although MCT is specifically for people experiencing (or at risk of) psychosis, the typical structure of MCT sessions may be useful for exploring the impact of disturbances in communication related to schizophrenia. Adapting this protocol could involve group sessions broadly structured on the framework used in MCT. The structure might then incorporate the following elements: (1) metapragmatic awareness tasks and normalizing aspects of communication challenges; (2) discussion of extremes of these difficulties that may be associated with schizophrenia (either in terms of frequency of difficulties or nature of the challenges); (3) responses to challenges and implementation of new or alternative strategies; and (4) implementation exercises within the session itself and as home practice.

The normalizing process may be of particular significance. Relevance Theory is overt in identifying the fragility of the human pragmatic ability:

> Communication is governed by a less-than-perfect heuristic. On this approach, failures in communication are to be expected: what is mysterious and requires explanation is not failure but success (Sperber & Wilson, 1986/1995, p.45).

This type of acknowledgement could form part of the initial part of each session, utilizing specific examples of the "fallibility of human cognition in general" (Moritz & Woodward, 2007, p.621) but with a specific focus on pragmatic processes. The discussion of the extremes of difficulties which may be faced when living with schizophrenia may involve acknowledging that typical difficulties may occur more frequently or that the nature of the challenges may be unique. For example, while most people will have some difficulty starting conversations in certain contexts, if a person with schizophrenia experiences a lot of anxiety around communication, these difficulties may occur in most, rather than some, social contexts. In contrast, a unique challenge may occur if a person is delusional, which may pose a particular challenge to the mutual cognitive environment. The third element of a pragmatic intervention structured in a similar way to MCT could involve consideration of strategies. Such strategies should be generated from a coherent theoretical grounding, given the argument put forward in this chapter. For this reason, it is argued that the clinician should be extremely well versed in whatever pragmatic theory she/he is applying (in this case Relevance Theory) and use that single coherent theory across the intervention. This coherence could be considered important for continuity and implementation of strategies. For example, one can imagine a session addressing dealing with misunderstandings that utilizes the notion of the mutual cognitive environment. Equally, the same concept could be included in considering conversation initiation. The strategies can then be built around the theoretical construct. The use of a strong theoretical construct, such as the mutual cognitive environment as one component of the intervention content, also acts to avoid simple rote 'solutions' or conversational strategies. For example, and based on a personal experience, a person approaching a stranger at a bus stop and launching into a comment about a personal interest and a movie they have just seen, may be perceived as socially awkward. However, in the context of an understanding of the mutual cognitive environment, the person may be able to stop and consider what is potentially perceivable and relevant to that individual, and begin the conversation differently (for example, if the bus is due, they may decide to comment, "I only just made it on time it seems; the movie I've come from was longer than I anticipated"). The implementation exercises should ideally utilize a lot of the session time and be exercises conducted in 'real-time', rather than considering materials about interactions in a more abstracted sense. Tasks which approximate real-time processes and are *experienced* rather than *represented* interactions (Begeer et al., 2010) may prove to be useful in this regard. The paired conversations about a video (described above), are one such example.

Addressing the collaborative nature of conversational competence: The role of conversation partners

Both Cognitive Pragmatics Theory and Relevance Theory emphasize the collaborative nature of communication. The clinical application of Cognitive

Pragmatics Theory has thus far confined itself to the individual with the disorder. The exploration of communication disability from a Relevance Theory perspective has also largely focused on the individual with the 'diagnosis', although considerations of the role of the conversation partner have also been presented across different clinical groups (Jagoe, 2015; Jagoe & Smith, 2017; Neuvonen, Jagoe, Launonen, Smith, & von Tetzchner, in submission). Given that these theories overtly discuss the roles of both interlocutors in the process of communication, the role of conversation partners when assessing and intervening with regards to pragmatics should not be ignored. Indeed, communicative competence should ideally be seen as arising within an interactional context:

> It is possible to extend our notion of communicative competence beyond consideration of how competence is vested in the individual, by recognizing competence as arising from the interactive relationship of communication partners as they negotiate messages (Ferguson, 1996, p.56).

In this light, it is not sufficient merely to 'assess' the individual with schizophrenia in order to uncover (dis)ability. The significant conversation partners also need to be part of the assessment and intervention process.

Consideration of the communication skills and resources of conversational partners is now a practice common within speech and language therapy, approached in different ways. Communication partner training for significant others of people with aphasia and dementia, and to some extent Traumatic Brain Injury, are relatively well established (e.g., Behn, Togher, Power, & Heard, 2012, in TBI; Morris, Horne, McEvoy, & Williamson, 2018, for review in dementia; Simmons-Mackie, Raymer, Armstrong, Holland, & Cherney, 2010, for review in aphasia), as well as opportunities for support, discussion, information and skill acquisition. Frontline and healthcare staff may also be trained to support communication, as has been done in settings in which people with acquired communication disorders reside or are treated. Although the strategies may be distinct, this practice may be very useful in promoting successful engagement between people with schizophrenia and those friends, family and professionals with whom they interact. In fact, research within the realm of communication and psychiatry has argued that interventions targeted at improving patient–clinician communication have favourable outcomes and should be pursued in research and clinical practice (e.g., McCabe et al., 2016). In the participatory action research study by Schneider and colleagues

(2004), the ability of the mental healthcare professionals to support successful interactions with people with schizophrenia emerged as a powerful theme. The SLT, with experience in training communication partners, may be well placed to engage other healthcare professionals, or even work alongside people with schizophrenia to improve the communication strategies used by medical staff.

Practically, the engagement of significant others may involve a process of appraising their own communication skills and strategies. Again, it is argued that this appraisal should be done from a coherent theoretical standpoint. Such an appraisal may yield a profile of current patterns and strategies of communication that may assist in planning intervention, as has been used in other populations. The members of the individual's social network can then be "encouraged and facilitated to communicate more effectively with the person with a [mental health disorder] in a way which promotes shared understanding and a positive communicative experience" (Walsh, 2008, pp.337–338). A skill appraisal may not be appropriate for other mental health professionals, who are likely to form a significant part of the individual's social network. In these instances, sensitizing staff to general principles of facilitating successful engagements may be useful.

An RT perspective may have application in sensitizing conversation partners of those with schizophrenia to the communication profiles of individuals. While conversation partners may helpfully adjust their communication strategies to accommodate for an individual assumed to be less communicatively 'competent' (Garcia, Metthé, Paradis, & Joanette, 2001), such an assumption also has the possibility of eroding successful engagement. Particularly in a disorder in which stigma is rife, an assumption of mental illness may lead to a subsequent assumption of 'incompetence', an avoidance of engagement (Walsh, 2008). In addressing a similar issue in relation to communication of people with neurological impairment, Garcia and colleagues suggest:

> ... a conversational partner can decide not to interpret a statement as relevant if he or she believes or has been told that this person is 'incompetent'. The partner might also decide that it is not worth the effort to work on keeping the conversation coherent. This means that the partner has the option of not inventing or inferring the necessary discourse links. Likewise if the speaker is judged to be incompetent, such a label may lead to an interpretation of irrelevance even when not warranted (Garcia et al., 2001, p.19).

Conversely, sensitizing the conversation partners of an individual with schizophrenia to the notion that the individual is aiming for relevance within their own framework of assumptions may lead to a more positive approach to interaction. In the event of recognizing the fallibility of pragmatic performance, taking a Relevance Theory perspective offers a very clear way in which to approach this issue with family members. The components of the proposed pragmatic approach above, which address normalizing those pragmatic difficulties which may occur in typical speakers and using these as a foundation to understand more extreme difficulties in those with schizophrenia, may form a useful foundation for the training of conversation partners.

Conclusion

In order to achieve appropriate assessment intervention with the aim of targeting pragmatic ability, the design of assessment processes and direct intervention programmes must consider the cognitive-pragmatic foundation of the clinical design. It is argued that a coherent theoretical foundation is of clinical importance, not merely of academic interest. An appropriate theoretical foundation allows for a consistent 'thread' to be woven into the intervention protocol and provides a 'pragmatic map' for the clients with whom we work. Cognitive Pragmatic Treatment has gone some way to establishing itself as a potentially efficacious approach in this regard. Other pragmatic theories, such as Relevance Theory, also have potential for effective clinical application. Ingenious task design will be required if intervention is going to maintain a level of 'real-time' processing while at the same time intensively challenging specific skills. Developing novel and sophisticated ways of assessing the complex domain of pragmatic competence and building on approaches to intervention should impact on the quality of the service provided to individuals with schizophrenia and ultimately their ability to more readily navigate the social world.

It is recognized that direct intervention of this sort may not be appropriate or relevant for all individuals. Indeed, pragmatic ability, or pragmatic disability, cannot be situated within the individual alone and theoretical perspectives may also offer conceptual tools to guide conversation partner training. However, for those individuals with schizophrenia actively seeking to work on their communication we as clinicians should be able to provide intervention which is theoretically sound and appropriately focused. Only then are we meeting the needs of this client group to the degree that we are able to offer focused therapy in more developed areas of the profession. The pragmatic nature of the difficulties offers a particular challenge to the field, a challenge that is only met when we respond with assessment and intervention practices that "get closer to the action" (Davis, 2007, p.113) of cognitive-communication processes.

References

Airenti, G., Bara, B.G., & Colombetti, M. (1993). Conversation and behavior games in the pragmatics of dialogue. *Cognitive Science, 17*(2), 197–256.

Angeleri, R., Bosco, F.M., Zettin, M., Sacco, K., Colle, L., & Bara, B.G. (2008). Communicative impairment in traumatic brain injury: A complete pragmatic assessment. *Brain and Language, 107*(3), 229–245.

Angeleri, R., Bosco, F.M., Gabbatore, I., Bara, B.G., & Sacco, K. (2012). Assessment battery for communication (ABaCo): Normative data. *Behaviour Research Methods, 44*(3), 845–861.

Anonymous. (2011). Language games, paranoia, and psychosis. *Schizophrenia Bulletin, 37*(6), 1099–1100.

Apperly, I.A., Riggs, K.J., Simpson, A., Chiavarino, C., & Samson, D. (2006). Is belief reasoning automatic? *Psychological Science, 17*(10), 841–844.

Bara, B.G. (2010). *Cognitive Pragmatics: The Mental Processes of Communication.* London: MIT Press.

Barker, M. & Givón, T. (2005). Representation of the interlocutor's mind during conversation. In B.F. Malle & S.D. Hodges (Eds), *Other Minds: How Humans Bridge the Divide between Self and Others* (pp.223–238). London: Guildford Press.

Barr, D.J. & Keysar, B. (2005). Mindreading in an exotic case. In B.F. Malle & S.D. Hodges (Eds), *Other Minds: How Humans Bridge the Divide between Self and Others* (pp.271–283). London: Guildford Press.

Begeer, S., Malle, B., Nieuwland, M., & Keysar, B. (2010). Using Theory of Mind to represent and take part in social interactions: Comparing individuals with high-functioning autism and typically developing controls. *European Journal of Developmental Psychology, 7*(1), 104–122.

Behn, N., Togher, L., Power, E., & Heard, R. (2012). Evaluating communication training for paid carers of people with traumatic brain injury. *Brain Injury, 26*(13–14), 1702–1715.

Bellack, A.S. (2004). Skills training for people with severe mental illness. *Psychiatric Rehabilitation Journal, 27*(4), 375–391.

Bora, E., Yucel, M., & Pantelis, C. (2009). Theory of mind impairment in schizophrenia: Meta-analysis. *Schizophrenia Research, 109*(1–3), 1–9.

Bosco, F.M., Angeleri, R., Zuffranieri, M., Bara, B.G., & Sacco, K. (2012). Assessment battery for communication: Development of two equivalent forms. *Journal of Communication Disorders, 45*(4), 290–303.

Bosco, F.M., Gabbatore, I., Gastaldo, L., & Sacco, K. (2016). Communicative-pragmatic treatment in schizophrenia: A pilot study. *Frontiers in Psychology, 7* (February), 1–12.

Bosco, F.M., Parola, A., Angeleri, R., Galetto, V., Zettin, M., & Gabbatore, I. (2018). Improvement of communication skills after traumatic brain injury: The efficacy of the cognitive pragmatic treatment program using the communicative activities of daily living. *Archives of Clinical Neuropsychology, 33*(7), 875–888.

Brophy, J. (2007). Working alongside people with schizophrenia: Directions for speech and language therapy practice. Unpublished MSc Thesis, Trinity College Dublin.

Colle, L., Angeleri, R., Vallana, M., Sacco, K., Bara, B.G., & Bosco, F.M. (2013). Understanding the communicative impairments in schizophrenia: A preliminary study. *Journal of Communication Disorders, 46*(3), 294–308.

Cummings, L. (2009). *Clinical Pragmatics*. Cambridge: Cambridge University Press.

Cummings, L. (2014). *Pragmatic Disorders*. London: Springer

Davidson, L., Shahar, G., Stayner, D.A., Chinman, M.J., Rakfeldt, J., & Tebes, J.K. (2004). Supported socialization for people with psychiatric disabilities: Lessons from a randomized controlled trial. *Journal of Community Psychology, 32*(4), 453–477.

Davis, B., Guendouzi, J., Savage, M., Blackburn, W.L., & Williams, M. (2015). Politeness strategies in response to prompted directives in a preliminary English version of the ABaCO Battery. *Journal of Interactional Research in Communication Disorders, 6*(2), 115–129.

Davis, G.A. (2007). Cognitive pragmatics of language disorders in adults. *Seminars in Speech and Language, 28*(2), 111–121.

Ferguson, A. (1996). Describing competence in aphasic/normal conversation. *Clinical Linguistics & Phonetics, 10*(1), 55–63.

Frith, C.D. (1992). *The Cognitive Neuropsychology of Schizophrenia*. Hillsdale, NJ: Lawrence Erlbaum.

Gabbatore, I., Bosco, F.M., Geda, E., Gastaldo, L., Duca, S., Costa, T., … Sacco, K. (2017). Cognitive pragmatic rehabilitation Program in schizophrenia: A single case fMRI study. *Neural Plasticity*, Article ID 1612078.

Gabbatore, I., Sacco, K., Angeleri, R., Zettin, M., Bara, B.G., & Bosco, F.M. (2015). Cognitive pragmatic treatment: A rehabilitative program for traumatic brain injury individuals. *The Journal of Head Trauma Rehabilitation, 30*(5), E14-28.

Garcia, L.J., Metthé, L., Paradis, J., & Joanette, Y. (2001). Relevance is in the eye and ear of the beholder: An example from populations with a neurological impairment. *Aphasiology, 15*(1), 17–38.

Haas, M.H., Chance, S.A., Cram, D.F., Crow, T.J., Luc, A., & Hage, S. (2015). Evidence of pragmatic impairments in speech and proverb interpretation in schizophrenia. *Journal of Psycholinguistic Research, 44*(4), 469–483.

Jagoe, C. (2013). Schizophrenia and metarepresentational abilities in conversation: A preliminary analysis of question interpretation. In A. Piskorska (Ed.), *Relevance Theory: More than Understanding* (pp.261–278). Cambridge: Cambridge Scholars Publishing.

Jagoe, C. (2015). Collaborative meaning-making in delusional talk as a search for mutual manifestness: A Relevance Theory approach. *Journal of Interactional Research in Communication Disorders*, *6*(1), 53–70.

Jagoe, C. & Smith, M. (2017). Balancing multimodality and relevance. In M. Smith & J. Murray (Eds), *The Silent Partner? Language Learning and Language Use in Aided Communication* (pp.231–248). Guildford: J&R Press.

Joyal, M., Bonneau, A., & Fecteau, S. (2016). Speech and language therapies to improve pragmatics and discourse skills in patients with schizophrenia. *Psychiatry Research*, *240*, 88–95.

Kurtz, M.M. & Mueser, K.T. (2009). A meta-analysis of controlled research on social skills training for schizophrenia. *Journal of Consulting and Clinical Psychology*, *76*, 491–504.

Langdon, R., Davies, M., & Coltheart, M. (2002). Understanding minds and understanding communicated meanings in schizophrenia. *Mind and Language*, *17*(1&2), 68–104.

Lavelle, M., Healey, P.G.T., & McCabe, R. (2013). Is nonverbal communication disrupted in interactions involving patients with schizophrenia? *Schizophrenia Bulletin*, *39*(5), 1150–1158.

Liberman, R.P., Glynn, S., Blair, K.E., Ross, D., & Marder, S.R. (2002). In vivo amplified skills training: Promoting generalization of independent living skills for clients with schizophrenia. *Psychiatry: Interpersonal and Biological Processes*, *65*(2), 137–155.

McCabe, R., John, P., Dooley, J., Healey, P., Cushing, A., Kingdon, D., ... & Priebe, S. (2016). Training to enhance psychiatrist communication with patients with psychosis (TEMPO): Cluster randomised controlled trial. *The British Journal of Psychiatry*, *209*(6), 517–524.

McCabe, R., Leudar, I., & Antaki, C. (2004). Do people with schizophrenia display theory of mind deficits in clinical interactions? *Psychological Medicine*, *34*(3), 401–412.

McCabe, R., Skelton, J., Heath, C., Burns, T., & Priebe, S. (2002). Engagement of patients with psychosis in the consultation: conversation analytic study. *BMJ*, *325*(7373), 1148–1151.

Meilijson, S.R., Kasher, A., & Elizur, A. (2004). Language performance in chronic schizophrenia: A pragmatic approach. *Journal of Speech, Language, and Hearing Research*, *47*(3), 695–713.

Mercier, H. & Sperber, D. (2011). Why do humans reason? Arguments for an argumentative theory. *Behavioral and Brain Sciences*, *34*(2), 57–74.

Moritz, S. & Woodward, T.S. (2007). Metacognitive training in schizophrenia: From basic research to knowledge translation and intervention. *Current Opinion in Psychiatry*, *20*(6), 619.

Morris, L., Horne, M., McEvoy, P., & Williamson, T. (2018). Communication training interventions for family and professional carers of people living with dementia: A systematic review of effectiveness, acceptability and conceptual basis. *Aging & Mental Health*, *22*(7), 863–880.

Mueser, K.T. & Bellack, A.S. (2007). Social skills training: Alive and well? *Journal of Mental Health*, *16*(5), 549–552.

Muir, N. (2001). Introduction to management and patient care. In J. France & N. Muir (Eds), *Communication and Mental Illness* (pp.147–153). London: Jessica Kingsley.

Neuvonen, K., Jagoe, C., Launonen, K., Smith, M., & von Tetzchner, S. (under revision). Expectations and interpretations in the context of conversations involving aided communication.

Pilling, S., Bebbington, P., Kuipers, E., Garety, P., Geddes, J., Martindale, B., ... Morgan, C. (2002). Psychological treatments in schizophrenia: II. Meta-analyses of randomized controlled trials of social skills training and cognitive remediation. *Psychological Medicine, 32*(5), 283–291.

Sacco, K., Angeleri, R., Bosco, F.M., Colle, L., Mate, D., & Bara, B.G. (2008). Assessment Battery for Communication — ABaCo: A new instrument for the evaluation of pragmatic abilities. *Journal of Cognitive Sciences, 9*(2), 111–157.

Sacco, K., Gabbatore, I., Geda, E., Duca, S., Cauda, F., Bara, B.G., & Bosco, F.M. (2016). Rehabilitation of communicative abilities in patients with a history of TBI: Behavioral improvements and cerebral changes in resting-state activity, *Frontiers in Behavioural Neuroscience, 10*(4), 1–10.

Schneider, B., Scissons, H., Arney, L., Benson, G., Derry, J., Lucas, K., ... Sunderland, M. (2004). Communication between people with schizophrenia and their medical professionals: A participatory research project. *Qualitative Health Research, 14*(4), 562–577.

Simmons-Mackie, N., Raymer, A., Armstrong, E., Holland, A., & Cherney, L.R. (2010). Communication partner training in aphasia: A systematic review. *Archives of Physical Medicine and Rehabilitation, 91*(12), 1814–1837.

Sperber, D. & Wilson, D. (1986/1995). *Relevance: Communication and Cognition.* Oxford: Blackwell.

Sprong, M., Schothorst, P., Vos, E., Hox, J., & van Engeland, H. (2007). Theory of mind in schizophrenia: Meta-analysis. *The British Journal of Psychiatry, 191*, 5–13.

Walsh, I.P. (2008) Language socialisation among people with mental health disorders. In P.A. Duff & N. Hornberger (Eds), *Encyclopedia of Language & Education*, 2nd ed. (pp.327–340), Vol 8. New York, NY: Springer.

Wilson, D. & Sperber, D. (2004). Relevance Theory. In L.R. Horn & G. Ward (Eds), *The Handbook of Pragmatics* (pp.607–632). Oxford: Blackwell.

7 Medical humanities and constructions of 'self': Invoking literary autobiography to educate healthcare students in communication and mental health disorder

Irene P. Walsh

> "I became an instant third person, or even personless ..."
> (Janet Frame)

Introduction

The academic discipline of medical humanities is a multidisciplinary field of study incorporating, along with the study of medicine, the disciplines of humanities (e.g., philosophy, history), social sciences (e.g., sociology, anthropology, psychology) and arts (e.g., literature, music and visual arts) (Batistatou, Doulis, Tiniakos, Anongiannaki, & Charalabopoulos, 2010). However, the medical humanities are positioned in varied and disproportionate ways across (allied) healthcare education and given significantly greater prominence in medical education where its visibility is increasing across curricular activities (e.g., see Peterkin, 2016). Medical humanities have not yet found a place within some allied healthcare professional courses, with speech and language therapy being a case in point.

Evolving curricular development in allied healthcare courses prompts consideration of an explicit introduction of medical humanities into course and clinical practicum. Medical humanities have the potential to offer a context where experiences of clinical conditions can be viewed as part of the human condition and illustrated through art, literature and film media. In this way, students are exposed to stimulating and engaging material to deepen and enrich learning.

The focus in this chapter is to consider a medical-humanities' 'take' on communication difficulties that may be core or associated with mental health disorders. In other words, the discussion in this chapter poses a question: what can literary or autobiographical accounts of mental ill health tell us of the communication struggles so often associated with psychiatric disturbance? The impetus for such consideration stems from the fact that understanding communication challenges in the context of mental health disorders is less than easy, for two main reasons. Firstly, the complexity of the psychiatric clinical presentation and its treatment may complicate and interfere with a person's speech and language functioning, for example through the illness process or side effects of medication (Sinha, Vandana, Lewis, Jayaran, & Enderby, 2015; Walsh, Regan, Sowman, Parsons, & McKay, 2007). Secondly, any communication breakdown is most usually seen to lie with the person with a mental health diagnosis and not a product of the two-way interaction where responsibility for communication breakdown is shared (Jagoe, 2013, 2015; Walsh, 2008; Walsh-Brennan, 2001).

Following some consideration of medical humanities in allied healthcare education and the use of autobiography as a resource within such contexts, the chapter will exemplify – through invoking the literary autobiographical work of the New Zealand novelist Janet Frame (*Janet Frame: The Complete Autobiography, 1989*) – how including different or supplementary routes to learning (aside from accessing formal academic textbooks) can educate and inform. Frame experienced significant mental health issues for most of her adult life and was diagnosed as having schizophrenia. This diagnosis was often questioned during her lifetime – not least at times by Frame herself. Even after her death in 2004, her diagnosis was still questioned, with some researchers discussing features of her presentation (through analysis of her writings) as possibly more characteristic of high functioning autism (e.g., Abrahamson, 2007; Oettli, 2007). Regardless of her diagnosis, Frame's experiences of mental ill health and her numerous hospitalizations informed both her biographical and fictional works. In fact, it could be said that an illness narrative pervaded her writings. Cohen (2008, p.38) explains that the illness narrative:

> ... tells us about how life problems are created, controlled and made meaningful. They are shaped by our cultural values and social relations, and will affect our self-perception of illness and health as well as the way we monitor our body and act towards bodily symptoms and complaints.

The discussion in the latter part of this chapter will centre on Frame's experiences as narrated by her, with a particular focus on how her social relations – and hence her communication – were affected by schizophrenia-like symptoms within the context of a general mental illness. Considering that personal experiences of mental illness can differ widely but can include 'conceptions of self' (Cohen, 2008, p.183), an analysis of Frame's writing through the lens of the notion of 'selves' (Lysaker & Lysaker, 2008, 2010) helps to explore her accounts of communication distress. Of particular interest is how multiple selves can be both self-shaped and other-constructed by experiences and social interactions. Understanding how self and identity are co-constructed by communication, or how communication co-constructs identity, is the challenge here. Examples from Frame's accounts show that communication seems central to her identity, her emotional angst, and her efforts to construct a healthy or recovering self.

The chapter will conclude with some implications for consideration of identity in clinical interactions and for a place for medical humanities in teaching and learning activities in the domain of communication and mental health disorder. Supplementary routes to learning via medical humanities can result in a far greater appreciation of how mental (ill-)health can impact identity and the communication experience for all concerned.

Medical humanities in (allied) healthcare education

Traditionally, the discipline of medical humanities has been better developed in the United States (Greaves & Evans, 2000), featuring at first in the 1960s and 1970s. However, more recent developments in the United Kingdom and Ireland have seen its growth in popularity in healthcare curricula and clinical practice education. A dedicated journal to the field, entitled *Medical Humanities*, was first published in 2000 and is an official journal of the Institute of Medical Ethics, published by that institute with the British Medical Journal (BMJ) Publishing Group. The growth of the medical humanities' focus in Ireland has gained momentum in recent times, especially with the work of O' Neill and colleagues (e.g., Moss & O' Neill, 2012, 2017; O' Neill et al., 2016) and the establishment of initiatives such as medical health and humanities (e.g., see https://www.tcd.ie/trinitylongroomhub/medical-humanities/) within university research groups.

Put simply, the field of medical humanities attempts "to emphasise the subjective experience of patients within the objective and scientific world of medicine" (Oyebode, 2010, p.242). The US National Library gives a more detailed definition as follows:

> The study of the intersection of medicine and humanistic disciplines such as philosophy, religion, literature, and the fine and performing arts. This field emphasizes the humane aspects of medicine and health care and has expanded to include research in social sciences disciplines that are informed by humanistic scholarship, such as cultural studies, anthropology, and medical sociology. The literature is diverse, and includes scholarly research, reflective essays, and critical interpretations of artistic and literary works. (https://www.nlm.nih.gov/tsd/acquisitions/cdm/subjects57.html)

The focus, then, is on the truly 'humane' aspects of health care. As O' Neill et al. (2016) state:

> ... our vision of the medical humanities is that it constitutes a vital aspect of the epistemology of what it is to be human and the nature and experiences of health, illness and healthcare (p.109).

Engaging with a medical humanities' curriculum aims to facilitate and nurture a greater and better understanding of health and illness experiences, through accessing the visual arts (e.g., painting/conceptual art and objects, to film and television media) and literature (e.g., fiction and non-fiction, biography and autobiography). It is about interrogating such sources in critical ways, to stimulate learners to reach beyond clinical textbook and other academic accounts to explore depictions of health, illness and healthcare with the human experience at the core. Additionally, medical humanities' resources can be used to explore clinical skills, such as those involved in interviewing patients or clients where roles and processes are key. For example, Waxman, Alexander,

Kirkpatrick and Blasco (2005, pp.125–129) give a review of a number of films that can be used to stimulate learning about aspects of clinical interviewing, including 'active listening', 'dealing with awkward moments' and 'interruptions'. Likewise, Hooper et al. (2005, pp.131–136) review some film media useful for exploring what they call "the professional and personal self of the physician", which includes exploration of physician–patient interaction, professional behaviour, legal and gender issues in medicine, among other areas.

Such teaching and learning within medical humanities, be it with a clinical skills or clinical presentation focus, should not be just 'additive' to existing curricula but 'integrative' so that "the experiential nature of suffering be brought within the scope of medicine's explanatory models, if necessary by reappraising those models" (Evans & Greaves, 1999, p.1216). However, integrating medical humanities into medical education in an authentic interdisciplinary manner – where both the disciplines of arts and medicine "have equal standing and contribution"– has been found to be problematic (Wachtler, Lundin, & Troein, 2006, p.16). Regardless, there are helpful accounts in the literature outlining the steps taken (or to be taken) to integrate a medical humanities' curriculum (e.g., Jones & Verghese, 2003, and Peterkin, 2016).

However, these attempts have largely focused on medical education taking place in medical schools for the education of future doctors or physicians. Yet there is some evidence of a shift in this regard to include other healthcare disciplines. For example, the University of Rochester in New York offers a Masters' programme in medical humanities which aims to include both healthcare and allied healthcare students, such as nursing, dentistry, social work, occupational therapy and physical therapy (see https://www.urmc.rochester. edu/education/graduate/masters/medical-humanities.aspx). Furthermore, Crawford and colleagues in a discussion paper (Crawford, Brown, Tischler, & Baker, 2010) call for a broadening of the concept of the 'medical humanities' discipline to consider 'health humanities', one that is:

> … a more inclusive, outward-facing and applied discipline
> … which both embrace interdisciplinarity and engage with
> the contributions of those marginalised from the medical
> humanities – for example, allied health professionals, nurses,
> patients and carers (p.4).

Of interest here is Crawford at al.'s dual focus on allied healthcare professionals and inclusion of 'patients and carers'. They exemplify the case of mental healthcare in their discussion, claiming that "for a specialism where communication is so central, it is perhaps surprising that the medical humanities are not further advanced in mental health care" (Crawford et al., 2010, p.6). This chapter redresses this point in its focus on how an allied healthcare discipline, such as speech and language therapy, could explore literature from a mental health context.

Medical humanities: Autobiography as resource

As referred to above, there are many sources from which to draw material for teaching and learning through a medical humanities' context. For example, the use of cinema and film is popular in medical education (e.g., see Alexander, Lenahan, & Pavlov, 2005; and Darbyshire & Baker, 2012). In psychiatry, specific resources have been identified and exemplified from cinema (e.g., Roberts, 2011) and via images and objects (e.g., Allan, Turri, Stein, Da Silva, & Harris, 2016). Literature too is popular (e.g., drama, fiction/non-fiction and poetry). Biographies and autobiographical accounts are also a source to exploit in this context (the latter being exemplified in this chapter). As Oyebode (2010) comments, an autobiographical account:

> ... lets the reader into the patient's experience and at the same time reminds them that just as physicians appraise the patient's condition in their role as clinicians, humanity is also being reciprocally judged by the patient. In other words, there is reciprocity of evaluation going on (p.243).

Moreover, intimate autobiographies allow a view through the window of the lived, or 'living' experience of an illness, that is, the day-to-day, often moment-by-moment troubling or distressing illness-related experiences that may not manifest or warrant comment or consideration in a more formalized clinical setting. Such a consideration is all the more applicable when communication may be affected by the anxieties of the doctor–patient clinical interview or when communication impairment can affect the interaction. Therefore, gaining access to such accounts is invaluable to enhance understanding and care, as Oyebode further outlines:

> Patients present to doctors with clinical symptoms but these symptoms in the home setting have a personal, indeed an intimate, dimension which operates at a register quite

distinct from the clinical wherein the intention is to collect and collate in order to reach a diagnosis (p.244).

Gaining insight about and into the communicative experiences of a person with a mental health disorder is crucial to effective practice in psychiatry, not least in the discipline of speech and language therapy, given that as a discipline its place is still nascent in many mental health service contexts (Walsh et al., 2007).

The work of Janet Frame and a subjective stance

Janet Frame (1924–2004) told her own story of her experiences of mental distress, through both her autobiographical works and, somewhat vicariously, through her novels. This widely-published and internationally renowned author was driven to tell her story by the depth of her experiences and frustration with communication. Yet her rich and eloquently written accounts belie this frustration with the spoken word. Frame's accounts provide rich data for analysis, allowing for an exploration of 'selves' (Lysaker & Lysaker, 2008, 2010) from many different (co-) constructions. It will be shown in this chapter that the constructions of such selves are self- and other-constructed in social interactions. In addition, given the timeline of her life, the construction of these selves could also be said to be historically sensitive.

Underpinning the discussion in this chapter are the subjective experiences of mental ill health, not the objective consideration of disorders and symptoms often characteristic of textbook accounts. Stanghellini's (2004) statement considers the perils of only considering objective accounts when he states:

> Amputating madness from the man who embodies it and amputating both from the life world: this represented the first serious side effect of wanting to make psychopathology into an objective *science* [sic] (p.46).

Staying close to subjective accounts within people's 'life worlds' seems crucial to even begin to attempt to understand the despair when communication is compromised and distorted in mental illness contexts. Analysis of Frame's accounts show that both communication partners are implicated in the communication breakdown, revealing that both must work together to repair the damage. The impact of so-called communication 'success' or indeed 'failure' on identity is also worth exploring.

Identity, self (selves) and recovery

'Identity', 'self' and 'recovery' are complex and weighty concepts, requiring at least some definition within the context of this chapter. Firstly, 'identity' and 'self' are closely interrelated concepts. Walton (2015) refers to social identity theory (as discussed by Tajfel and Turner, 1986) to clearly explain concepts of identity, as used in discourse analysis:

> ... the way they [individuals] might think, feel and act, is supposed to be based upon and made relevant by their relatively stable membership of any number of social groups. An individual's identity might be supposed from what we might know about them – for example, their sex, age, ethnicity or sexuality. In contrast, within discourse analytic approaches, identity is highly dynamic [...]. It is both a social construction and a social accomplishment managed and achieved through speakers' orientations to interactional concerns. In this sense, identity is a participant's resource, constructed and mobilized in a 'bottom-up' manner rather than being imposed on them by the researcher in a 'top-down' way (p.187).

Walton (2015, p.187) explains (while exemplifying a discourse analytic approach to interview transcripts from ex-soldiers) that identities can be constructed through an individual's discourse with reference to the social categories of which they believe they are members (e.g., 'army') or which they attribute to others (e.g., 'non-army' or 'civilians'), "and the normative behaviours that are culturally associated with members of those categories". In this way, identity becomes both "a topic within talk" (the social construction) and "an effect of talk" (the social accomplishment) (ibid., p.187) as identities emerge from, and are constructed by, what is said and how it is said in discourse.

To extend the notion of 'identity' a step further in this chapter, it is also useful to consider the psychological dimension of the 'self' or the 'dialogical self', as discussed in some detail in relation to schizophrenia by Lysaker and Lysaker (2002, 2008). Lysaker and Lysaker refer to philosophers and theorists, such as Bakhtin and Dostoyevsky, who helped explain the nature of self-experience, "stressing that the self is inherently 'dialogical', or the produce of ongoing conversations both within the individual and between the individual and others" (Lysaker & Lysaker, 2002, p.209). This notion of 'self', then, is social in origin and dialogical in function, whereby it reflects and appropriates the voices of society and significant others. Lysaker and Lysaker (2010) explain that the 'self' can be construed as:

> ... an inter-animating constellation of elements, or better still, moments (whose genesis is a braid of biological and social forces as well as personal experiences) (p.336).

Thus, 'social forces' and 'personal experiences' acted out in 'moments' of interaction, can be seen to shape our sense of self (or selves) in interesting ways.

Language, communication and discourse, then, serve to construct identity (e.g., Walton, 2015) and seem to have a role in the emergence of self (or selves) (Lysaker & Lysaker, 2010). There is evidence for the close relationship between communication and identity from first-person accounts. Personal accounts are a form of discourse through which we can explore expressions of identity as well as communication. First-person accounts are important. They can reveal social constructions of identity and construals of 'self' (or multiple 'selves'). This chapter focuses on Janet Frame's expression of self, as mediated through and by communication, and as a way of attempting to understand the dilemma of communication in mental illness contexts. The search for her accounts of explicit (or implicit) references to identity or self as 'communicator' or 'in communication' form the material under scrutiny here, aided by the principles of a discourse analysis approach.

The notion that society may influence sense of self and influence identity has particular resonance in the context of people with mental health disorders. People with mental health disorders are particularly prone to misunderstandings in and by society, despite efforts by the individual, families and mental health services to ebb the flow of such misapprehensions. The adoption of the Recovery Model (Anthony, 1993) in psychiatry has gone some way to support acceptance of self as a means to develop a "new meaning and purpose in one's life as one grows beyond the catastrophic effects of psychiatric illness" (Anthony, 1993, p.527). Barham and Hayward, taking a person-centred approach to reclaim one's own personhood in psychiatry, urge us to consider a question in this context of recovery, that is: "Who and what existed *before* the illness and who and what endure *during and after*?" (Barham & Hayward, 1995, p 2). Adopting a recovery model means not being defined or shaped by the mental health disorder – or by society's often negative stigmatizing attitudes – but living beyond mental illness in a positive and proactive way. One way of aiding and supporting this recovery is by paying attention to the stories or accounts that people tell of their experiences.

Janet Frame: The writer

Before exploring Frame's accounts of communication and recovery, it is important to give the biographical background of this writer. Janet Frame was a novelist and poet from New Zealand. She published many novels in her lifetime, along with collections of short stories and books of poetry, in addition to her autobiographical works (see Appendix). Throughout her writing career she won many literary and other awards, including being awarded a Commander of the Order of the British Empire (CBE) in 1983 and the Order of New Zealand (ONZ) in 1990. Frame received two honorary doctorates from New Zealand universities and was also awarded an Arts Foundation Icon Award in 2003, and the Inaugural Prime Minister's Award for Literature in the same year.

Frame became as well known for her dramatic personal history recounted in her autobiographies as for her writing of poetry and prose and was a 'household name' in New Zealand. Douglas Martin, in writing an obituary in *The New York Times* on the day after her death, commented on the fact that:

> A continuing discussion among critics was whether her
> autobiographical work was mostly fiction or whether her
> fiction was mostly autobiographical (Martin, 2004).

Born 1924 in Dunedin, Frame's father was a railroad engineer and her mother was a maid, who sold her own poetry door-to-door. Frame's early life was blighted by deprivation and sadness with the drowning of two of her sisters (in separate incidents) and the family caring for a very ill brother with epilepsy. Accounts show that her family was viewed as 'different' in their community.

In her early adult years, Frame experienced acute aloneness and reportedly was often found seeking respite sitting among gravestones in her local graveyard writing poetry. Such was the depth of her despair, she reportedly attempted suicide in 1943. While at teacher training college, she experienced what was called at the time a 'nervous breakdown' during teacher training practice in 1945, which triggered admission to a psychiatric hospital.

Over the next eight years (1945-1953), Frame was repeatedly readmitted (often voluntarily) to psychiatric hospitals, experiencing over 200 electroconvulsive therapy (ECT) treatments. The diagnosis attributed to her was schizophrenia. A scheduled 'lobotomy' was cancelled when she was due to be awarded a literary prize (in 1951). She was discharged from psychiatric care in 1954 and moved to the UK in 1956.

Having been diagnosed in New Zealand as having schizophrenia, this diagnosis was later disputed while she was living in the UK (during the early 1960s), where psychiatrists described her as being 'different' but in 'need of professional help' just the same and as a result of her protracted stays in psychiatric institutions (Frame, 1993). In her distress, she explained how she felt 'robbed' of her diagnosis:

> The loss was great. At first the truth seemed to be more terrifying than the lie. Schizophrenia, as a psychosis, had been an accomplishment, removing ordinary responsibility from the sufferer. I was bereaved. I was ashamed. How could I ask directly when there was 'nothing wrong with me'? (p.116).

Frame returned to her home country in 1963 but was a frequent visitor to Europe and the USA afterwards.

Throughout her life, Frame remained a loner, always writing prolifically. During the 1980s, she wrote her autobiography from which most of the data in this chapter is drawn. In the 1990s, Frame had two mild strokes. However, her ill health did not deter her from writing and publishing up until her death in Dunedin in 2004 from leukemia. Frame's works and accounts of her life have been the subject of many studies in film (e.g., Jane Campion's (1990) film *An Angel at my Table*) and writing (e.g., Brennan, 2015; Fuentes-Vásquez, 2013; Gambaudo, 2012; Hopgood, 2006).

The construction of selves by and through language and communication

Before examining a construction of selves by and through examples of communication from the autobiographical data, other identities have been described by, and attributed to, Frame which help to map her biographical detail as outlined above.

Frame invoked the idea of 'selves' in her own work, most especially in *The Envoy from Mirror City*, where she talks about the need for multiple selves to cooperate in the completion of a piece of work, when acting as an

'Envoy' she must travel to and from to the 'Mirror City' (her imagination) to complete her writing:

> The self must be the container of the treasures of Mirror City, the Envoy as it were, and when the time comes to arrange to list those treasures for arranging into words, the self must be the worker, the bearer of the burden, the chooser, placer and polisher. And when the work is finished and nothingness must be endured, the self may take a holiday, if only to reweave the used container that awaits the next visit to Mirror City (p.405).

Hawes (1995), in her consideration of Frame's work as 'self as other/othering the self', explains that Frame narrates many identities in her 'quest for belonging'. Hawes lists these identities as five major phases of Frame's life as follows:

1. The intelligent sensitive child of *To the Is-Land* (Frame, 1982).

2. The poetic scholar who the narrator describes as "the stoical solitary heroine suffering in silence" (Frame, 1989, p.127).

3. The obedient student, the narrator of *An Angel at My Table* describes as "'I', almost a nothingness, like a no-woman's land" (Frame, 1989, p.161).

4. The schizophrenic 'madwoman', "'she', one of 'them'" (Frame, 1989, p.194).

5. The writer.

Hawes then concentrates on the latter identity – Frame as 'the writer' – in her 1995 work as 'the guise she [Frame] has kept' (at the point of writing the article in the mid-1990s). Shifting the lens to a focus on communication meant reviewing the autobiography for evidence of accounts where communication issues, both successes and struggles, were salient.

Frame's accounts demonstrate mental anguish and social aloneness with a need for, yet resistance to, social interaction. Language and communication seem central to her being and were important to her. Her writing draws on how others behave around her, how others relate to her and talk about her, and how they perceive her and her 'self'. What is of interest is how her 'self'/'selves' is/are co-constructed by and through her intra-personal and inter-personal dialogues. The question is posed: *Can a sense of these dialogues help us understand the communication dilemma that is mental ill health and accompanies it?*

For the purposes of this chapter, three 'selves' will be discussed, as follows:

I. Self as 'other'

II. Self as 'mad person'

III. Self as 'in recovery'

Accounts supporting the discussion of these 'selves' are all taken directly from Frame (1989) with page numbers specified, with the exception of Extract 6, which is taken from King's (2000) biography of Frame.

I. Self as 'other'

Feeling as an 'other', positioned outside of social and communication interactions, is depicted in the following accounts. In Extract 1, while on a visit to her sister's house, Frame describes her feelings of being outside looking in, when members of her family "*enclosed one another*":

Extract 1 p.215

"*My stay with my sister and her husband was not successful. They and their infant son enclosed one another and while I stood awkwardly in the background, and if anyone called and looked my way, my shyness and self consciousness, arising from my feeling of being nowhere, increased when my sister's friends asked, 'How is she?' 'Does she like being in Auckland?'* "

A feeling of '*being nowhere*' was exacerbated by others present talking about her in the third person ("*How is she?*"), a point also explicitly referred to in Extract 2 below where she describes herself as being spoken about in the 'third person':

Extract 2 p.215

"*I had become a third person, at home at Willowglen and now here in Auckland. Sometimes, as if I were my own obituary, people asked, 'What was she?' As if an archaeological find stood before them and they were applying with eyes, heart and mind, a 'carbon' test to name, date and place me - and if only I had a place!*"

Additionally, Frame's analogy of being like 'an archaeological find' further described her sense of being displaced from and not belonging to the interaction, ending with the exclamation – "*if only I had a place!*"

Being considered in the '*third person*' also gave way to a feeling of being '*personless*' as Frame recalls a note made about her in a hospital file:

> **Extract 3 p.191**
>
> "*No one thought to ask me why I had screamed at my mother, no one asked me what my plans were for the future. I became an instant third person, or even personless, as in the official note made about [me], 'Refused to leave hospital'.*"

Finally, returning to her perceptions of how family viewed her, and recalling how their behaviour "*had changed in subtle ways*", Frame invokes a powerful analogy of being spider-like, weaving a web:

> **Extract 4 p.194**
>
> "*I noticed that the behaviour of my family had changed in subtle ways related to my having been a patient in Seacliff where the loonies lived*"
>
> "*...I had, like a spider, woven about me numerous threads which invisibly reached all those who 'knew' and bound them to a paralysis of fixed poses and expressions and feelings that made me unhappy and lonely but gave me also a recognition of the power of having spun the web and the powerlessness of those trapped within it*".

"*Fixed poses and expressions*" of those who "*knew*" (about her illness) suggest a non-engagement with the "*loonies*" by others, including family. A hint of more positivity emerging from the unhappiness caused is evident in the latter part of this extract, where a "*power*" is acknowledged as the weaver of the web and the "*powerless of those trapped in it*".

II. Self as 'mad person'

Frame was aware of how others, family included, construed her. A construal as a '*mad person*', not to be taken seriously, can be found in the following extract:

> Extract 5 p.215
>
> *"I wrote my poems, showing them to no one. A member of my family had found and read a story I wrote and voiced the strong opinion that I would never be a writer. Sometimes when I began to say what I really felt, using a simile or metaphor, an image, I saw the embarrassment in my listener's eyes – here was the mad person speaking."*

Here in a communicative situation, Frame talks about her listener and the 'embarrassment' she thinks she is causing by the creative figurative language she uses (e.g., similes or metaphors). Communication and her very identity and sense of self are compromised, it seems, by the reactions of those around her.

Continuing with what she feels her listeners might think, Frame describes her difficulty in communicating in a hospital context, where '*questioning*' may ensue:

> Extract 6 Frame (1949 in King, 2000, p.103)
>
> *"I cannot talk about myself. I cannot. Every month I go to the hospital and [see] one of the doctors from Seacliff...I have been able scarcely to say a word to them...I just go into a kind of dream probably to escape their questioning. And my voice won't work. And if it did it would utter what they would think to be utter nonsense...I keep silent because physically, I cannot speak."*

Describing how her voice '*won't work*' and anticipating what '*they*' (i.e., the medical staff) may think of what she has to say (i.e., 'to be utter nonsense') numbs Frame: "*I keep silent because physically, I cannot speak*". Such silence and silencing are distressing, as is the hint at an identity of perhaps a silly person who may talk 'nonsense'.

Being othered as a '*mad person*' is also described by Frame, when she refers to a division of '*ordinary*' and '*secret*' people, including herself in the latter category as those coming from the mental hospital:

> Extract 7 p.193
>
> *"I felt as if my life was overturned by this sudden division of people into 'ordinary' people in the street, and these 'secret' people whom few had seen or talked to but whom many spoke of with derision, laughter, fear."*

Here again communication is referenced by Frame: few people talk to these 'secret' people, but instead talk about them with 'derision, laughter and fear'. Again, we see constructions of otherness, and construals of madness in Frame's descriptions, mediated by communication and talk.

III. Self as 'in recovery'

Despite the challenges of being 'othered', and outside communication, some of Frame's accounts resonate with concepts of the Recovery Model (Anthony, 1993). In Extract 8, Frame talks of belonging to the "*world of the mad*" but reconstrues this as a means to "*survive*":

> ### Extract 8 p.198
>
> "*I was taking my new status seriously. If the world of the mad were the world where I officially belonged (lifelong disease, no cure, no hope), then I would use it to survive I would excel in it. I sensed it did not exclude my being a poet.*"

Acknowledging to herself that being mentally ill did not rule her out as 'being a poet' is freeing in and of itself. On discovering that Vincent van Gogh and others in the arts had serious mental health issues, she described their artistic ability as the "pearl of their schizophrenia" and asserts how:

> ### Extract 9 p.201
>
> "*My place was set, then, at the terrible feast. I had no illusions about 'greatness' but at least I could endow my work and – when necessary – my life with the mark of my schizophrenia.*"

Using her diagnosis in a positive way to endow her work has echoes of the 'living with' and 'beyond' mental illness, so core and pivotal to recovery.

Reflections on emergence of selves

It would seem from the few examples taken from Frame's accounts of her mental illness experience that surrounding discourses interpenetrated Janet's sense of self and identity. It is apparent that she was deeply affected by these accounts of 'disability', communication included. All her identities, or selves (summarized in Figure 7.1), were socially (i.e., by family, others), situationally (i.e., environmentally and contexts of interaction), and self-constructed, while mediated through language and communication.

However, Frame was eventually able to rise above, or at least 'with', the discourses surrounding her as she assumed a way of being that included her mental illness and struggles. In addition to the more positive '*Self as in recovery*', another self could be said to emerge in her accounts. It could be said that '*Self as communicator*' also emerges, given that she was a (written) language user who was in a social interaction or relationship with her reader. In other words, she was a social being engaging in 'social acts' (in this case of writing) which can be similar to that which may be achieved in speaking (van Dijk, 1997, p.4). It seems too that expressing herself through language was an expression of her identity that helped to heal the pain of being 'othered'. Wisdom, Bruce, Saedi, Weis and Green (2008) point out in their discussion of identity and recovery in accounts of mental illness that:

> Efforts to publish personal accounts that focus on strengths-based patient-centred stories, rather than on deficits, could be helpful. In particular, stories that provide examples of individuals recovering from mental illness, of those who have moved through their illness identities to identify new competencies, and of constructing, new or reclaiming old,

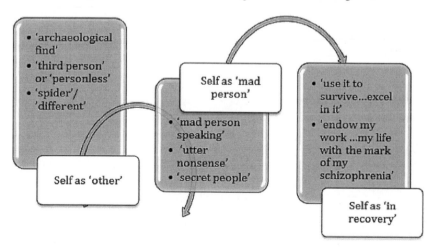

Figure 7.1 Summary of how Frame communicated her various selves.

selves may provide important guidance and hope for both
patients and clinicians (p.8).

Moreover, Wisdom et al. (2008, p.8) add that "education about the value of
competency, rather than dysfunction" could have a real role to play in recovery,
as Green (2004) and others have argued. The education here could equally apply
to the student learning about mental health disorders and communication where
the potential to "reveal ability amidst disability" (Walsh, 2002, 2003) is key.

Medical humanities and (allied) healthcare education

The small and limited number of extracts given in this chapter, taken solely from
her literary autobiography (and not from her many other works), of course do
not do justice to Frame's accounts of the struggles associated with her mental
health issues, the source of which, in many cases, was communication challenges
with family, friends and medical staff. However, a humanities-based enquiry,
such as that suggested in this chapter, goes some way to educate and reveal
what a person with mental health difficulties may experience in the day-to-day
communicative interactions that are so taken for granted. Frame's accounts are
not only *about* communication but describe *instances of* communication and
how these moments are experienced and responded to both by herself and,
as she perceives, by others. Thus, they provide a multidimensional, nuanced
'take' on communication in all its complexity. The rich and detailed narratives
open up communication experiences in mental health for closer examination
and consideration in ways that academic textbook accounts do not. It seems, as
Cohen (2008, p.32) states, that "the humanities are also turning to narratives as
a more valid way of understanding peoples' lives than traditional methods of
research". For the student in mental healthcare, or indeed the practitioner (be
they doctors, nurses, social workers, occupational therapists, etc.), narrative
accounts such as these may prompt reflection on communication processes,
not just those of the person they are working with (e.g., with the identified
'diagnosis'), but of their own discourse style. In turn, then, such explorations
may prompt reflection on learning or honing of clinical skills, especially those
related to communication (e.g., rapport building, interviewing, counselling,
etc.) and on identity – of both patient/client and practitioner alike.

Such accounts, as those described here, certainly beg the question: Were
the accounts of her reactions to mental ill health unique because she was
an accomplished writer? It seems no, when one compares the core thematic

content of many other accounts of communication distress as part of a mental illness where similar themes arise (e.g., see Brophy, 2009; Walsh, Brophy, & Hendy, 2013; Walsh, Delmar, & Jagoe, 2018). What perhaps is unique for Frame, however, is the literary eloquence of her writing and the 'power' that she harvested from it, despite her distressing struggles to orally communicate at times or converse 'in the moment'. Her writing was her main means of language expression amidst the chaos of her mental ill health, isolation and hospitalization. The value she gained is best summed up in her own words, as reported by Martin (2004): "*Writing is a boon, analgesic, and so on. I think it is all that matters to me. I dread emerging from it each day*". This chapter has attempted to shown how Frame's writing can inform and educate in ways the author herself may not have anticipated.

Clinical considerations and implications

First and foremost, hearing the voice of the service user – and not just in mental health contexts – is core to developing good and meaningful professional practice. The 'missing voice' in evidence-based practice is discussed by Kovarsky and Curran (2007). Whether this voice is heard through biographical and/or literary accounts or through the spoken word, the person's 'voice' is key. Cohen (2008, p.2) urges professionals to "take at face value what we see and hear from the one source that lies at the heart of the mental health debate but is often ignored – from the service user themselves". Despite some interpretations made in this chapter through the concept of selves, it is hoped that the integrity of Frame's own words and self-conceptions (as a service user herself) has not been lost in the process. Rather, it is hoped that depicting her accounts in this way demonstrates how such accounts can be used to inform and educate in both academic and clinical contexts.

In many clinical contexts, adults with mental health disorders have been regarded as outside the scope of practice of speech and language therapy, though there are exceptions given the proven need (e.g., see Emerson & Enderby, 1996; Walsh et al., 2007). This is due to a number of reasons, including that the clinical presentations of people with mental health issues are seen to be primarily psychologically or emotionally-based, and therefore not perceived as a primary area of expertise within the discipline. Furthermore, treatment or intervention is seen to 'belong to', most usually, specialists of psychology or psychiatry. Wisdom et al. (2008) explain that people with mental illness often describe "a loss of self and identity" (p.1) or experience "identity dilemmas" (p.6), taking away "a person's sense of self" (p.4). Language and communication play a role in this challenge to identity, in varying ways, evidence for which we see in an individual's own testimonies and words. The Speech and Language Therapist (SLT) is uniquely placed to work with individuals who may face challenges in communication due to their mental health issues or due to others' reactions to how that illness manifests in communication interactions.

It has been argued in this chapter that selves or identities can be both self- and other-constructed and mediated through language and communication. This is particularly relevant to a consideration of identity or multiple identities as constructed and shaped by the discourse(s) of both patient/client and the healthcare practitioner, as they interact and work together in clinical settings. Individuals' discourse(s) of identity through a process of co-construction may collide, coalesce, or even act in conflict with one another. The collective resultant discourse of identity may be a healthy one or, alternatively, a faulty and disabling one, within the clinical context. The dynamics of 'disabling evaluations in clinical and social contexts' is discussed by Kovarsky, Duchan and Maxwell (1999) in their edited volume *Constructing (in)competence*. Examples of such 'disabling evaluations' that can construct what Goffman termed a 'spoiled identity' (Goffman, 1963) are discussed by Kovarsky, Kimbarow and Kastner (1999) and Kovarsky, Shaw and Adingono-Smith (2007). Kovarsky et al. (1999, p.304) describe the "competency lowering communicative practice" that can characterize some speech and language therapy interactions in the case of a group therapy session with people with traumatic brain injury (TBI). Instead of facilitating communicative competence to emerge (i.e., a goal of any speech and language therapy intervention), perceived incompetence is exposed and prompts correction by the therapist; reasonable and relevant response attempts are rejected as they are not the predetermined, intended or desirable ones in the set therapy activity, for example. This practice is not uncommon in speech and language therapy contexts, an issue well explained and discussed by Kovarsky and Maxwell (1992), Panagos (1996), and Simmons Mackie and Damico (1999). Kovarsky et al's (2007) discussion of identity within the context of a therapeutic context highlights the need for practitioners to attend to a client's multiple identities as constructed by self or others in the contexts of interactions.

Conclusion

The discipline of 'medical humanities' - or perhaps the more inclusive term 'health humanities' – has much to offer the education of healthcare professionals, SLTs included.

It is important to consider the introduction of medical humanities for both tutor-guided teaching and self-directed learning. Specific teaching and learning activities have potential for both college- and clinic-based work, bridging the theory-to-practice gap in innovative ways. A focus on exploring the arts and humanities may serve to capitalize on young people's often-common preference for varied teaching methods, involving consulting and critiquing popular or historical media of many kinds (literature, film, drama, etc.). For maximum effect, medical humanities' introduction must be carefully tailored and worked strategically into the curriculum at key stages of learning. If educators can strive to truly integrate arts and humanities into their healthcare teaching in engaging and interesting ways, their students can only gain from a deeper learning experience and creative environment where the human (illness) condition, with all its attendant care practices, can be critically and authentically discussed. Finally, reflecting on how selves and identities are co-constructed in real-time clinical interactions for patient/client and practitioner has the potential to tell us not only a lot about ourselves and our professional practice, but also about the people we purport to guide and support in therapeutic interactions.

Acknowledgement

I would like to acknowledge the support of Professor Judy Duchan (Emeritus Professor, University at Buffalo, New York) in the shaping of ideas and in the writing of this chapter. Any errors and misinterpretations that remain are my own.

References

Abrahamson, S. (2007). Did Janet Frame have high-functioning autism? *The New Zealand Medical Journal, 120,* 1263.

Alexander, M., Lenahan, P., & Pavlov, A. (Eds) (2005). *Cinemeducation: A Comprehensive Guide to Using Film in Medical Education*. Oxford: Radcliffe Publishing.

Allan, C.L., Turri, M.G., Stein, K., Da Silva, F.N., & Harris, J. (2016). Exploring psychiatry through images and objects. *Medical Humanities, 42,* 205-206.

Anthony, W.A. (1993). Recovery from mental illness: The guiding vision of the mental health service system in the 1990s. *Psychosocial Rehabilitation Journal, 16*(4), 11-23.

Barham, P. & Hayward, R. (1995). *Relocating Madness: From the Mental Patient to the Person*. London: Free Association Books.

Batistatou, A., Doulis, E.A, Tiniakos, D., Anongiannaki, A., & Charalabopoulos, K. (2010). The introduction of medical humanities in the undergraduate curriculum of Greek medical schools: Challenge and necessity. *Hippokratia, 14*(4), 241-243.

Brennan, F. (2015). Janet Frame's "An Electric Blanket": Love, loss, and "the bitter seed of moment". *Journal of Palliative Care, 31,* 193-195.

Brophy, J. (2009) Working alongside people with schizophrenia: Directions for speech and language practice. (Unpublished Master's Thesis). Trinity College Dublin.

Campion, J. (Director). (1990). *An Angel at my Table.* [Motion Picture]. New Zealand: Channel Four Films, New Zealand Film Commission, Hibiscus Films, Television New Zealand & Australian Broadcasting Corporation.

Cohen, B.M.Z. (2008). *Mental Health User Narratives: New Perspectives on Illness and Recovery.* Basingstoke: Palgrave Macmillan.

Crawford, P., Brown, B., Tischler, V., & Baker, C. (2010). Health humanities: The future of medical humanities? *Mental Health Review Journal, 15*(3), 4-10.

Darbyshire, D. & Baker, P. (2012). A systematic review and thematic analysis of cinema in medical education. *Medical Humanities, 38,* 28-33.

Emerson, J. & Enderby, P. (1996). Prevalence of speech and language disorders in a mental illness unit. *European Journal of Disorders of Communication, 31*(3), 221-236.

Evans, M. & Greaves, D. (1999). Exploring the medical humanities. *British Medical Journal, 319,* 1216.

Frame, J. (1982). *To the Is-land.* New York: Braziller.

Frame, J. (1989). *Janet Frame: The Complete Autobiography.* London: The Women's Press.

Frame, J. (1993). *The Envoy from Mirror City - Autobiography 3.* London: Flamingo.

Frame, J. (1994). *The Envoy from Mirror City.* Auckland: Vintage Collector's Edition.

Fuentes-Vásquez, C.L. (2013). *Dangerous Writing: The Autobiographies of Willa Muir, Margaret Laurence and Janet Frame.* New York: Rodopi.

Gambaudo, S. (2012). 'Melancholia in Janet Frame's Faces in the Water.' *Literature and Medicine, 30*(1), 42-60.

Goffman, E. (1963). *Stigma: Notes on the Management of a Spoiled Identity.* New York: Simon & Schuster.

Greaves D. & Evans M. (2000). Medical humanities. *Medical Humanities, 26,* 1-2.

Green, C.A. (2004). Fostering recovery from life-transforming mental health disorders: A synthesis and model. *Social Theory & Health, 2,* 293-314.

Hawes, T. (1995). Janet Frame: The self as other/othering the self. *Deep South* v.1.n.1.(February).

Hooper, S.P., Alexander, M., Allbright, T.A., Wan, C. Burks, J.K., & Lenahan, P. (2005). The professional and personal self of the physician. In M. Alexander, P. Lenahan, & A. Pavlov (Eds), *Cinemeducation: A Comprehensive Guide to using Film in Medical Education* (pp.131-136). Oxford: Radcliffe Publishing.

Hopgood, F. (2006). Unraveling the myth of the mad genius in An Angel at My Table. *Journal of Interdisciplinary Gender Studies, 10*(1), 53-76.

Jagoe, C. (2013). Schizophrenia and metarepresentational abilities in conversation: A preliminary analysis of question interpretation. In E. Walaszewska & A. Piskorska (Eds), *Relevance Theory: More than Understanding* (pp.261-278). Cambridge: Cambridge Scholars Publishing.

Jagoe, C. (2015). Collaborative meaning-making in delusional talk as a search for mutual manifestness: A relevance theory approach. *Journal of Interactional Research in Communication Disorders*, 6(1), 53–71.

Jones, T. & Verghese, A. (2003). On becoming a humanities curriculum: The Center for Medical Humanities and Ethics at the University of Texas Health Science Center at San Antonio. *Academic Medicine*, 78(10), 1010-1014.

King, M. (2000). *Wrestling with the Angel: A Life of Janet Frame*. London: Picador.

Kovarsky, D. & Curran, M. (2007). A missing voice in the discourse of evidence-based practice. *Topics in Language Disorders*, 27(1), 50-61.

Kovarsky, D., Duchan, J., & Maxwell, M. (1999). *Constructing (in)competence: Disabling Evaluations in Clinical and Social Interaction*. New Jersey: Lawrence Erlbaum.

Kovarsky, D., Kimbarow, M., & Kastner, D. (1999). The construction of incompetence during group therapy with traumatically brain injured adults. In D. Kovarsky, J. Duchan, & M. Maxwell (Eds), *Constructing (in)competence: Disabling Evaluations in Clinical and Social Interaction* (pp.291-311). New Jersey: Lawrence Erlbaum.

Kovarsky, D. & Maxwell, M. (1992). Ethnography and the clinical setting: Communicative expectancies in clinical discourse. *Topics in Language Disorders*, 12(3), 76-84.

Kovarsky, D., Shaw, A., & Adingono-Smith, M. (2007). The construction of identity during group therapy among adults with traumatic brain injury. *Communication & Medicine*, 4(1), 53-66.

Lysaker, P. & Lysaker, J. (2002). Narrative structure in psychosis: Schizophrenia and disruptions in the dialogical self. *Theory & Psychology*, 12(2), 207-220.

Lysaker, P. & Lysaker, J. (2008). *Schizophrenia and the Fate of the Self*. Oxford: Oxford University Press.

Lysaker, P. & Lysaker, J. (2010). Schizophrenia and alternations in self-experience: A comparison of 6 perspectives. *Schizophrenia Bulletin*, 36(2), 331-340.

Martin, D. (2004, January 30). Janet Frame, 79, Writer Who Explored Madness. *New York Times*. Retrieved from http://www.nytimes.com/2004/01/30/books/janet-frame-79-writer-who-explored-madness.html

Moss, H. & O'Neill, D. (2012). Medical humanities – serious academic pursuit or doorway to dilettantism? *Irish Medical Journal*, 105, 261-262.

Moss, H. & O' Neill, D. (2017). Narratives of health and illness: Arts-based research capturing the lived experience of dementia. *Dementia*. Article first published online: October 12th, 2017 https://doi.org/10.1177/1471301217736163

Oettli, S. (2007). Janet Frame and autism? Response from a Frame scholar. *The New Zealand Medical Journal*, 120, 1265.

O' Neill, D., Jenkins, E., Mawhinney, R., Cosgrave, E., O' Mahony, S., Guest, C., & Moss, H. (2016). Rethinking the medical in medical humanities. *Medical Humanities, 42,* 109-114.

Oyebode, F. (2010). The medical humanities: Literature and medicine. *Clinical Medicine, 10*(3), 242-244.

Panagos, J. (1996). Speech therapy discourse: The input to learning. In M. Smith & J. Damico (Eds), *Childhood Language Disorders* (pp.41-63). New York: Thieme.

Peterkin, A. (2016). Curating the medical humanities curriculum: Twelve tips. *Medical Humanities, 42*(3), 147-148.

Roberts, R. (2011). *Real to Reel: Psychiatry at the Cinema.* Ross-on-Wye, UK: PCCS Books.

Simmons-Mackie, N. & Damico, J. (1999). Social role negotiation in aphasia therapy: Competence, incompetence, and conflict. In D. Kovarsky, J. Duchan & M. Maxwell (Eds), *Constructing (in)competence: Disabling Evaluations in Clinical and Social Interaction* (pp.313-341). New Jersey: Lawrence Erlbaum.

Sinha, P., Vandana, V.P., Lewis, N.V., Jayaran, M., & Enderby, P. (2015). Evaluating the effect of risperidone on speech: A cross-sectional study. *Asian Journal of Psychiatry, 15,* 51-55.

Stanghellini, G. (2004). *Disembodied Spirits and Deanimated Bodies: The Psychopathology of Common Sense.* Oxford: Oxford University Press.

Tajfel, H. & Turner, J.C. (1986). The social identity theory of intergroup behavior. In S. Worchel & W.G. Austin (Eds), *The Psychology of Intergroup Relations* (pp.7-24). Chicago: Nelson-Hall.

van Dijk, T.A. (1997). Discourse as interaction in society. In T.A. van Dijk (Ed.), *Discourse as Social Interaction* (pp.1-37). London: Sage.

Wachtler, C., Lundin, S., & Troein, M. (2006). Humanities for medical students? A qualitative study of a medical humanities curriculum in a medical school program. *BioMedCentral Medical Education, 6,* 16.

Walsh, I.P. (2002, 2003). Revealing ability amidst perceived disability: A nice idea or a clinical imperative? *Journal of Clinical Speech & Language Studies, 12-13,* 118-145.

Walsh, I.P. (2008). Whose voice is it anyway? Hushing and hearing 'voices' in speech and language therapy interactions with people with chronic schizophrenia. *International Journal of Language & Communication Disorders, 43*(supp 1), 81-95.

Walsh-Brennan, I.P. (2001). *'Speak to me...speak to me please'.* Conversational sociability amidst perceived disability in chronic schizophrenia. Unpublished doctoral dissertation. Trinity College, Dublin.

Walsh, I.P., Brophy, J., & Hendy, D. (2013). Experiences of communication 'disorder' and difference in the world of mental health disorders. Paper presented at 'A Narrative Future for Health Care', June 19-21, 2013, King's Guy's Hospital Campus, London.

Walsh, I.P., Delmar, P., & Jagoe, C. (2018). "It's not the Asperger's that causes the anxiety, it's the communication": Person-centered outcomes of hope and recovery in a cultural–clinical borderland. *Topics in Language Disorders, 38*(2), April/June 108–125.

Walsh, I.P., Regan, J., Sowman, R., Parsons, B., & McKay, A.P. (2007). A needs analysis for the provision of a speech and language therapy service to adults with mental health disorders. *Irish Journal of Psychological Medicine, 24*(3), 89-93.

Walton, C. (2015). Doing discourse analysis. In E. Lyons & A. Coyle (Eds), *Analysing Qualitative Data in Psychology* (pp.182-201). London: Sage.

Waxman, D., Alexander, M., Kirkpatrick. H.A., & Blasco, P. (2005). Interviewing skills. In M. Alexander, P. Lenahan, & A. Pavlov (Eds), *Cinemeducation: A Comprehensive Guide to using Film in Medical Education* (pp.125-129). Oxford: Radcliffe Publishing.

Wisdom, J.P., Bruce, K., Saedi, G.A., Weis, T., & Green, C.A. (2008). 'Stealing me from myself': Identity and recovery in personal accounts of mental illness. *Australian and New Zealand Journal of Psychiatry, 42*(6), 489-495.

Appendix

Selected works of Janet Frame:

Novels

1957 *Owls Do Cry*. Christchurch: Pegasus Press.

1961 *Faces in the Water*. Christchurch: Pegasus Press; New York: Braziller.

1962 *The Edge of the Alphabet*. Christchurch: Pegasus Press.

1963 *Scented Gardens for the Blind*. London: W.H. Allen.

1965 *The Adaptable Man*. London: W.H. Allen.

1966 *A State of Siege*. New York: Braziller.

1968 *The Rainbirds*. London: W.H. Allen. (Published in the US with Frame's preferred original title, *Yellow Flowers in the Antipodean Room*. New York: Braziller, 1969.)

1970 *Intensive Care*. New York: Braziller.

1972 *Daughter Buffalo*. New York: Braziller.

1979 *Living in the Maniototo*. New York: Braziller.

Short stories

1963 *The Reservoir: Stories and Sketches/Snowman Snowman: Fables and Fantasies*. New York: Braziller (Edited selection published in the Commonwealth edition *The Reservoir and Other Stories*, London: W.H. Allen, 1966).

1983 *You Are Now Entering the Human Heart*. Wellington: Victoria University Press.

Poetry

1967 *The Pocket Mirror*. New York: Braziller.

Autobiography

1982 *To the Is-Land* (Autobiography 1). New York: Braziller.

1984 *An Angel at My Table* (Autobiography 2). New York: Braziller.

1984 *The Envoy From Mirror City* (Autobiography 3). Auckland: Century Hutchinson.

1989 *An Autobiography* (Collected edition). Auckland: Century Hutchinson (Posthumously reprinted under the title *An Angel at My Table*, London: Virago, 2008).

8 Reflecting on hope: Communication and mental health

C. Jagoe, P. Delmar, A. Sheehy and I.P. Walsh

"Hope will never be silent" (Harvey Milk)

Introduction

The growing interest in positive psychology and wellbeing has seen an increase in the focus on *hope* as a therapeutic construct. This chapter will address hope as it applies within the field of mental health, and in relation to communication abilities. The argument made and supported by clinicians across different healthcare contexts, including Speech and Language Therapists (SLTs), is that hope plays a role in the therapeutic dynamic. Clinicians are encouraged to be cognisant of hope in their encounters with clients. However, it is worth exploring what challenges language and communication difficulties in the context of mental health disorder might raise, and how the clinician working within this field might harness hope to optimize the therapeutic dynamic and desired outcomes.

At the outset of the chapter, it is necessary to highlight the fact that addressing hope is unlikely to be the primary focus of speech and language therapy intervention or explicitly addressed by most healthcare professionals. Indeed, across health professions, hope-enhancement occurs within the context of professional roles and practice. In other words, while engaging in assessment, intervention or support strategies, awareness of ways in which hope can be assessed and enhanced may lead to better outcomes for the individuals within the therapeutic relationship. This chapter will begin by considering concepts and constructions of hope, before a brief history of hope in healthcare is outlined. Communication, hope and the role of the SLT will also be discussed with a specific focus on how principles in the hope literature might need adaptation in the context of communication difficulties. The chapter will close with some intentional exploration (or 'assessment') of hope, along with a consideration of hope-enhancing strategies in therapy contexts.

Concepts and constructions of hope

The difficulty of defining hope is apparent in the literature, with various authors offering different perspectives (Edey & Jevne, 2003). It is not the intention here to identify a singular definition of hope, but rather to provide an overview of some of the proposals put forth by researchers to show the depth and diversity of this concept.

Firstly, Dufault and Martocchio (1985) identify two spheres of hope: 'particularized hope' which is directed towards a goal or a desire, and 'generalized hope' which is the expectation that the future will be good and is not specific to any given situation. Their multidimensional model of hope (across the spheres of the 'particularized' and 'generalized'), share six common dimensions – affective, cognitive, behavioural, affiliative, temporal and contextual – thereby challenging earlier unidimensional constructs of hope (e.g., Stotland, 1969). Their model was developed based on their work with two relatively small sample groups of elderly people with cancer and patients with terminal illness. The two spheres of hope are inter-related and reciprocal. Research with people with aphasia has similarly suggested that people may operate within two spheres of hope – framed by Bright and colleagues (2013) as *simply having hope* and *actively hoping*. Hope, though at first appearing a relatively simple construct, is rather a complex and dynamic one, not so easily defined or described.

Most definitions of hope focus on the nature of the 'particularized hope' or the active, more goal-directed nature of hope. Snyder and colleagues (Snyder et al., 1991; Snyder, Lopez, Shorey, Rand, & Feldman, 2003) are specific in their formulation of hope, which takes on a narrower motivational stance. They propose two inter-related components: *agency* which "refers to a sense of successful determination in meeting goals in the past, present and future", and *pathways* which "refers to a sense of being able to generate successful plans to meet goals" (Snyder et al., 1991, p.570). The two elements are "reciprocal, additive, and positively related" (Snyder et al., 1991, p.571). Simpson (2004) focused her discussion of hope on its relevance to illness and health. She identified four aspects of hope: the role of desires and wants; the connection to values and goals; the role of imagination and its link to uncertainty; and the action component. In this conceptualization, Simpson addresses goal-oriented hope, which has an action component but also acknowledges the uncertainties which are intrinsic to hope. The notion of uncertainties raising 'openings' or possibilities for action is also articulated in the work of Solnit (2016) who summarizes her understanding of hope as follows:

> It's important to say what hope is not: it is not the belief that everything was, is, or will be fine...The hope I am interested in is about broad perspectives with specific possibilities, ones that invite or demand that we act. It's not a sunny everything-is-getting-better narrative, though it may be a counter to the everything-is-getting-worse one. You could call it an account of complexities and uncertainties, with openings (p.xi).

Hope as a construct is also defined by those who 'live it' or aspire to it in their own personal illness context. For example, O' Malley-Keighran and Coleman (2014) analyzed illness narratives in Irish press media and found hope to be central to many of these accounts. Some accounts showed a wish to "return to a place where life felt 'normal' again" and not to be pitied (p.184). They illustrate this way of viewing hope with an account from a person with Motor Neurone Disease (MND), as follows:

> I neither want nor need pity. I am full of hope. The word hope and MND do not go together in this country. Hope is not about looking for a cure to disease. Hope is a way of living. We often think we are entitled to a long and fruitful Coca-Cola life, but life is a privilege, not a right. I feel privileged to be alive. That's hope (O' Malley-Keighran & Coleman, 2014, p.184).

Bland and Darlington (2002) extend the consideration of hope to include family caregivers in mental health contexts, a notion which resonates with the desire from people with communication impairments "that people be hopeful with them" (O' Malley-Keighran & Coleman, 2014, p.184). The complexity of hope, encompassing specific goals which capture a previous way of being, but in the acknowledgment that life is different, is captured in this family member's account:

> I still grieve and hope optimal treatment can offer Susan a
> new freedom to be herself again, a new self different from
> what I knew, but hopefully still inhabited by this unique
> flame that is her essence. I hope to play music again with
> Susan one day. I hope this day is not so far off. Most of all, I
> hope she and I will regain the joy of sharing simple things,
> simple thoughts, simple notes (Demers, 2002, p.188).

Hope experienced as relational is a strong theme in the research and is clearly expressed in the following account by Hartman (2002, p.414):

> Hope, sometimes even blind hope, must somehow be
> grasped. It is best grasped not by a lone sentry of the night,
> but within true community: a place to go, to feel worthy,
> to nourish a self-respect: a job, a friend, a neighbour, a
> lover. This is the true lifeblood, and it is this that incessant
> mental disease steals.

It can be concluded from these few examples of accounts of hope that the idea of hope as a return to a pre-morbid self (i.e., that sense of self before the diagnosis or illness) is unusual. Instead, hope may more typically exist in the context of recognizing a different but hopeful life in interaction with others.

A brief history of the concept of hope in relation to healthcare

Hope, as it applies to healthcare, can seem like an abstract concept. Hope was historically viewed as being the territory of theology and philosophy, only moving into the realm of modern medicine in the 20th century (Elliot, 2005).

Hope appears across the history of medicine, including in the 1847 Code of Ethics of the American Medical Association (AMA, 1871). The reference to hope in these contexts was typically as "a universal balm" (Coulehan, 2011) rather than as a feature of human psychological, social and cognitive life that could be assessed, measured and modulated. Karl Menninger, a psychiatrist, argued that hope should not be confined to the realms of theology and philosophy; rather, that medical professionals had a responsibility to consider, research, and advocate for the "validity of Hope in human development" (Menninger, 1960, p.11). In his lecture (reprinted in the 1960 paper), Menninger highlighted the lack of scientific research in the area of psychiatry and called upon his colleagues to focus "attention upon a basic but elusive ingredient in our daily work – our teaching, our healing, our diagnosing, [...] hope" (p.11). He emphasized the role of the healthcare professional in considering hope in their interactions with their patients and held that the nurturing and sustaining of hope could improve patient recovery and survival. Menninger thus viewed hope as a resource that can be strengthened or weakened. Since Menninger's paper, hope has become widely researched in healthcare, perhaps most prominently in oncology, with Brown (2015) arguing that this field has demonstrated the most prolific investigation of hope. Nursing, as a profession, has led in terms of the exploration of the concept of hope in healthcare contexts (see Tutton, Seers, & Langstaff, 2009 for an exploration of the concept as it relates to nursing practice). Specific application in fields of chronic illness, allied health and rehabilitation exist but have been more limited (Schiavon, Marchetti, Gurgel, Busnello, & Reppold, 2017). In the rehabilitation literature, hope has been found to act as a safeguard against the development of poor psycho-emotional wellbeing (following illness or accident) and to improve the identification and achieving of goals (Kortte, Stevenson, Hosey, Castillo, & Wegener, 2012; Snyder, Lehman, Kluck, & Monsson, 2006) by developing motivating emotions and ways of thinking and identifying ways to achieve goals. Positive states of wellbeing have been found to improve attention, strategic and creative problem solving, goal-oriented behaviours, and active participation in activities of daily living (Huppert, 2009). Hope, therefore, whether explicitly considered or not, plays an integral role across the journey of recovery and engagement with health services, and is thus of relevance in any therapeutic alliance.

Hope in the context of modern mental health research and practice is nestled within the concept of personal recovery, where it has been shown to have an impact on functional outcomes (Schrank, Stanghellini, & Slade, 2008). O' Callaghan (2003) discusses hope as pivotal to his recovery from clinical depression. For O' Callaghan (2003, p.184), recovery meant "success in reaching a new level in my life, within what was possible, beyond the old routines and destructive habits". This description is in keeping with Anthony's (1993, p.17) definition of personal recovery, that is, not a cure or return to a pre-morbid self but:

> ...a deeply personal, unique process of changing one's attitudes, values, feelings, goals, skills and/or roles. It is a way of living a satisfying, hopeful and contributing life even

with limitations caused by illness. Recovery includes the development of new meaning and purpose in one's life as one grows beyond the catastrophic effects of mental illness.

While the importance of hope is acknowledged within healthcare, there is a documented concern about the potential for 'false hope' (Edey & Jevne, 2003; Snyder & Rand, 2003; Snyder, Rand, King, Feldman, & Woodward, 2002; Soundy et al., 2010). When faced with a patient with an incurable illness, a progressive disease and/or a plateaued recovery, do healthcare professionals risk causing harm by not tempering any 'false hope'? The first-person accounts explored through the quotes in the previous section suggest a hope tempered by realism or hope in the space of uncertainties. In addition, research does not appear to support the concern about 'false hope'. Hope and realism can co-exist (e.g., Mack et al., 2007). According to Snyder (2002), studies have found that while people with high hope levels do have "slightly positively biased self-referential views", these views are not extreme or "illusion-based" (p.264). People with high hope levels have been found to not only adapt their hopes and goals based on their circumstances (Kwon, 2002), but to have better coping mechanisms when challenges arise or goals are not realized (Snyder, 2002). Furthermore, people with high hope levels have been found to be more flexible and to independently identify new opportunities and solutions to challenges (Edey & Jevne, 2003; Irving, Snyder, & Crowson, 1998), and to persist in their goal-achievement (Snyder, 2002).

Communication and hope

The role of the Speech and Language Therapist is to optimize communication and thereby maximize participation, wellbeing and quality of life. Hope, as presented above, has a central role in wellbeing and is particularly important in the face of challenges, including illness (Dufault & Martocchio, 1985; Edey & Jevne, 2003), and therefore healthcare professionals, including SLTs, should have an awareness of hope (Bright et al., 2013). The highly abstract concept of hope, and the factors which appear to influence hope, are intertwined with language. Asking about hopes (in the context of desired outcomes, for example), articulating goals, facilitating interpersonal connections are all hope-related clinical activities which are intrinsically based on communication. Using the model proposed by Bright and colleagues (2013), different levels of engaging with hope in the therapeutic dynamic are possible: awareness of hope, intentional exploration of hope and active intervention to enhance hope. Each of these will be briefly presented in the context of work in mental health, and the communication considerations will be highlighted.

Awareness of hope

Perhaps one of the key reasons that SLTs should be aware of hope is the common finding that hope is associated with interpersonal connectedness and affirming relationships, highlighted in research on hope and personal recovery in people with schizophrenia (Noh, Choe, & Yang, 2008) and older adults after stroke (e.g., Bays, 2001). Given that communication difficulties impact on interaction, individuals who experience barriers to interpersonal connections (such as those with communication difficulties) may have greater challenges in maintaining hope. SLTs should be aware that facilitating these interpersonal connections impacts not only on communicative participation but is likely to have a ripple effect into other domains of recovery, through the mediating impact of hope. Expressing, or verbally articulating, goals is also important for hope. Bright and colleagues (2013) suggest that actively hoping (the goal-oriented, particularized form of hope) is strongly language-based. Their conclusion that actively hoping may therefore be more difficult for people with communication impairment following stroke (e.g., aphasia) may be relevant for other groups, including people with mental health disorders and communication difficulties. Supporting individuals with communication difficulties to articulate goals within a framework of their hopes may therefore be an important role for the Speech and Language Therapist.

Intentional exploration of hope or 'assessing' hope

Research into hope has, since the 1970s, resulted in a number of instruments designed to 'measure' hope. The discourse of measurement is dominant within the healthcare literature on hope, and has received some critique (e.g., Brown, 2015). Intentionally exploring people's hope and hopes may be a useful way to consider their preferred futures and direct conversations around goal setting (Bright et al., 2013). Formal 'measurement' may not be useful or appropriate for everyone or in every context. However, scales to assess hope do exist.

In a review of the literature published on hope in psychiatry in 2008, Schrank and colleagues identified 32 scales for assessing hope (Schrank et al., 2008). As the understanding of hope has developed, so too has the focus of assessment tools. While earlier assessments (e.g., Gottschalk, 1974) used Stoner's (1969) definition of hope as an expectation of goal achievement, assessments including the Herth Hope Scale (Herth, 1992), the Hope Index Scale (Obayuwana et al., 1982) and the Miller Hope Scale (Miller & Powers, 1988), developed more multidimensional approaches, addressing such concerns as interpersonal elements, including emotional and behavioural responses; both time oriented and non-time oriented senses of hope; and the impact of interpersonal relationships, as well as goal achievement (Herth, 1992). This section will discuss two examples of commonly used tools to assess hope (i.e., *Synder Hope Scales*, and *Herth Hope Index*). It should be noted that all of the existing scales are language-based and none has been specifically adapted to be accessible for those with more significant communication difficulties.

Snyder Hope Scales

The Dispositional Hope Scale (DHS) was developed by Snyder et al. in 1991 and examines hope as an enduring trait of an individual. It has been found to be reliable and valid (Schrank et al., 2008). The DHS is a 12 item self-rating scale that is based on Snyder et al.'s definition of hope (as outlined above) as comprising of *pathways* (the individual's perception that it is possible to achieve a goal), and *agency* (the individual's perception that they are able to take specific actions to achieve that goal) (Brouwer, Meijer, Weekers, & Baneke, 2008). Four of the items in the DHS relate to pathways, four to agency, and four are distractors. Patients self-rate these items on an eight-point Likert Scale that ranges from 'definitely false' to 'definitely true'. In recognition that hope can fluctuate in response to specific circumstances, the State Hope Scale (SHS) (Snyder et al., 1996) was developed. It consists of six items, three related to pathways and three to agency, that examine the patient's *current* state of hope. Studies support the SHS's reliability, validity, and sensitivity to change (Schrank et al., 2008). A paediatric version of Snyder Hope Scales, The Children's Hope Scale (CHS), has also been developed (Snyder et al., 1997).

Herth Hope Index

The Herth Hope Index (HHI) was developed by Kaye Herth in 1992, as an adaptation of the Herth Hope Scale (Herth, 1991). Its aim is "to capture the multidimensionality of hope [...], to reflect clearly the unique dimensions of hope in the clinical populations, and to reduce the number and complexity of items and so render the tool more clinically useful" (Herth, 1992, p.1252). Its reliability, validity, and sensitivity to change have been found to be strong (Schrank et al., 2008). The HHI consists of 12 items to be rated by the patient using a Likert scale that ranges from 1 (strongly disagree) to 4 (strongly agree). These items address three dimensions of hope based on Dufault and Martocchio's Model of Hope (Dufault & Martocchio, 1985): (i) cognitive-temporal, defined by Herth as "the perception that a positive, desired outcome is realistically probable in the near or distant future"; (ii) affective-behavioural, "a feeling of confidence with initiation of plans to affect the desired outcome"; and (iii) affiliative-contextual, "the recognition of the interdependence and interconnectedness between self and others and between self and spirit" (Herth, 1992, p.1253).

The healthcare professional working with someone with communication difficulties should evaluate whether hope is an explicit outcome which needs to be measured and, if so, to consider (i) the patient's readiness and comfort with facing their feelings about hope, and discussing those feelings; (ii) the amount of effort and energy involved in completing what is likely to be one more of many assessments; and (iii) the accessibility of the language used in the assessment (Herth, 1992). In other words, a formal measure of hope may not be necessary or appropriate in a clinical context, although an awareness of hope is likely to be beneficial.

Actively employing hope-enhancing strategies

Conveying hope has been identified as important by mental health service users (Borg & Kristiansen, 2004) and therefore SLTs working in the context of mental health services should arguably conduct their work with sensitivity to the ways in which hope (and therefore recovery) can be fostered. Hope can be developed within a therapeutic relationship, described by Magyar-Moe (2014, p.244) as "a malleable strength that can serve as an important therapeutic change agent". Hope can be viewed, then, as something that can be shaped and nurtured as a positive force in therapy interactions to promote wellbeing, including in the context of speech and language therapy (Walsh, Delmar, & Jagoe, 2018). Hope (or hopefulness) in such contexts often goes unnamed but could be described as an attitude or stance adopted by those involved and which proactively permeates positive clinical interactions.

Therefore, hope-enhancing strategies can be a part of the clinical encounter in order to foster recovery, without any specific focus on hope as a primary outcome. A range of strategies have been identified in the literature, with five of the most promising candidate interventions to improve hope in people with mental health disorders identified through a systematic review (Schrank et al., 2008):

(i) collaborative strategies for illness management

(ii) fostering relationships

(iii) peer support

(iv) helping clients to assume control and to formulate and pursue realistic goals

(v) specific interventions to support multiple positive factors such as self-esteem, self-efficacy, spirituality and wellbeing.

These strategies are generic and the authors of the systematic review outline them as potential approaches relevant across mental health. However, they are all heavily reliant on successful communication and good language abilities. For people with communication difficulties associated with, or intrinsic to, mental health disorders, the speech and language therapist may have a role to play both in enhancing hope and enabling access to other interventions which could increase hope and promote recovery. Walsh, Delmar and Jagoe (2018) discuss an example of a person with a diagnosis of Asperger's Syndrome, with concomitant mental health challenges and communication difficulties, where hope became an active dynamic within the therapeutic relationship while enhancing communication skills and wellbeing.

Conclusion

Health professionals, including SLTs, working within mental health services, should consider how hope might be nurtured within, or incorporated into, their practice. Listening and responding to clients' conversations about recovery can provide opportunities to foster hopeful therapeutic interactions in which hope is not just a by-product but rather something that is core to the success of the therapeutic dynamic. Individuals with mental health disorders and communication difficulties may need specific consideration with regards to how the language-dependent processes of goal-setting, fostering relationships and nurturing connectedness can be appropriately supported in order to optimize hope and recovery.

References

American Medical Association. (1871). *Code of Ethics of the American Medical Association Adopted May 1847*. Philadelphia: Turner, Hamilton.

Anthony, W.A. (1993). Recovery from mental illness: The guiding vision of the mental health service system in the 1990s. *Psychosocial Rehabilitation Journal, 16*(4), 11–23.

Bays, C.L. (2001). Older adults' descriptions of hope after a stroke. *Rehabilitation Nursing, 26*(1), 18–27.

Bland, R. & Darlington, Y. (2002). The nature and sources of hope: Perspectives of family caregivers of people with serious mental illness. *Perspectives in Psychiatric Care, 38*(2), 61–68.

Borg, M. & Kristiansen, K. (2004). Recovery-oriented professionals: Helping relationships in mental health services. *Journal of Mental Health, 13*(5), 493–505.

Bright, F.A.S., Kayes, N.M., McCann, C.M., & McPherson, K.M. (2013). Hope in people with aphasia. *Aphasiology, 27*(1), 41–58.

Brouwer, D., Meijer, R.R., Weekers, A.M., & Baneke, J.J. (2008). On the dimensionality of the Dispositional Hope Scale. *Psychological Assessment, 20*(3), 310–315.

Brown, N. (2015). Metrics of hope: Disciplining affect in oncology. *Health: An Interdisciplinary Journal for the Social Study of Health, Illness and Medicine, 19*(2), 119–136.

Coulehan, J. (2011). Deep hope: A song without words. *Theoretical Medicine and Bioethics, 32*(3), 143–160.

Demers, M.-F. (2002). First person account: Susan's cello. *Schizophrenia Bulletin, 28*(1), 187–189.

Dufault, K. & Martocchio, B.C. (1985). Symposium on compassionate care and the dying experience. Hope: Its spheres and dimensions. *The Nursing Clinics of North America, 20*(2), 379–391.

Edey, W. & Jevne, R.E. (2003). Hope, illness, and counselling practice: Making hope visible. *Canadian Journal of Counselling, 37*(44–51).

Eliott, J.A. (2005). What have we done with hope? A brief history. In J.A. Elliott (Ed.), *Interdisciplinary Perspectives on Hope* (pp.3–45). Hauppauge, NY: Nova Science Publishers.

Gottschalk, L.A. (1974). A Hope scale applicable to verbal samples. *Archives of General Psychiatry, 30*(6), 779–785.

Hartman, C.E. (2002). Personal accounts: Life as death: Hope regained with ECT. *Psychiatric Services, 53*, 413–414.

Herth, K. (1991). Development and refinement of an instrument to measure hope. *Scholarly Inquiry for Nursing Practice, 5*(1), 39–51.

Herth, K. (1992). Abbreviated instrument to measure hope: Development and psychometric evaluation. *Journal of Advanced Nursing, 17*(10), 1251–1259.

Huppert, F.A. (2009). Psychological well-being: Evidence regarding its causes and consequences. *Applied Psychology: Health and Well-Being, 1*(2), 137–164.

Irving, L.M., Snyder, C.R., & Crowson, J.J. (1998). Hope and coping with cancer by college women. *Journal of Personality*, *66*(2), 195–214.

Kortte, K.B., Stevenson, J.E., Hosey, M.M., Castillo, R., & Wegener, S.T. (2012). Hope predicts positive functional role outcomes in acute rehabilitation populations. *Rehabilitation Psychology*, *57*(3), 248–255.

Kwon, P. (2002). Hope, defense mechanisms, and adjustment: Implications for false hope and defensive hopelessness. *Journal of Personality*, *70*(2), 207–231.

Mack, J.W., Wolfe, J., Cook, E.F., Grier, H.E., Cleary, P.D., & Weeks, J.C. (2007). Hope and prognostic disclosure. *Journal of Clinical Oncology*, *25*(35), 5636–5642.

Magyar-Moe, J.L. (2014). Infusing multiculturalism and positive psychology in psychotherapy. In J. Teramoto Pedrotti & L.M. Edwards (Eds), *Perspectives on the Intersection of Multiculturalism and Positive Psychology* (pp.235–252). New York, NY: Springer.

Menninger, K. (1960). Hope. *Pastoral Psychology*, April, 11–24.

Miller, J.F. & Powers, M.J. (1988). Development of an instrument to measure hope. *Nursing Research*, *37*(1), 6–10.

Noh, C., Choe, K., & Yang, B. (2008). Hope from the perspective of people with schizophrenia (Korea). *Archives of Psychiatric Nursing*, *22*(2), 69–77.

O' Callaghan, G. (2003). *A Day Called Hope: A Personal Journey Beyond Depression*. London: Hodder & Stoughton.

O' Malley-Keighran, M.-P. & Coleman, M. (2014). 'I am not a tragedy. I am full of hope': Communication impairment narratives in newspapers. *International Journal of Language & Communication Disorders*, *49*(2), 174–188.

Obayuwana, A.O., Collins, J.L., Carter, A.L., Rao, M.S., Mathura, C.C., & Wilson, S.B. (1982). Hope Index Scale: An instrument for the objective assessment of hope. *Journal of the National Medical Association*, *74*(8), 761–765.

Schiavon, C.C., Marchetti, E., Gurgel, L.G., Busnello, F.M., & Reppold, C.T. (2017). Optimism and hope in chronic disease: A systematic review. *Frontiers in Psychology*, *7*.

Schrank, B., Stanghellini, G., & Slade, M. (2008). Hope in psychiatry: A review of the literature. *Acta Psychiatrica Scandinavica*, *118*(6), 421–433.

Simpson, C. (2004). When hope makes us vulnerable: A discussion of patient-healthcare provider interactions in the context of hope. *Bioethics*, *18*(5), 428–447.

Snyder, C.R. (2002). Hope theory: Rainbows in the mind. *Psychological Inquiry*, *13*(4), 249–275.

Snyder, C.R. & Rand, K.L. (2003). The case against false hope. *American Psychologist*, *58*(10), 820–822.

Snyder, C.R., Harris, C., Anderson, J.R., Holleran, S.A., Irving, L.M., Sigmon, S.X., Yoshinobu, L., Gibb, J., Langelle, C., & Harney, P. (1991). The will and the ways: Development and validation of an individual-differences measure of hope. *Journal of Personality and Social Psychology*, *60*(4), 570–585.

Snyder, C.R., Hoza, B., Pelham, W.E., Rapoff, M., Ware, L., Danovsky, M., Highberger, L., Rubenstein, H., & Stahl, K.J. (1997). The development and validation of the Children's Hope Scale. *Journal of Pediatric Psychology, 22*(3), 399–421.

Snyder, C.R., Lehman, K.A., Kluck, B., & Monsson, Y. (2006). Hope for rehabilitation and vice versa. *Rehabilitation Psychology, 51*(2), 89–112.

Snyder, C.R., Lopez, S.J., Shorey, H.S., Rand, K.L., & Feldman, D.B. (2003). Hope theory, measurements, and applications to school psychology. *School Psychology Quarterly, 18*(2), 122–139.

Snyder, C.R., Rand, K.L., King, E.A., Feldman, D.B., & Woodward, J.T. (2002). "False" hope. *Journal of Clinical Psychology, 58*(9), 1003–1022.

Snyder, C.R., Sympson, S.C., Ybasco, F.C., Borders, T.F., Babyak, M.A., & Higgins, R.L. (1996). Development and validation of the State Hope Scale. *Journal of Personality and Social Psychology, 70*(2), 321–335.

Solnit, R. (2016). *Hope in the Dark: Untold Histories, Wild Possibilities.* Chicago: Haymarket Books.

Soundy, A., Smith, B., Butler, M., Lowe, C.M., Helen, D., & Winward, C.H. (2010). A qualitative study in neurological physiotherapy and hope: Beyond physical improvement. *Physiotherapy Theory and Practice, 26*(2), 79–88.

Stotland, E. (1969). *The Psychology of Hope.* San Francisco, CA: Jossey-Bass.

Tutton, E., Seers, K., & Langstaff, D. (2009). An exploration of hope as a concept for nursing. *Journal of Orthopaedic Nursing, 13*(3), 119–127.

Walsh, I.P., Delmar, P., & Jagoe, C. (2018). "It's not the Asperger's that causes the anxiety, It's the communication": Person-centered outcomes of hope and recovery in a cultural–clinical borderland. *Topics in Language Disorders, 38*(2), 108–125.

Section 3

Communication and mental health: Growing practice

9 The role of speech and language therapy in guiding service user involvement for mental health service users with communication support needs

Jennifer Brophy and Stephanie O'Connor

"There's really no such thing as the 'voiceless'. There are only the deliberately silenced or the preferably unheard." Arundhati Roy, *The Ordinary Person's Guide to Empire* (2006, p.330).

Introduction

There is increasing emphasis on people being able to play a more active role in their communities and lives, both as citizens and as service users. This has become a shared focus across all areas of health and social care, including mental health care. In recent years, mental health services have moved from institutionalized care as their primary focus to care in the community. This transition is driven by and facilitates a focus on recovery which is led by people with lived experience of mental health difficulties (Dermody, Ní Chaoláin, & Gardner, 2015). People with lived experience are experts by virtue of their experience of using mental health services and the importance of this perspective is increasingly acknowledged (Tait & Lester, 2005). These trends have provided the opportunity for the involvement of people with lived experience in their own mental health care and the development of services provided to them and their peers (Dermody et al., 2015).

Lawn (2015, p.1) describes participation in mental health services as encompassing three areas:

1. "... individually focused collaborative, respectful inclusion of mental health service users in care decisions within their interpersonal encounters with service providers and systems"

2. "... engagement with the notion of having a mental illness and seeking or accepting support"

3. "... participation at service and system level as peer workers and as advocates for policy and practice change".

A growing body of research shows positive outcomes from developing a collaborative approach to mental health care (Miller, Chambers, & Giles, 2015; Tait & Lester, 2005). There are benefits to both individuals and services when a good model of service user involvement is apparent within a service:

- Promotion of strong person-centred values (i.e., equality, dignity, respect, choice)
- Provision of opportunities to share knowledge and expertise
- Development of new skills, confidence and self-esteem
- Challenge to discrimination and stigma
- Shaping and informing campaign issues
- Focus on continuous improvement
- Delivery of positive outcomes for people who use services.

(Good Practice Guide: *Service User Involvement*, Turning Point Scotland, 2011, p.2)

Importantly, everyone has the right to have the support they need in order to be involved and to have their say (Charter for Involvement, 2015). However, it has become increasing apparent that some groups (including people with communication difficulties) may face more barriers than others in being involved. This reinforces the difficulties that they face and excludes important perspectives from being heard (Beresford, 2013). Being able to communicate is central to our ability to participate in society. Given that policymakers expect services and organizations to co-produce and engage with people who use their services, it is important that adjustments are made in order to reduce barriers and inequality.

The purpose of this chapter is to outline an area of developing practice: the ways in which Speech and Language Therapists (SLTs) can involve mental health service users with speech, language and communication needs (SLCNs) in their own care and in services in general. Drawing on existing best practice guidelines and extensive clinical experience in specialist roles within mental health services, this chapter aims to provide guidance for SLTs working in the area.

The challenge of service user involvement for mental health service users with SLCNs

There is strong agreement that it is difficult for people with SLCNs to become involved (Beresford, 2013)in health services. For people with both mental health difficulties and SLCNs, there may be extra challenges (see Figure 9.1).

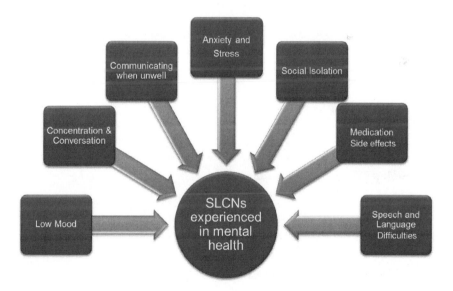

Figure 9.1 Speech, language and communication needs experienced in mental health.

These difficulties can be viewed from two perspectives:

1. Barriers due to SLCNs which are intrinsic to or related to the person and their mental health difficulty.

2. Barriers due to a mental health service which fails to take communication support needs into account.

These are not mutually exclusive, but merge and interplay with each other, thus increasing the cumulative effect.

Barriers due to SLCNs which are intrinsic to or related to the person and their mental health difficulty

The SLCNs of people experiencing mental health difficulties were explored by Brophy (2009). This study identified, through interviews with people living with schizophrenia, some experiences of barriers to communication.

These barriers, described in people's own words below, exist as challenges for service users in being involved in their own care and in services in general:

- Difficulties with concentration and attention in interaction was described by a participant in Brophy's (2009, p.45) study by saying that *"I wouldn't retain what they have said, it might be that they have said something but my mind is thinking of something else"*.

- Another participant in the study commented on other people with schizophrenia and their difficulties with communication. She said, *"They would be maybe a little more debilitated and not able to get across exactly what they mean...or what they need to get across, how they're feeling"* (Brophy, 2009, p.49).

- Feeling anxious during interactions with others was a shared experience for the participants in Brophy's study. One participant stated that *"if I get nervous, I rush my speech, people can't understand me"* (Brophy, 2009, p.50).

McDaid (2009), a researcher who also identifies as a person with lived experience of mental health difficulties, highlights some of the barriers to people being involved in committees in mental health services. Many of these barriers relate to the SLCNs also described in Brophy (2009):

- *"As most service users do not have third level education, professionals have to build up our self-esteem, to build up communication skills, to build up negotiation skills, to build up what's being said and what others are saying, to see these committees as a changing tool, a way forward"* (male participant, aged 50) (McDaid, 2009, p.49)

- *"I remember some things and I don't remember some things, and I don't know how I remember some, and not others. And sometimes I find it hard to take in information as well, you know. It just depends on what form I am in at the time"* (female participant, aged 47) (McDaid, 2009, p.24)

- *"... too much information, but not good information, not understandable"* (McDaid, 2009, p.21).

The cumulative impact of difficulties experienced can be devastating when these needs are not fully recognized and accommodated for within mental health services (Figure 9.2).

Figure 9.2 Barriers due to SLCNs which are intrinsic to or related to the person and their mental health difficulty.

Barriers due to a mental health service which fails to take communication support needs into account

Health services have developed general guidelines around accessibility (e.g., *National Guidelines: Accessible Health and Social Care Services*, HSE & NDA,

2014). However, many barriers exist which are specific to mental health services and the SLCNs experienced by people with mental health difficulties. If the mental health service has not considered the process of making their services more accessible to people with SLCNs as recommended in policy, then the specific difficulties experienced by people with mental health and communication difficulties are unlikely to be considered and adjusted for.

Hagiliassis et al. (2006, p.4), in their guidelines for providing counselling services to clients with disabilities and complex communication needs, acknowledge that "most leading models of counselling are based on speech and listening processes". Indeed, most mental health services are verbally mediated (e.g., phone calls to make appointments, initial interviews with service providers and formulation of mental health plans).

Involving the person in their own care is a central tenet of mental health services in Ireland (Mental Health Commission, 2012) and is regularly audited as part of the Mental Health Commission standards (see Standards 1.1.2): "The development of the individual care and treatment plan has input from the service user, the multidisciplinary team (MDT), and the family/chosen advocate, where appropriate" (Mental Health Commission, 2007). Opportunities afforded within the mental health service for the person to participate in their own care and in wider service involvement may be missed due to the service not responding with appropriate communication supports.

Service users have identified a range of barriers which reduce the opportunity to get and stay involved in making a difference to how services are delivered. (See Figure 9.3 for examples of impact of barriers.) Key barriers include:

- Devaluing or not listening to service users

- Tokenism – involvement being a publicity exercise so that organizations can say that people have been consulted

- Stigma – the fear of being treated differently as a result of your mental health difficulty

- Confidence and skills – service users' own sense of self-worth, lack of knowledge of systems, processes and the hidden 'rules of the game'

- Language and culture – use of jargon and inaccessible language are widely recognized as frequent barriers

- Gatekeepers – people in a position to support or obstruct the involvement of service users

- Power and control – service provider interests dominating the conversations

- Impact of physical and mental health (e.g., difficulties concentrating, understanding what is being said, anxiety/stress, lack of energy and stamina.

(Beresford, 2013; McDaid, 2009)

The role of the SLT embedded in the mental health team includes working with the service to ensure that all people using services have the opportunity to be equally included: "Speech and Language Therapists (SLTs) are key players in promoting communication inclusion. It is embedded firmly in some specialisms. However, it is equally relevant across all speech and language therapy services" (Money et al., 2016, p.5).

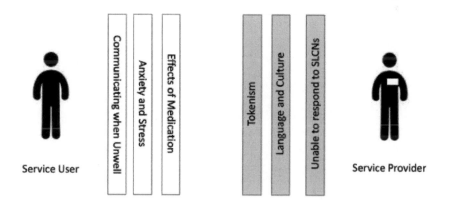

Figure 9.3 Barriers due to a mental health service which fails to take communication support needs into account.

Recovery and speech and language therapy

The concept of recovery in mental health is considered a fundamental principle upon which all mental health services should be based.

The term 'recovery' has been described in different ways as a process, an outlook, a vision, and a guiding principle. It does not refer purely to the remission of clinical symptoms but is a wider concept which views the person's life as a whole. A recovery approach aims to "support an individual in their own personal development, building self-esteem, identity and finding a meaningful role in society" (Allott & Loganathan, 2003). Anthony (1993, p.527) defines recovery as a:

> ...deeply personal, unique process of changing one's attitudes, values, feelings, goals, skills and/or roles. It is a way of living a satisfying, hopeful and contributing life even with limitations caused by illness. Recovery includes the development of new meaning and purpose in one's life as one grows beyond the catastrophic effects of mental illness.

The values which underpin recovery are also those which inform SLT practice (Table 9.1). SLTs who work in Mental Health are thus able to easily adapt their social model approaches to fit with the recovery values of mental health work.

Table 9.1 Shared values of recovery and speech and language therapy practice in mental health.

Recovery in mental health	Speech & Language Therapy Practice
'Living with' mental health difficulty	'Living with' communication difficulty
Person as an active agent in the Recovery process	Goal setting from the perspective of the person
Recovery is something a person does, not something that is done to them	Authentic involvement of the person
Collaboration	Partnership

SLTs support the inclusion of people with mental health difficulties and can make a substantial contribution to this process in mental health services (Figure 9.4).

Firstly, due to the nature of their work with people who have SLCNs, SLTs are aware of the importance of hearing the voice of the person who uses services and also of the factors which can make it more difficult for their voice to be heard. Enshrined within speech and language therapy practice is a view of the person as an 'expert by experience'. Valuing the lived experience of service users ensures that services are based on what people need and want and not on what service providers think they need (Byng & Duchan, 2005). The person is seen as an active agent who acts in collaboration with the healthcare professional during the therapy process. This means that there is a point of entry that starts with the issues that matter most to the individual in terms of living with a speech, language and/or communication difficulty and mental health problems (Duchan & Black, 2001; Kagan, Simmons-Mackie, Rowland, Huijbregts, et al., 2007). In fact, service users have reported that they value professionals who listen to their specific needs and concerns and who tailor therapy accordingly (Cott, 2004).

Secondly, 'problems' are not seen as located solely within the individual.

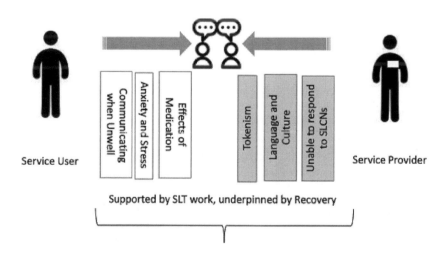

Figure 9.4 SLT role: Reducing barriers to involvement.

Speech and language therapy practice in mental health presumes that SLCNs are a consequence of *interactions* between health conditions and the physical and social environment (Simmons-Mackie, 2004). While this includes impairment effects (e.g., restrictions in activity due to having a language difficulty), it also embraces 'barriers to doing' (e.g., environmental and social obstacles such as lack of accessible information, noise) and 'barriers to being' (stigmatizing behaviour of others which can reduce self-esteem) (Thomas, 1997).

In essence, this view of the role of SLT in adult mental health allows for a more equal relationship between the person and service providers which, in turn, creates the space for the real and direct involvement of service users in their own care as well as the provision of services generally.

A model of involvement for service users with SLCNs in mental health services

As mental health services have developed, the scope of practice for a SLT on a mental health team has evolved. The IASLT Guidance Document for SLTs working in Mental Health in Ireland (IASLT, 2015) describes the work of the SLT as supporting:

- the person
- their environment
- the wider community.

Within this approach, the involvement of the service user is fundamental. SLTs working in mental health focus on each of the levels described above alongside the service user. In order to best facilitate involvement at each of these levels, the following model of inclusive communication, first described by Money and Thurman (2002) is a helpful model and is used in this chapter to outline how SLTs in mental health can support meaningful involvement for service users with mental health difficulties and SLCNs.

The following sections use the model to describe how SLTs in mental health services can build the capacity of service users and service providers to ensure that people with SLCNs are included and have opportunities to influence the decisions which affect them.

The Basis of Service User Involvement

Figure 9.5 Means, Reasons and Opportunities (based on Money & Thurman, 2002)

1. *Reasons* to be involved: the purpose and motivations

2. *Means* to be involved: a Communication Support Plan

3. *Opportunities* to be involved: reducing the barriers to involvement and supporting a service that is committed to meaningful service user involvement and has developed the communication supports to facilitate this.

Communication and *reasons* to be involved

The first element in Money and Thurman's (2002) framework for inclusive communication is *Reasons*, that is, the *why* of communication. Communication is the most fundamental of human capacities. People need to be able to communicate in order to fulfil their social, educational, emotional and vocational potential. People have many reasons for communication, for example to express feelings, needs and wants, to give their opinion, to protest/deny, to make choices, to negotiate, plan and influence.

For many service users, becoming involved in how services are delivered is linked to the desire to make things better and bring about change (Beresford & Croft, 1993; Cott, 2004; Neech, Scott, Priest, Bradley, & Tweed, 2018). People who use mental health services are experts by experience. They have an unparalleled perspective on how services are delivered and how they can be changed. This experience is the very basis of involvement. Using this experience can influence the support and services received. For many service users, the starting point for involvement is based on past negative experiences they had without any involvement at all: "*Having gone through the things I've been through in my life, I thought getting involved would help me and other people*" (Beresford, 2013, p.27). Because of this, service users emphasize the importance of seeing outcomes of their involvement: "*Having your views acted on, it's no good having your views heard if they are not acted on*" (Beresford, 2013, p.27).

Service users have also reported valuing the opportunity to come together within their own organizations to share experience and knowledge (Branfield et al., 2006). A group of service users in a study by Neech (2015) described how it was important for them to bear witness to the changes they helped to create. There was a collective desire to bring about change in service user experiences for the better by instilling hope, representing those without a voice and making meaning of their own experiences: "*I'm not just complaining. I want things to change, and I know it won't happen immediately...I'm doing it more for people in the future*" (Neech, 2015, p.68).

On a personal level, service users talk about the psychological, social, occupational and other benefits of coming together in terms of improving quality of life and quality of service provision: "*sometimes you don't know things and involvement helps you*" (Beresford, 2013, p.29). Service users have also described how being involved was inextricably linked to wellness: "*I was looking for something that would build my confidence, which had been severely dented, and self-esteem. And it's certainly done that*" (Neech, 2015, p.67). However, wellness was seen along a continuum, whereby involvement sometimes also had negative effects: "*I have to remember that AFTERWARDS, the next couple of days, I'm gonna need extra sleep...look after myself AFTER that. And I do wonder whether the people that organise it are AWARE that it's not just that DAY I'm giving*" (Neech, 2015, p.68).

Research undertaken by Beresford (2013) with groups of service users whose voices are often harder to access (including people with communication difficulties) highlighted different reasons and benefits of being involved depending on whether participation was with user led groups versus non-user led groups. A greater variety of positive experiences were described by service users who were involved in user led groups. A recurring theme in the research was the importance of service users having the opportunity to come together themselves to bring about positive changes as individuals and for service users more widely. This gives a chance to build greater confidence and skills and to be part of a collective group in which to get involved in other participatory activities – from a position of greater strength.

Communication and *means* to be involved

One of the ways SLTs can support service users to be involved in their own care and contribute to the service in general is through the completion of a Communication Support Plan. Communication Support Plans exist within a number of specialisms in SLT. However, none of these formats fully meet the needs of SLTs working within mental health services, where there is a necessity to work with both the values of speech and language therapy and those of recovery. The format of the Communication Support Plan described below was devised in response to the needs of service users in a mental health service. Table 9.2 shows how the component parts of the Communication Support Plan meet the requirements of service provision for SLTs working in mental health (IASLT, 2015).

The sections focus on the following areas:

1. **What I want**: SLTs work with people to help them explore what has most meaning for them. This forms the basis of all future speech and language therapy work and gives the person the experience of self-determination.

Table 9.2 Linking the speech and language therapy provision and the Communication Support Plan.

Level of speech and language therapy provision	Communication Support Plan Section
Person	What I want How I communicate What I can do differently
Environment	Things I would like others to do differently
Wider community	Things the mental health service and/or society can do to support me

2. **How I communicate**: The work in speech and language therapy sessions often begins with an exploration of the person's experiences in communication situations. This may take the form of self-assessment. Sometimes, but not always, this work will include more formal assessment and diagnosis when the person wants to gain a greater understanding of the basis of their communication experiences.

3. **Things I can do differently**: Focusing on the person's ability to change, and exploring how this change can be maintained, supports an ownership of some of the difficulties in communication situations, and helps shift power and autonomy back to the person.

4. **Things I can ask others to do differently**: It is vital that communication partners also hold responsibility for communication breakdown. This work supports the person to advocate for themselves in asking for support from other individuals and from their service.

5. **Things the mental health service and/or society can do to support me**: During SLT intervention, it often becomes evident that the mental health service itself, and also wider society, can present a barrier to the person's SLCNs being best supported. The process of acknowledging this, of identifying the changes that would be beneficial and of finding a way within the service of having their voice heard, can open new doors.

Communication Support Plan and recovery

The Communication Support Plan aligns with an important conceptual framework for personal recovery in mental health called CHIME (Leamy, Bird, Le Boutillier, Williams, & Slade, 2011). This framework is a form of patient reported outcome measurement and is often used for planning support. In using this framework, the SLT ensures that interventions are founded upon recovery concepts, as described previously. CHIME encompasses all the key concepts which many different recovery approaches touch upon:

- Connectedness
- Hope and optimism
- Identity
- Meaning
- Empowerment

Table 9.3 Links between levels of speech and language therapy support, Communication Support Plan and recovery.

Levels of speech and language therapy input	Communication Support Plan section	Recovery
Person	What I want How I communicate What I can do differently	Meaning Identity Hope
Environment	Things I would like others to do differently	Connectedness
Wider community	Things the mental health service and/or society can do to support me	Empowerment

The resonance between the Communication Support Plan and the key concepts of CHIME is illustrated in Table 9.3.

Communication Support Plan: Example from practice

Eoin was referred to speech and language therapy by his psychiatrist for assessment of communication. He reported a discrepancy between what he wanted to be able to express and what he could actually say, with specific difficulties retaining verbal information. This problem was present since childhood and affected his performance in school. He was assessed for dyslexia as a child, and his parents queried a diagnosis of Autism Spectrum Disorder in adulthood. Of note, he also experienced a brain injury involving loss of consciousness as a child. Eoin lives at home with his parents and is unemployed.

The SLT carried out formal language assessment, but it was difficult to quantify any significant language difficulties. However, in conversation in the clinic

Name	Eoin
Age	43 years
Date of Plan	October 2018
People involved	Eoin, SLT, Eoin's friend Paul

What I want:
I want to learn how to do interviews so that I can get a job.
I want to understand why I struggle with conversations with people. I've lost touch with many of my friends from the past because of this.

How I communicate:
When I get anxious I lose track of conversations.
It feels like the communication part of my brain stops working.
Sometimes I know what I want to say, but when it comes to the moment I say what's convenient rather than what I really mean.
I feel more comfortable when I'm talking with someone I know.
I do better in conversations when I've an idea of the subjects we might be talking about.

Things I can do differently:
I can make sure that I'm on time
I can spend time thinking beforehand about what I want to talk about
When I start to feel anxious or worried, I can take a breath and reconnect with the feeling of my feet on the ground.

Things I can ask others to do differently:
I can ask them to give me time
If someone's explaining a task to me, I'll need them to clearly explain and demonstrate the task and to give me time to practice it.

Things the MH service and/or society can do to support me:
I'd like there to be a form that I could fill in before coming to my appointment with the psychiatrist. That way I could prepare my answers to the questions instead of feeling like I'm put on the spot.

I'd like the world to slow down. Why do we all need to do things so fast?

Figure 9.6 Eoin's Communication Support Plan.

it was clearly evident that Eoin was experiencing difficulties in communicating with others. Informal speech and language therapy assessment over a number of sessions uncovered anxiety as playing a major role in determining the level to which Eoin was able to access his own language abilities in general conversation. The informal assessment process was driven by the structure of the Communication Support Plan, and was therefore focused on him achieving his goals of finding employment and renewing old friendships.

The understanding Eoin gained through this process allowed him to see himself as an able communicator and as someone who needed to find strategies to manage his anxiety. Eoin was able to take part in a speech and language therapy session including his friend Paul, where the Communication Support Plan was the basis to his explanation of his experiences in conversation and which facilitated him asking Paul to give him extra time and pauses when they meet up for a drink.

Eoin is currently re-engaging with acquaintances from his past and is working with Occupational Therapy in finding a road back to employment. He is on the waiting list to attend an anxiety management group.

The Communication Support Plan is an important recovery tool in the following ways:

1. It supports the service user to set goals in therapy.

2. It establishes the basis of speech and language therapy intervention to be a process of co-production.

3. It supports the service user to experience autonomy.

4. It helps the service user to find words to describe the difficulties they experience in communication, thus giving them greater understanding and ownership of their own communication experience.

5. It gives the service user a voice.

6. It provides a tool which the service user can utilize in informing and training others about their communication support needs.

7. It supplies a format by which the SLT and service user can write joint reports on the outcomes of the therapy

8. It supports the service user to experience a greater degree of power and control within a clinical intervention.

9. It focuses on the future which has the potential to instil a sense of hope.

10. It facilitates involvement in mental health services.

Communication and *opportunities* to be involved

Finally, without the *opportunity* within services to participate, the *means* and the *reasons* will not be enough to ensure service users' voices are heard within the mental health services they access.

While service user involvement is a goal for many mental health services, being able to do it effectively has proven challenging, particularly for the groups of service users (e.g., with SLCN) whose voices go unheard. Barriers arise in terms of translating the rhetoric of involvement into a reality in many clinical contexts (Borg, Karlsson, & Sim, 2009). Service users have reported that the opportunities they are offered for involvement in services are often excluding and do not accommodate to access issues well (Beresford, 2013).

Jabeer Butt (cited in Beresford, 2013) examined the characteristics of social care organizations which successfully promote diversity and concluded that: "Diversity means taking account of the complexities of the lives of individuals, of groups of people, and the impact these complexities have on their experience of discrimination and disadvantage" (Beresford, 2013, p.14).

Neech's (2015) study, which explored service user experience of involvement in service delivery found that those who were most articulate and educated were more inclined to be part of activities, emphasizing the need to support service users with SLCNs to avail of opportunities to be involved: "*When people know that you've used services...they either expect NOTHING from you, or when you can string a sentence together, EVERYTHING from you*" (Neech, 2015, p.66).

These barriers (and others described previously) combine to undermine equal opportunities for participation in committee and/or other service structures which exist for decision making and service planning.

Overcoming the barriers: The role of speech and language therapy support

In Beresford's (2013) research, service users emphasized two elements as being essential for inclusive involvement:

1. *Access*: ensuring all service users have pathways into organizations and decision-making forums.

2. *Support*: building skills and confidence, offering practical ways of helping people to work together and build capacity so that service users are getting involved from a position of strength.

SLTs in mental health services can contribute significantly to both of these elements in terms of the creation of opportunities for involvement.

Access

Frequently, the term 'access' is narrowly associated with physical access (e.g., can a wheelchair get into a building). The access needs of service users with SLCN may be invisible to organizations so their voices may be excluded or assumed to be included. Through the development of the Communication Support Plan service users have a better chance of being involved meaningfully. However, the organization also needs to reflect on its own way of working in order to address access issues. Communication access issues can range from the most obvious, for example the lack of accessible signage, to the most fundamental – an organizational culture that treats service users with a lack of respect.

Beresford (2013, p.49) advises that "a helpful rule of thumb (as yet to be disproved) is that everybody can express themselves, get involved in some way and contribute, if their access needs are met. This may be through the use of photographs, facial expression, through making noises, through movement, through new technology".

SLTs working in mental health services play an important role in facilitating access for people with SLCN who want to be involved in their own care as well as involvement in how services are shaped and delivered. SLTs have an understanding and awareness of the impact that communication difficulties can have on people becoming more involved in their own care. The role of the SLT on a mental health team will involve supporting team members to ensure that the supports they are offering are designed to reduce many of the barriers to involvement experienced by people with SLCNs related to mental health difficulties (e.g., ensuring information is given in an accessible format, asking questions which are easily understood by the person, being flexible with timing and length of sessions/meetings).

When considering service user involvement activities, it is important to be clear about the purpose of participation. Various types of involvement can slot into a number of different levels and can be viewed as a pathway to service users developing their own power and responsibility in involvement activities.

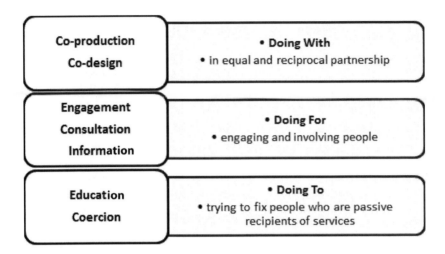

Figure 9.7 The Ladder of Participation (adapted from Arnstein, 1969).

Figure 9.7 shows an adapted form of the Ladder of Participation (Arnstein, 1969). SLTs and other service providers can identify the levels of increasingly meaningful and active involvement, with increasing levels of reflection and dialogue.

Typically, a combination of approaches is likely to be needed and the SLT has a role in facilitating access for people with SLCNs at each level. Table 9.4 gives examples of involvement activities which can be used at each stage of the Ladder of Participation and outlines some examples of where SLTs can have a role in supporting service user opportunities to be involved.

Support

The requirement for support does not come about because service users with SLCNs cannot participate in society, but because their participation is made difficult for them. Beresford (2013) highlights at least five elements to support, which includes communication support:

- Support for personal development to increase people's expectations, confidence and self esteem.
- Support to develop skills needed to participate (e.g., speaking and writing skills for traditional ways that people are involved (see Table 9.5 for an example from practice).

Table 9.4 Involvement activities and the role of the SLT.

Level	Activity focus	Examples	SLT role
Informing	Giving information about the services available for people, their families and communities	Print Website Face-to-face Videos	Providing clear and accessible information
Consulting	Asking for feedback on service users' needs and experiences	Meetings Workshops Focus groups Interviews Surveys Website	Involvement in planning of consultation approaches to ensure inclusive communication standards are met Asking about the impact of SLCN on involvement in individual care and services in general
Engaging	Seeking representative opinions and perspectives on care and services	Membership on committees Links with service user groups	SLT as mentor for people to ensure active participation in service structures (e.g., committees/groups)
Co-desiging	Working together to seek solutions to problems	Advisory and reference groups Parallel structures Co-design of engagement activity	Exploring, in partnership with service users, how to improve supports for people with SLCNs and mental health difficulties
Co-producing	Sharing ideas and perspectives Recognizing strengths and expertise of all involved	Working together as equal partners to improve and deliver health and wellbeing outcomes	SLT and service users with SLCN work together to design and deliver services in equal partnership

- Practical support including accessible and timely information, expenses, payment, childcare

- Support for equal opportunities so that everybody can be included including people with SLCNs.

It is only when these supports are provided that the invitation to be involved can be considered real and genuinely inclusive.

Open Dialogue: An opportunity with service user involvement at its core

No discussion of service user involvement in mental health services can be complete without considering the Open Dialogue approach. This revolutionary service developed in Western Lapland in the 1980s as a response to people presenting with first episode psychosis. Its use has spread to America, England, Ireland, Germany and many other European countries. The approach has achieved dramatic treatment outcomes including avoiding hospitalizations, lowering use of medication, and getting people through crises.

Open Dialogue takes a consistent family and social network approach to mental health care – particularly in crisis situations. All interventions are carried out with the service user's support system present. The aim of Open Dialogue is to develop a dialogical communication between the patient and their support system as a therapeutic intervention (Razzaque & Wood, 2015).

One of the key elements of Open Dialogue is to develop a common verbal language. This can allow the person's experiences to be processed within a supportive presence in a way that all involved with the person can understand, rather than their experience remaining embodied in the person's internal system. The emphasis on developing a common language gives the person, their family, their friends and their mental health team a way of constructing a dialogue which all can participate in. The work is 'done with' rather than 'done to' the person.

Thus, we can see this is a radically different approach, where the person's voice is at the centre of their understanding of their current experiences. As discussed by Borg et al. (2009, p.287) in their discussion of the challenges of encompassing the service user perspective, "When a service user comes in contact with a mental health professional for service, it is through a discourse between the service user and the professional practitioner a determination of mental health problems gets formulated". They also reference Mishler (1984), "...two voices, the service user's voice of everyday life and the professional's voice of medicine, often tend to clash and do not meet to reconcile different perspectives from which two parties see problems."

Table 9.5 Example from Practice of SLT role in supporting service user involvement.

Example from practice

Skills for Change: Speech and Language Therapist as mentor for participation

Given the changing shape of mental health services in Ireland, the need for service user involvement is an increasing requirement.

Resulting from research focused on building capacity for service user and family members' involvement in local mental health services in Dublin (Dermody, 2016), a training and information programme was developed. This programme was designed for service users and family members who wanted to know more about or become directly involved in service planning and evaluation. It included information on:

- Mental health services, structures and roles
- Committee skills
- Leadership and communication skills
- Advocacy
- Using our own story.

In built into the design of the training was the support of a mentor for participants in the training programme. Examples of the role of the mentor were to provide:

- Guidance and support problem solving to develop strategies for personal responsibility, e.g., promoting dialogue with group
- Encourage self-reflection to identify strategies for overcoming barriers to participation
- Sign posting to other services during and after training course that will enhance their skills and strengths to take on the role of effective representative
- Focus on continued or extra learning that will support effective committee membership.

The mentor was required to meet with the person once a week for six weeks during the training programme and once a month for the following four months.

In addition, each participant had completed an individualized learning plan to support them for the duration of the programme.

During the initial meetings with participants, the trainers identified two individuals with speech, language and communication needs. As a result, a SLT who worked within the local adult mental health services was asked to be the mentor for both these people. Neither of these people had been previously known to SLT. The role of SLT as mentor in this context was clearly distinguished from treatment.

The role of SLT as mentor was to:

- Identify and explore speech, language and communication strengths and areas for support
- Discuss barriers and facilitators to participation based on the identified needs above and others which emerged through the mentor-mentee relationship
- Identify strategies to enable participation in specific contexts, e.g., how to take notes at a meeting, how to prepare what to say, how to manage anxiety about speaking in a group, how to make small talk before a meeting begins, how to use your story and experiences to make a contribution

Outcomes:

- Active participation of service users with SLCN in the system
- Identifying and empowering the person to get their communication support needs met in contexts of committees and other relevant groups within services.

When Open Dialogue becomes the approach within a mental health service, the voice of the service user is the key to understanding the issue, and opportunities to explore the person's lived experience is the basis for all interventions. Thus, the person can see themselves as the agent of change in their own life, with the support of their family, their friends and their mental health team.

SLTs can be seen to have a key role in a service where the foundation of treatment is the person's voice. When someone is experiencing barriers to having their voice heard, their whole treatment approach will be affected. But when this approach is fully employed, many of the barriers which can exist in mental health services, such as stigma, effects of medications, loss of esteem, are already removed. The Open Dialogue approach is in itself a tool which reduces communication barriers.

Conclusion

This chapter has outlined how SLTs can support the meaningful involvement of service users through the use of the Means, Reasons and Opportunities Model (Money & Thurman, 2002). As service user involvement in mental health services continues to be emphasized in healthcare policy, there is a need to identify how speech and language therapy, as a profession, can define our role in this domain. It is important that the contribution of speech and language therapy in supporting and developing the capacity for service user involvement is made clear in order to ensure that the seldom-heard voices of people with SLCN and mental health difficulties are heard.

Research is needed which further explores, defines and quantifies the barriers experienced by people with SLCNs and mental health difficulties. This work must be grounded in a clear understanding of the values of co-production. Qualitative research which helps uncover the experiences of service users will add to our understanding of these barriers and how the barriers can begin to be addressed. Research should involve both the mental health service and its service users, and should involve SLTs whose work is underpinned by recovery values.

References

Allott P. & Loganathan, L. (2003). Discovering hope for recovery from a British perspective: A review of a sample of recovery literature, implications for practice and systems change. West Midlands Partnerships for Mental Health, Birmingham www.wmpmh.org.uk

Anthony, W.A. (1993). Recovery from mental illness: The guiding vision of the mental health service system in the 1990s. *Psychosocial Rehabilitation, 16*, 11-23.

Arnstein, S.R. (1969). A ladder of citizen participation. *Journal of the American Planning Association, 35*, 216-224.

Beresford, P. (2013). *Beyond the Usual Suspects: Towards Inclusive User Involvement.* London: Shaping Our Lives.

Beresford, P. & Croft, S. (2016). Citizen Involvement: A Practical Guide for Change. London: Macmillan.

Borg M., Karlsson B., & Kim H.S. (2009). User involvement in community mental health services – principles and practices. *Journal of Psychiatric and Mental Health Nursing, 16*, 285–292.

Branfield, F., Beresford, P., Andrews, E., Chambers, P., Staddon, P., Wise, G., & Williams-Findlay, B. (2006). *Making User Involvement Work: Supporting Service User Networking and Knowledge.* York: Joseph Rowntree Foundation.

Brophy, J. (2009). Working alongside people with schizophrenia: Directions for speech and language therapy practice. Unpublished MSc Thesis. Trinity College Dublin.

Byng, D. & Duchan, J. (2005) Social model philosophies and principles: Their applications to therapies for aphasia. *Aphasiology, 19*(10-11), 906-922.

Charter for Involvement (2015). Let's get involved. National Involvement Network, Scotland: Association for Real Change. Retrieved from https://arcscotland.org.uk/wp-content/uploads/ARC-final-charter-297mmx297mm-12.12.14.pdf

Cott, C. (2004). Client centred rehabilitation: Client perspectives. *Disability and Rehabilitation, 26*(24), 1411-1422.

Dermody, A., Ní Chaoláin, S., & Gardner, C. (2015). Our service, our say: A report on the views of people with self-experience, their supporters, and service providers in the Dublin 10 area, on the inclusion of people with self-experience of mental health difficulties and their supporters on decision making bodies. Dublin: Ballyfermot Partnership.

Duchan, J. & Black, M. (2001). Progressing toward life goals: A person-centred approach to evaluating therapy. *Topics in Language Disorders, 22*, 37-49.

Good Practice Guide (2011). Service user involvement: Making services fit. Turning Point, Scotland. Retrieved on 25th January 2019 from http://www.turningpointscotland.com/wp-content/uploads/2011/08/Service-User-Involvement-Good-Practice-Guide.pdf

Hagiliassis, N., Di Marco, M., Gulbenkoglu, H., Iacono, T., & Watson, J. (2006). *Beyond Speech Alone: Guidelines for Practitioners Providing Counselling Services to Clients with Disabilities and Complex Communication Needs.* Victoria, Australia: Scope.

Health Service Executive (HSE) & National Disability Authority (NDA) (2014). National Guidelines on Accessible Health and Social Care Services, Ireland: National Disability Authority. Retrieved from https://www.hse.ie/eng/services/yourhealthservice/access/natguideaccessibleservices/natguideaccessibleservices.pdf

Irish Association of Speech and Language Therapists (IASLT) (2015). Speech and language therapy in mental health services: A guidance document. Dublin, Ireland: IASLT.

Kagan, A., Simmons-Mackie, N., Rowland, A., Huijbregts, M., Shumway, E., Threat, T., & Sharp, S. (2007). Counting what counts: A framework for capturing real-life outcomes of aphasia intervention. *Aphasiology, 12*, 1-23.

Lawn, S. (2015). Integrating service user participation in mental health care: What will it take? *International Journal of Integrated Care, 14*, 1-5.

Leamy, M., Bird, V.J., Le Boutillier, C., Williams, J., & Slade, M. (2011). A conceptual framework for personal recovery in mental health: Systematic review and narrative synthesis. *British Journal of Psychiatry, 199*, 445-452.

McDaid, S. (2009). An equality of condition framework for user involvement in mental health policy and planning: Evidence from participatory action research. *Disability & Society, 24*, 461–474.

McDaid, S. (2006). Equal and inclusive user involvement in the Mental Health Services in Ireland: Results from participatory action research. Retrieved from https://recoverycontextinventory.com/images/resources/Shari_McDaid_Equal_and_Inclusive_User_Involvement_2006.pdf

Mental Health Commission (2007). Quality Framework Mental Health Services in Ireland, Retrieved from https://www.mhcirl.ie/File/qframemhc.pdf

Mental Health Commission (2012). Guidance Document on Individual Care Planning Mental Health Services. Retrieved from https://www.mhcirl.ie/file/GuidanceOn_ICPMHS.pdf

Miller, S., Chambers, M., & Giles, M. (2015). Service user involvement in mental health care: An evolutionary concept analysis. *Health Expectations, 19*, 209–221.

Mishler, E.G. (1984). *The Discourse of Medicine: Dialectics of Medical Interviews.* New Jersey: Ablex.

Money, D. & Thurman, S. (2002). Inclusive communication – coming soon near you? *Speech and Language Therapy in Practice*, Autumn Edition.

Money D., et al. (2016). Inclusive communication and the role of Speech and Language Therapy. Royal College of Speech and Language Therapists Position Paper. RCSLT: London; www.rcslt.ie

Neech, S. (2015). User involvement in adult mental health settings: User motivations and benefit. Thesis submitted in partial fulfilment of the requirements of Staffordshire and Keele Universities for the jointly awarded degree of Doctorate in Clinical Psychology. From http://eprints.staffs.ac.uk/2248/1/Neech%20Sophie%20DClinPsy%20thesis%20July%202015.pdf

Neech, S., Scott, H., Priest, H., Bradley, E., & Tweed, A. (2018). Experiences of user involvement in mental health settings: User motivations and benefits. *Journal of Psychiatric and Mental Health Nursing, 25*, 327–337.

Razzaque, R. & Wood, L.E. (2015). Open Dialogue and its relevance to the NHS: Opinions of NHS staff and service users. *Community Mental Health, 51*, 931–938.

Roy, A. (2004). *The Ordinary Person's Guide to Empire*. London: Harper Collins.

Simmons-Mackie, N. (2004). Social approaches to aphasia intervention. In R. Chapey (Ed.), *Language Intervention Strategies in Aphasia and Related Neurogenic Communication Disorders*, 4th ed. (pp.246–277). Philadelphia: Williams & Wilkins.

Tait, L. & Lester, H. (2005). Encouraging service user involvement in mental health services. *Advances in Psychiatric Treatment, 11*, 168–175.

Thomas, P. (1997). What can linguistics tell us about thought disorder. In J. France, & N. Muir (Eds), *Communication and the Mentally Ill Patient: Developmental and Linguistic Approaches to Schizophrenia* (pp.30–42). London: Jessica Kingsley.

10 Language and communication needs of young offenders

Karen Bryan and Pamela Snow

Introduction

This chapter outlines the evidence concerning speech, language and communication needs (SLCNs) in youth offenders, and the implications of such difficulties for psychosocial functioning and academic achievement. We also consider the relationship between language development and mental health in childhood and adolescence, as a basis for considering some of the developmental trajectories that lead to a small but highly challenging number of young people becoming engaged with the justice system in the developmental period. The term 'mental health disorders' is used in this chapter to refer to both internalising disorders (e.g., anxiety of various forms and depressed mood) as well as externalising disorders (e.g., conduct and attentional disorders). Whilst these are typically discussed as being separate, in reality they commonly co-occur in vulnerable adolescents (Ryan & Redding, 2004). Many major psychiatric conditions have their onset in adolescence, and involve a complex interplay of genetic factors, perinatal exposure to environmental insults, neurodevelopmental problems and/or early adversity such as maltreatment (e.g., abuse and/or neglect), family lifestyle factors, and individual personality characteristics such as coping styles (Meyer & Feldon, 2010; Sadock & Sadock, 2007). It is against this sometimes extremely complex background that the ongoing development and refinement of language skills needs to continue, across both spoken and written domains.

Adolescence is an important developmental period

Adolescence is associated with key developmental achievements in domains such as cognition, self-actualisation, moral and spiritual development, and sense of self (Arnett, 2014). It is also characterized by increased peer influence and risk-taking behaviour (Barkus & Murray, 2010). During adolescence, a process of 'neuronal pruning' occurs in the cerebral cortex in order to increase the efficiency of neural networks that underpin executive functions, such as attention, concentration, learning, impulse control, self-regulation, perspective taking, abstract thinking and complex reasoning (Best & Miller, 2010). This process of neuronal pruning continues into the early to mid-20s, occurring last in the prefrontal regions (those areas most closely associated with the executive functions listed above). Until this process is complete, the adolescent brain remains vulnerable to poor decision making, particularly when in the presence of similar-age peers (Blakemore, 2008).

Early and problematic exposure to alcohol and other drugs can further compromise cognitive development (e.g., using cannabis may affect verbal memory) (Barkus & Murray, 2010), as well as reducing motivation and capacity for cognitive effort (Lynskey & Hall, 2002), which are critical for academic success. In many developed cultures, alcohol is widely used by adolescents in patterns of consumption that elevate risk of both short- and long-term harm (Toumbourou, Williams, Snow, & White, 2003), and vulnerable young people display earlier initiation into alcohol and other drug use and more chronic and problematic patterns of use (Dube et al., 2003). In their investigation into the language skills of a sample of 50 young male offenders completing community-based orders, however, Snow and Powell (2008) investigated associations with substance abuse and reported higher rates of cannabis use by youths in the *non*-language impaired subgroup. Snow and Powell (2008) speculated that this finding may reflect the fact that substance use in young people is related to social networks, which may be lacking in the lives of young offenders with poor language skills.

Language development in adolescence

During adolescence, young people must continue to develop all aspects of oral expressive and receptive language skills, as these are important underpinnings of both ongoing academic achievement (where spoken and text-based demands increase considerably over time) and social development (Nippold, 2007). Discourse-based developments (e.g., across the conversational, expository, persuasive and narrative genres) are particularly important academically, and place demands on all levels of the language system (in particular vocabulary, syntax, and morphology), as well as requiring ongoing development of pragmatic competence (Law, Rush, Clegg, Peters, & Roulstone, 2015; Paul & Norbury, 2012). Skills in these discourse genres, such as high-level inferencing and perspective-taking, also need to draw down on developments occurring in other domains, most notably in executive functions (Blakemore & Mills, 2014).

Language plays a key role in creating and maintaining adolescent peer groups, and is used to demonstrate status, cohesion, trust, and entitlement to knowledge, within and between members of the peer group (Eckert, 2005). Rejection by family and peer groups is thought to be a significant factor underpinning gang cultures (Patten, 1998). Further, the 50 gang members interviewed in Patten's study were all failing in school. It has also been suggested that in gang cultures, simple language, including nonverbal hand signals, are used to convey difference and to enforce hierarchies (Hasan & Harry, 1998).

Language disorders, psychosocial development, and education

During the school years, loneliness and peer rejection may contribute to adverse mental health outcomes for young people with compromised language skills (Durkin & Conti-Ramsden, 2010; Fujiki, Brinton, Hart, & Fitzgerald, 1999). Evidence also suggests that a contributing factor to poor social relationships for children with language impairment is difficulty recognizing emotion conveyed by others' prosody in narrative (Fujiki, Spackman, Brinton, & Illig, 2008) and also difficulty inferring others' affective states from their facial expressions (Ford & Milosky, 2008). These social cognition difficulties with peer interaction have previously been shown to create vulnerability for association with people already involved in crime (Quinton, Pickles, Maughan, & Rutter, 1993). Further, pragmatic language problems have been described in children with attention deficit hyperactivity disorder (Green, Johnson, & Bretherton, 2014; Martin, 2014), which in itself is over-represented in youth offending populations and is a commonly self-reported diagnosis by young offenders with language difficulties in such samples (Snow & Powell, 2008).

Language-based academic difficulties may, however, be masked in primary and secondary school years by mental health issues such as social anxiety, performance anxiety, depressed mood (Conti-Ramsden, 2008), and disruptive behaviour (Cohen et al.,1998). Some researchers (e.g., Cohen et al., 1998; Snow, 2014; Snow & Powell, 2011a, b) have suggested that primary school-aged children who present with behaviour disturbances should undergo a thorough language assessment in order to determine the contribution of unidentified language difficulties to problematic classroom behaviours, such as poor compliance with instructions and causing disruption to other children. Language assessment should also be considered for adolescents who experience academic and social difficulties, given the role of oral language competence in supporting both the academic and social-emotional developmental domains (Bryan, Garvani, Gregory, & Kilner, 2015; Starling, Munro, Togher, & Arciuli, 2011).

Once children enter secondary school, their communication difficulties are more likely to attract a diagnosis of emotional/behavioural disorder (Cohen, 2001; Vallance, Im, & Cohen, 1999). The tendency towards a psychological diagnosis in adolescence may reflect the young person developing secondary behavioural problems (or dysfunctional coping strategies), or the tendency for the externalising behaviour to be the focus of others' concern. It may also reflect the greater availability of welfare specialists over speech-language specialists in such settings, hence influencing the types of referrals made. Speech, language and communication needs (SLCN) make young people vulnerable in educational settings, both academically and socially (Snow, 2009, 2014; Starling et al., 2011; Whitmire, 2000). Unfortunately, however, when such language difficulties go unrecognized and undiagnosed, conditions favour the development of complex behavioural and emotional disorders in the classroom, suspensions and exclusions, and an overall pattern of academic under-achievement.

Language skills and academic success

It is well established that spoken language abilities are essential for the transition to literacy and the development of written language skills that underpin educational achievement (Dockrell, Lindsay, & Palikara, 2011; Durkin & Conti-Ramsden, 2010; Paul & Norbury, 2012; Snow, 2016; Snowling & Hulme, 2012). Comprehension difficulties in particular make children vulnerable in relation to educational progress (Ford, Farah, Shera, & Hurt, 2007; Hooper, Roberts, Zeisel, & Poe, 2003), and poor oral language skills in the early years have also been linked to later academic difficulties (Bishop & Edmundson, 1987; Conti-Ramsden, Durkin, Simkin, & Knox, 2009; Roth, Speece, & Cooper, 2002; Snow, Sanger, Caire, Eadie, & Dinslage, 2014; Zucker, Cabell, Justice, Pentimonti, & Kaderavek, 2013). However, such difficulties are not always identified and some children with early language difficulties are unrecognized as such in the classroom, being noticed only when they have failed to transition from 'learning to read' to 'reading to learn' by the middle years of primary school (Snow, 2014, p.15). Poor academic achievement is a well-established feature of the developmental histories of young offenders (Foley, 2001; Putnins, 1999), but it is only in recent years that the compromised oral language skills have been considered as a contributory factor in this picture (e.g., Snow & Powell, 2008, 2011a; Snow, Woodward, Mathis, & Powell, 2015). These high rates of psychosocial and economic disadvantage, combined with poor academic achievement and excessive rates of school suspensions and exclusions, have given rise to the term 'school to prison pipeline' in the literature (Christle, Jolivette, & Nelson, 2005).

Low socio-economic status (SES) is independently associated with impoverished language skills (Letts, Edwards, Sinka, Schaefer, & Gibbons, 2013; Locke, Ginsborg, & Peers, 2002; Roy & Chiat, 2014; Spencer, Clegg, & Stackhouse, 2012), risk of offending (Australian Institute of Health and Welfare, 2017; Defoe, Farrington, & Loeber, 2013; Graves, Openshaw, Ascione, & Ericksen, 1996), low academic attainment (Snow, 2016), and contact with child protection services (Drake & Jonson-Reid, 2014), and hence is a confounding variable in the discussion of language competence in vulnerable young people. Some children from low SES families and communities may not experience long-term detrimental effects of their early language disadvantage, perhaps because they receive early speech and language therapy intervention (Dockrell, Stuart, & King, 2006). However, early language and academic disadvantage in children with identified SLCN often persists into later years (Durkin, Simkin, Knoz, & Conti-Ramsden, 2009; Snowling, Adams, Bishop, & Stothard, 2001), and this is more likely to be the case where other adversities exist and access to services is limited. Notably, there is some evidence derived from research which included a low-SES comparison group that SES alone does not account for the language profiles of young people in the youth justice system (Snow & Powell, 2008); however, this relationship requires further investigation. Issues associated with SES and language and communication development are dealt with in detail in Chapter 2 (Clegg, this volume).

Evidence from other adolescent populations also suggests that SLCN may contribute to lack of achievement in education (Clegg, Stackhouse, Finch, Murphy, & Nicholls, 2009; Spencer, Clegg, Stackhouse, & Rush, 2017). These findings echo the earlier reports of Ripley and Yuill (2005) of an over-representation of language impairments in boys excluded from school on behavioural grounds, and Clegg's (2006) finding that over 60% of children facing school exclusion had SLCN. Further, Clegg et al. (2009) showed that over

60% of children facing school exclusion had SLCN. SLCN are also commonly associated with other developmental conditions such as attentional problems, intellectual disability and autism spectrum disorders (Paul & Norbury, 2012), which vary in severity and also persist into adolescence and beyond (O'Brien & Bell, 2004).

SLCN in community samples

Speech and language difficulties are relatively common in the developmental period; approximately 6% of all children in the UK have speech and language difficulties in the absence of other diagnosed developmental problems (Law, Garrett, & Nye, 2010) and some international estimates are even higher. Figures include around 14% of secondary students in Australia (McLeod & McKinnon, 2007), and 7% of preschoolers in the United States (Tomblin et al., 1997) but this figure may rise to 30% (Enderby & Pickstone, 2005) or even 50% (Locke et al., 2002) in areas of lower SES, or when children with other neurodevelopmental disorders are considered.

The UK Bercow report (Bercow, 2008) concerning children and young people (aged 0–19), and a follow-up review report 10 years later (Bercow, 2018), highlighted that many children with SLCN are either not identified or are not identified early enough, and that services to support them are frequently not available. Some vulnerable young people lead highly chaotic lives as a consequence of the psychosocial risks attached to their family and community environments. This dysfunction may contribute to non-identification of SLCN through low access to services, or non-attendance at appointments (and absence of service provider follow-up after such non-attendance). Under-identification of children with language difficulties is a particular problem when these difficulties are comorbid with or create secondary emotional/behaviour problems, which can mask SLCN and tend to take precedence over such needs in educational settings (Cohen, Davine, Horodezky, Lipsett, & Isaacson, 1993; Snow & Powell, 2011b; Stringer & Lozano, 2007).

SLCN in young offenders

Research suggests that at least 60% of young offenders in the UK have SLCN (Bryan, 2004; Bryan, Freer, & Furlong, 2007), though rates reported internationally are not quite as high as this (e.g., a rate of around 50% was reported in Australia by Snow and Powell (2011a)). Estimates vary between jurisdictions as a function of measures used, sample characteristics, and operational definitions of language disorder. Regardless of methodological differences, however, significantly elevated incidence figures have also been reported in young offender populations in the USA (Blanton & Dagenais, 2007; Sanger, Moore-Brown, Magnuson, & Svobada, 2001), and Australia (Snow & Powell, 2005, 2008, 2011a; Snow et al., 2015). All the studies to date have been cross-sectional and focus on slightly different offender populations (reflecting differences in criminal justice policies and practices across different countries) and contexts (community versus custodial contexts).

Standardized assessments such as the *Clinical Evaluation of Language Fundamentals* (Semel & Secord, 2006) have been used across a number of studies, and others (e.g., the *British Picture Vocabulary Scale* (BPVS-II) (Dunn, Whetton, & Burley, 1997) and *Test of Adolescent and Adult Language*, 3rd ed. (TOAL-3) (Hammill, Brown, Larsen, & Wiederholt, 1994)) have been used to measure relevant language constructs. Consistent findings have been reported of depressed language profiles across receptive and expressive domains at semantic and syntactic levels, and compromised skills at a discourse level. With respect to discourse, however, it is noted that the genre most studied in this population has been narrative (e.g., Snow & Powell, 2005), with some recent evidence that expository discourse skills are also compromised (Hopkins, Clegg, & Stackhouse, 2018). Little is known about conversational discourse at this time; however, extrapolation from the above findings would suggest that this genre would be the most compromised, given its real-time information-processing, linguistic, and interpersonal demands.

Young people in the youth justice system should not be assumed to be completely unaware of their communication difficulties (Hopkins, Clegg, & Stackhouse, 2016; Snow & Woodward, 2017) and may experience adverse impacts on their self-esteem as a result. Hopkins et al. (2016) further reported that young offenders with communication difficulties are likely to find themselves in dispute with authority figures and have difficulty verbally resolving such conflicts. This is consistent with evidence that young people who are convicted of particularly violent crimes display poorer language skills than other young offenders (Snow & Powell, 2011a), and raises the possibility that ambiguous social cues are resolved through physical rather than verbal means by the most verbally impoverished young offenders. This has significant implications for the design and delivery of anger management programmes for youth offenders (see further below).

Hughes et al. (2017) showed that co-morbidities with SLCN are common in young offenders, suggesting that detailed neurodevelopmental assessments are needed. Over-represented neurodevelopmental problems include: autism spectrum disorders, attentional problems, substance abuse problems, acquired brain injury, and learning disorders (Chitsabesan & Hughes, 2016; Hughes et al., 2017; Loucks, 2007; Mottram, 2007). Notably, fetal alcohol spectrum disorder (FASD) should also be considered in this population, given the wide-ranging executive function, behavioural, and academic difficulties with which it is associated (Kalberg et al., 2010). In their recent epidemiological study of a sample of young people in custody in Western Australia, Bower et al. (2018) reported that 36% were diagnosed with FASD. Further, Kippen et al. (2018) have identified that of the nearly 50% of a custodial sample of youth offenders in their Western Australian sample who were identified with language disorder, more than half had an associated diagnosis of FASD.

All of these neurobiological co-morbidities can independently compromise language and interpersonal skills; however, support to manage such difficulties in youth justice systems is highly variable (Talbot, 2010). It must be noted, too, that such additional diagnoses do not necessarily *account for* elevated rates of language impairment, and nor does low nonverbal IQ (Snow & Powell, 2011a; Snow et al., 2015). These high-prevalence co-morbidities need to be the subject of ongoing investigation in at-risk populations so that early trajectories and developmental needs can be better understood and responded to.

The types of SLCN that have been identified in the international literature in young people who access youth justice services consistently include expressive and receptive deficits in vocabulary, poor abstract language, poor listening comprehension, reduced narrative language skills, and difficulties using and understanding everyday figurative language (Blanton & Dagenais, 2007; Bryan, 2004; Sanger, Creswell, Dworak, & Schultz, 2000; Sanger, Spilker, Scheffler, Zobell, & Belau, 2008; Snow & Powell, 2004, 2005, 2008, 2011a; Snow et al., 2015). Importantly, very few young people in these studies indicated that they have had a prior diagnosis of a SLCN (Bryan et al., 2007). However, histories of school suspension and expulsion are so common as to be normative, occurring in 87% of a recent sample reported by Snow et al. (2015).

Consistent with the findings reported above, the speech and language therapy services run within two young offender institutions in the UK (Bryan, 2014; Bryan et al., 2007) documented a wide range of referrals, including:

- Language (developmental problems in understanding and using language to communicate)

- Specific developmental syndromes (e.g., ADHD/autism spectrum disorders)

- Communication difficulties associated with mental illness

- Speech disorders (e.g., dyspraxia)

- Hearing impairment

- Dysfluency.

In considering young people in the youth justice system, it is also important to note that a large proportion enter this system via child protection services. *Looked-after children* (a term used in the UK to describe children who are in the care of statutory authorities rather than their families) represent only 1% of the population in England, but make up 33% of boys and 61% of girls in custody in England and Wales (Kennedy, 2013). Involvement with child protection services due to substantiated histories of maltreatment (patterns of abuse and/or neglect of various forms) is also over-represented in Australian data (Stewart, Livingstone, & Dennison, 2008). Maltreatment, in turn, is associated with elevated risk for compromised language skills in childhood (Hagaman, Trout, DeSalvo, Gehringer, & Epstein, 2010; Lum, Powell, Timms, & Snow, 2015). Consistent with this, McCool and Stevens (2011) found that 63% of looked-after children in residential care had a language impairment. In the youth criminal justice service in the UK, 25% of young people were found to have special educational needs, 46% were under-achieving at school and 29% had difficulty with literacy and numeracy (HM Inspectorate of Prisons, 2002). It is therefore important for clinicians to be aware that young people presenting within youth justice services may have a complex developmental history, characterized by high rates of trauma-exposure and/or deprivation, resulting in a depressed and uneven profile of language skills. In countries such as Australia, children from Aboriginal and Torres Strait islander backgrounds are greatly over-represented in child-protection statistics (Australian Institute of Health and Welfare, 2017), which poses particular challenges to services with respect to the provision of care and support which is culturally and linguistically appropriate.

The fact that young people from indigenous backgrounds and other ethnic minorities are strongly over-represented in youth justice statistics (Kippin et al., 2018; Snow, 2019) has significant implications for assessment of their communication strengths and difficulties, and the design and delivery of intervention programmes. Few standardized measures have normative data on the language groups which are strongly represented in this population (which, in turn, vary in different jurisdictions) and this is an area of pressing need with respect to the provision of evidence-informed services.

Language skills and mental health in young offenders

Whilst there may be an interaction between mental health difficulties and SLCN, the link is not inevitable and the interaction may be bi-directional (Beitchman & Brownlie, 2014; Miller et al., 2008; Snow et al., 2015). For example, in their study of 100 young offenders completing custodial sentences, Snow and Powell (2011a) found that mental health problems (notably depression and anxiety) were not strongly represented, a finding which may reflect self-selection bias with respect to which young offenders are more likely to agree to take part in such studies. In a subsequent investigation, however, Snow et al. (2015) found that although mental health problems *were* prevalent in a sample of custodial young offenders, they were not significantly associated with scores on oral language measures. These researchers also found that alexithymia (difficulty finding words to describe one's own affective state) was strongly represented and was significantly correlated with the presence of mental health problems but not with language disorder. These findings suggest, therefore, that language difficulties and mental health problems in young offenders are important *co-morbidities*, without necessarily being *correlates*. Further research is needed to understand the nature of this complex interaction between language difficulties and mental health problems in this population.

There is no evidence that early language difficulties 'cause' young people to come into contact with the justice system. However, recent evidence reported by Winstanley, Webb and Conti-Ramsden (2018) suggests that early service provision for children identified with developmental language disorders may avert their risk of contact with the youth justice system. This is an important finding that lends support to the value of investing in early intervention services, particularly where multiple risk factors are present.

As Bond, Toumbourou, Thomas, Catalano and Patton (2005) remind us, risk and protective factors exist in a young person's life across four key levels: the individual, the family, the school, and the wider community. Such factors are often cumulative, so we need to consider the extent to which an overall developmental profile contributes to, or protects against, antisocial behaviour, educational disengagement/under-achievement, and contact with the youth justice system. It is likely that a bi-directional relationship exists between low educational attainment and poor oral language skills in vulnerable populations such as youth offenders, and longitudinal research is needed to disambiguate such relationships in terms of causal pathways.

The high incidence of suspensions and exclusions (i.e., 87% in a recent study by Snow et al., 2015) suggests that exposure to academic language via classroom experiences is reduced in many young offenders. Suspensions and exclusions are also associated with frequent changes of school, which disrupts curriculum mastery and continuity. There is a strong nexus between language difficulties and externalizing behaviour problems in early childhood (Brownlie et al., 2004; St Clair, Pickles, Durkin, & Conti-Ramsden, 2011), and it is clear that for a significant proportion of young people, such problems persist into adolescence, and may interfere with the ability to learn and adopt prosocial skills. It is not always clear, however, whether language problems precede behavioural difficulties, whether the reverse is true, or whether they have a common cause. It is likely that there are different subgroups for which different trajectories are more dominant. Complex outcomes have complex inputs, and this is nowhere more evident than in the case of young offenders' language profiles. Examination of the small number of international longitudinal studies available helps to shed light on the nature of the links between language and behaviour.

Evidence from the Ottawa Language Study (Beitchman et al., 2001; Brownlie et al., 2004; Johnson, Beitchman, & Brownlie, 2010), which has tracked a cohort of language-impaired 5-year-olds into adulthood, shows significantly elevated rates of anxiety, parent-reported delinquency, and educational/ vocational under-achievement in early adulthood relative to peers. Smart et al.'s (2003) longitudinal study showed that language-impaired boys were more likely than non-language-impaired peers to go on to offend in adolescence, and Clegg, Hollis, Mawhood and Rutter (2005) showed that one-third of children with SLCN developed mental health problems if untreated, with criminal involvement occurring in over half of cases. Evidence from a long-term Danish study (Mouridsen & Hauschild, 2009) suggested an association between language impairment and sexual offending, although the influence of intellectual disability in this particular study may have partially accounted for these findings. Nevertheless, clinicians providing specialist services to young sex offenders should consider the possibility of reduced language processing and production skills in the design and delivery of intervention programmes.

Assessment and intervention for SLCN in youth justice populations

Although the relationship between mental health difficulties and language difficulties is not well understood, current evidence indicates that clinicians should carefully assemble and review history and diagnostic information when a young person presents with mental health problems and/or communication difficulties, to identify possible co-morbidities. In settings such as young offender institutions, information on developmental history may not be easily accessible and clinicians need to be alert to the presence of difficulties that are not documented (Bryan et al., 2015).

There is currently only a modest evidence base for adolescent language interventions in general, and even less for youth offender language interventions in particular (Snow et al., 2014), although recent reports from the UK (Gregory & Bryan, 2011) and Australia (Snow & Woodward, 2017) indicate that youth offenders can successfully engage with speech-language services while in custody and can make meaningful and measurable gains. It is also possible to derive therapeutic principles from related research fields, such as child language interventions, that could be applied to adolescent offenders with impaired language skills. When working with adolescents presenting to speech and language therapy or psychology services, it is important to ascertain whether they experienced early language difficulties, whether they struggled with communication in school, at home, with authority figures or with peers, and whether they experienced academic difficulties (often a surrogate marker for unidentified expressive and/or receptive language problems). Ascertaining whether formal developmental assessments have taken place and accessing reports on these assessments is important. Engagement with the young person and encouraging discussion about *how* they interact with other people will often be informative. Use of self-report instruments with young people may be challenging given that they can be reluctant to admit to difficulties or weakness (Bryan et al., 2015). That said, self-report tools which are used in the context of a trusting therapeutic relationship can be beneficial in identifying intervention goals that have functional relevance to the young person, for example being able to resolve everyday misunderstandings (Snow & Woodward, 2017). It is also important to explore the presence of other developmental disorders such as autism spectrum disorder, ADHD, FASD, and/or learning difficulty. Such disorders may not have been formally diagnosed or may not be adequately documented in a young person's record (Hughes et al. 2017; Kippin et al., 2018; Talbot, 2010).

It is debatable as to whether all young people entering youth justice custodial settings should undergo a speech and language screening assessment, given the high prevalence rates of SLCN identified in this population. It may be more efficient to apply a universal assumption of compromised communication abilities, and design services accordingly. However, it is recognized that some young people will have especially complex needs and they need to be identified through a data triangulation process on entry to the system, with referral to formal assessment to identify their profile of communication strengths and difficulties. In 2015, Snow et al. (2015) published a modified Response to Intervention (RTI) framework that could be used to support the communication assessment and intervention planning for young people in youth justice settings (see Figure 10.1). This framework builds on the increasingly well-known RTI framework for use in mainstream educational settings, and proposes universal, small group and individual levels of intervention to strengthen oral language skills and promote academic engagement and attainment. This modified RTI framework offers a basis on which to target and prioritize services, as well as using ongoing assessment data to monitor progress and response to the services provided. This ongoing assessment data is critical if an evidence base is to be established to support the use of SLT services in such settings.

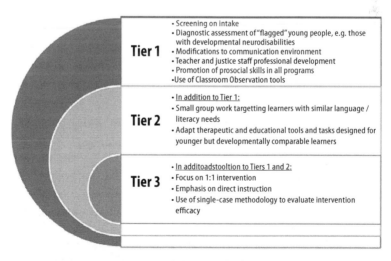

Figure 10.1 A modified Response to Intervention Framework for identifying and responding to SLCN in youth offenders (Snow et al., 2015). Reproduced with permission.

Because SLCN are so common, but are frequently not identified, information about expressive and receptive language difficulties should be provided by clinicians such as Speech and Language Therapists (SLTs) to members of the multidisciplinary team to aid their understanding of the young person's communication difficulties, and to highlight behavioural manifestations such as frustration, distractibility, and apparent rudeness or disinterest that these may cause (Gregory & Bryan, 2011). This information could also enable the young person's care plan to be adapted to ensure that other interventions utilise appropriate types and levels of language. Equally, it is vital to clarify areas of linguistic and communication strengths.

Language demands of youth justice interventions

Many interventions aimed at addressing young people's difficulties and reducing the risk of reoffending place a high demand on language skills. Verbally-mediated interventions such as psychotherapy, anger management programmes or any individual or group-based 'talk therapy' might need to be adjusted to require a lower level of language and reduced metacognitive demands. Cognitive Behaviour Therapy (CBT), for example, requires the young person to talk about their reflections on their thinking processes (Beck, 1995). Such intervention approaches may even be contra-indicated if the young person does not currently have sufficient expressive and receptive language skills, and it may be that intervention needs to be adapted, or alternative forms of expression, such as art and drama, could be employed (Bryan, 2014) (see also Brophy, Chapter 12, this volume). In forensic settings, however, failure to engage in a psychological intervention may reflect negatively on the young person and in some circumstances will delay their discharge. It is therefore vital that young people with SLCN are supported to strengthen their language skills in order to manage group and individual work, and that services are adapted to their particular needs. The input of an SLT may facilitate modification of language levels, may support staff to deliver interventions and, where necessary, may provide group or individualized therapy tailored to individual communication profiles (Gregory & Bryan, 2011).

Young people may have some awareness of their SLCN (Hopkins et al., 2016; Snow, Sanger, & Bryan, 2011; Snow & Woodward, 2017) and should be consulted about their aspirations regarding communication competence. Consultation is likely to increase the face validity of speech and language therapy and to foster therapeutic engagement (Snow & Woodward, 2017).

Although many custodial youth justice facilities offer literacy interventions, there are few international examples of settings that provide dedicated speech language therapy services. This is critical because of the fundamental nexus between oral language skills and the transition to literacy, and the need to address weak language skills in many struggling readers (Snow, 2016). As Snow and Powell (2011a, p.486) have observed, however, "Literacy programs do not resolve oral language deficits". There is a need, therefore, for the development and trialling of literacy interventions for young offenders that specifically address the known linguistic prerequisites for successful reading, notably vocabulary, phonemic awareness, decoding skills, comprehension, and fluency (Snow, 2016).

The ability of young people in contact with youth justice services to access education, and to benefit from interventions such as those provided by child and adolescent mental health services (CAMHS), may be significantly constrained by low language skills. In line with the modified RTI model described earlier, specialized speech and language therapy services should therefore be offered in order to provide detailed individual assessments of communication strengths and difficulties, as well as offering targeted 1:1 and/or group interventions, and secondary consultation to other mental health practitioners who work with young offenders.

Although the SLCN of young offenders have been well described in the literature, such issues are not yet a systematic focus of early identification processes via other channels, such as parenting provision, school referral units, and other services for young people who are excluded from school (e.g., child and adolescent mental health services, substance abuse services, and youth offending services in the community (Bryan et al., 2015)). These service gaps all contribute to, and perpetuate, the school-to-prison pipeline.

Non-specialist staff need training in relation to SLCN in young people who access youth justice and/or mental health services, and also need to note that, in many cases, such difficulties are masked by a range of maladaptive behavioural strategies such as avoidance and minimisation of social interaction. Behaviour should be considered by teachers and clinicians as a form of communication (Snow, 2014), with possible 'messages' underlying disordered conduct, including the fact that the young person does not understand the task demands of a particular situation or is not able to adequately regulate their affective state. Services for young people, such as CAMHS, should routinely screen young people with behaviour problems, poor clinical engagement and/ or compromised academic progress for unidentified SLCN.

Conclusion

Adolescence is a time of considerable development in terms of language, cognition, educational attainment, and social functioning. Children who enter adolescence with language difficulties are disadvantaged in terms of social and educational development, particularly if such difficulties have not been formally identified. Language difficulties, impaired social interaction skills, and lack of educational achievement are all factors associated with vulnerability for mental health problems and/or offending behaviour, particularly in the context of social disadvantage. Language difficulty may be a risk factor for offending in some already highly vulnerable young people, but this has not been established as a causal relationship, and there are complex interplays between both risk factors for offending and protective factors. Young people presenting to health and welfare services or to youth justice services may have complex developmental histories which clinicians need to understand and document. Many adolescents with SLCN do not have their difficulties recognized, assessed or formally diagnosed, and there is a need for more widespread access to speech and language therapy services for these adolescents. There is also a pressing need for research to identify optimal models for speech and language intervention with young people with SLCN in the youth justice system, so that their contact with such agencies can be therapeutic and result in improved life trajectories.

References

Arnett, J.J. (2014). *Adolescence and Emerging Adulthood*. New Jersey: Pearson Education.

Australian Institute of Health and Welfare. (2017*). Youth Justice in Australia 2015–16*. Retrieved from https://www.aihw.gov.au/reports/youth-justice/youth-justice-in-australia-2015-16/contents/table-of-contents

Barkus, E. & Murray, R.M. (2010). Substance use in adolescence and psychosis: Clarifying the relationship. *Annual Review of Clinical Psychology, 6*, 365–389.

Beck, J. (1995). *Cognitive Therapy: Basics and Beyond*. New York, NY: Guilford Press.

Beitchman, J. & Brownlie, E.B. (2014). *Language Disorders in Children and Adolescents*. Boston: Hogrefe.

Beitchman, J.H., Wilson, B., Johnson, C., Atkinson, L., Young, A., Adlaf, E., Escobar, M., & Douglas, L. (2001). Fourteen-year follow-up of speech language impaired and control children: Psychiatric outcome. *Journal of the American Academy of Child and Adolescent Psychiatry, 40*(1), 75–82.

Bercow, J. (2008). The Bercow Report: A review of services for children and young people (0-19) with speech, language and communication needs. London: Department for Children, Schools and Families.

Bercow, J. (2018). Ten years on: An independent review of provision for children and young people with speech, language and communication needs in England. London: ICAN and RCSLT.

Best, J.R. & Miller, P.H. (2010). A developmental perspective on executive function. *Child Development, 81*(6), 1641-1660.

Bishop, D.V.M. & Edmundson, A. (1987) Language-impaired 4-year-olds: Distinguishing transient from persistent impairment. *Journal of Speech and Hearing Disorders, 52*(2),156–173.

Blakemore, S. (2008). The social brain in adolescence. *Nature Reviews. Neuroscience, 9*(4), 267-277.

Blakemore, S. & Mills, K.L. (2014). Is adolescence a sensitive period for sociocultural processing? *Annual Review of Psychology, 65,* 187-207.

Blanton, D.J. & Dagenais, P.. (2007). Comparison of language skills of adjudicated and non-adjudicated adolescent males and females. *Language, Speech, and Hearing Services in Schools, 38*(4), 309-314.

Bond, L., Toumbourou, J.W., Thomas, L., Catalano, R.F., & Patton, G. (2005). Individual, family, school, and community risk and protective factors for depressive symptoms in adolescents: A comparison of risk profiles for substance use and depressive symptoms. *Prevention Science, 6*(2), 73–88.

Bower C., Watkins R.E., Mutch R.C., et al. (2018). Fetal alcohol spectrum disorder and youth justice: A prevalence study among young people sentenced to detention in Western Australia. *British Medical Journal, Open,* 8: e019605

Brownlie, E.B., Beitchman, J.H., Escobar, M., Young, A., Atkinson, L., Johnson, C., Wilson, B., & Douglas, L. (2004). Early language impairment and young adult delinquent and aggressive behaviour. *Journal of Abnormal Child Psychology, 32*(4), 453-467.

Bryan, K. (2004). Prevalence of speech and language difficulties in young offenders. *International Journal of Language and Communication Disorders, 39*(3), 391-400.

Bryan, K. (2014). Psychiatric disorders and communication. In L. Cummings (Ed.), *Handbook of Communication Disorders* (pp.300-318). Cambridge: Cambridge University Press.

Bryan, K., Freer, J., & Furlong, C. (2007). Language and communication difficulties in juvenile offenders. *International Journal of Language and Communication Disorders, 42*(5), 505-520.

Bryan, K., Garvani, G., Gregory, J., & Kilner, K. (2015). Language difficulties and criminal justice: The need for earlier identification. *International Journal of Language and Communication Disorders, 50*(6), 763-775.

Chitsabesan, P. & Hughes, N. (2016). Mental health needs and neurodevelopmental disorders amongst young offenders: Implications for policy and practice. In J. Winstone (Ed.), *Mental Health, Crime and Criminal Justice* (pp.109-130). London: Palgrave Macmillan.

Christle, C.A., Jolivette, K., & Nelson, C.M. (2005). Breaking the school to prison pipeline: Identifying school risk and protective factors for youth delinquency. *Exceptionality*, 13(2), 69-88.

Clegg, J. (2006). Childhood speech and language difficulties and later life chances. In J. Clegg & J. Ginsborg (Eds), *Language and Social Disadvantage: Theory into Practice* (pp.59-73). Chichester: John Wiley.

Clegg, J., Hollis, C., Mawhood, L., & Rutter, M. (2005). Developmental language disorders – a follow-up in later adult life: Cognitive, language and psychosocial outcomes. *Journal of Child Psychology and Psychiatry*, 46(2), 128-149.

Clegg, J., Stackhouse, J., Finch, K., Murphy, C., & Nicholls, S. (2009). Language abilities of secondary age pupils at risk of school exclusion: A preliminary report. *Child Language Teaching and Therapy*, 25, 123-139.

Cohen, N. (2001). *Language Impairments and Psychopathology in Infants, Children and Adolescents*. Thousand Oaks, CA: Sage.

Cohen, N.J., Davine, M., Horodezky, N., Lipsett, L., & Isaacson, L. (1993). Unsuspected language impairment in psychiatrically disturbed children: Prevalence and language and behavioral characteristics. *Journal of the American Academy of Adolescent Psychiatry*, 32(3), 595-603.

Cohen, N.J., Menna, R., Vallance, D.D., Barwick, M.A., Im, N., & Horodezky, N. (1998). Language, social cognitive processing, and behavioral characteristics of psychiatrically disturbed children with previously identified and unsuspected language impairments. *Journal of Child Psychology and Psychiatry*, 39(6), 853–864.

Conti-Ramsden, G. (2008). Heterogeneity of specific language impairment in adolescent outcomes. In C.F. Norbury, J.B. Tomblin, & D.V.M. Bishop (Eds), *Understanding Developmental Language Disorders. From Theory to Practice* (pp.115-129). Hove, UK: Psychology Press.

Conti-Ramsden, G.M., Durkin, K., Simkin, Z., & Knox, E. (2009). Specific language impairment and school outcomes. I: Identifying and explaining variability at the end of compulsory education. *International Journal of Language and Communication Disorders*, 44(1), 15-35.

Defoe, I.N., Farrington, D.P., & Loeber, R. (2013). Disentangling the relationship between delinquency and hyperactivity, low achievement, depression and low socioeconomic status: Analysis of repeated longitudinal data. *Journal of Criminal Justice*, 41(2), 100-107.

Dockrell, J.E., Lindsay, G., & Palikara, O. (2011). Explaining the academic achievement at school leaving for pupils with a history of language impairment: Previous academic achievement and literacy skills. *Child Language Teaching and Therapy*, 27(2), 223-237.

Dockrell, J., Stuart, M., & King, D. (2006). Implementing effective oral language interventions in preschool settings. In J. Clegg & J. Ginsborg (Eds), *Language and Social Disadvantage: Theory into Practice* (pp.177-187). Chichester: John Wiley & Sons.

Drake, B. & Jonson-Reid, M. (2014). Poverty and child maltreatment. In J.E. Korbin & R.D.Krugman (Eds), *Handbook of Child Maltreatment* (pp.131-148). Netherlands: Springer.

Dube, S.R., Felitti, V.J., Dong, M., Chapman, D.P., Giles, W.H., & Anda, R.F. (2003). Childhood abuse, neglect, and household dysfunction and the risk of illicit drug use: The adverse childhood experiences study. *Pediatrics, 111*(3), 564-572.

Dunn, L.M., Whetton, C., & Burley, J. (1997). *The British Picture Vocabulary Scale,* 2nd ed. National Foundation for Educational Research. Windsor: NFER-Nelson.

Durkin, K. & Conti-Ramsden, G. (2010). Young people with specific language impairment: A review of social and emotional functioning in adolescence. *Child Language Teaching and Therapy, 26*(2), 105-121.

Durkin, K., Simkin, Z., Knoz, E., & Conti-Ramsden, G. (2009). Specific language impairment and school outcomes, II: Educational context, student satisfaction, and post-compulsory progress. *International Journal of Language and Communication Disorders, 44*(1), 36-55.

Eckert, P. (2005). Stylistic practice and the adolescent social order. In A. Williams & C. Thurlow (Eds), *Talking Adolescence: Perspectives on Communication in the Teenage Years* (pp.93-110). New York: Peter Lang Publishing.

Enderby, P. & Pickstone, C. (2005). How many people have communication disorders and why does it matter? *Advances in Speech-Language Pathology, 7*(1), 8-13.

Foley, R.M. (2001). Academic characteristics of incarcerated youth and correctional educational programs. A literature review. *Journal of Emotional and Behavioural Disorders, 9*(4), 248-259.

Ford, J.A. & Milosky, L.M. (2008). Inferring emotional reactions in social situations. Differences in children with language impairment. *Journal of Speech, Language, and Hearing Research, 46*(1), 21-30.

Ford, S., Farah, M., Shera, D., & Hurt, H. (2007) Neurocognitive correlates of problem behaviour in environmentally at-risk adolescents. *Journal of Developmental Behavior Pediatrics, 28,* 376-385.

Fujiki, M., Brinton, B., Hart, C.H., & Fitzgerald, A.H. (1999). Peer acceptance and friendship in children with specific language impairment. *Topics in Language Disorders, 19*(2), 34-48.

Fujiki, M., Spackman, M.P., Brinton, B., & Illig, T. (2008). Ability of children with language impairment to understand emotion conveyed by prosody in a narrative passage. *International Journal of Language and Communication Disorders, 43*(3), 330-345.

Graves, R.B., Openshaw, D.K., Ascione, F.R., & Ericksen, S.L. (1996). Demographic and parental characteristics of youthful sexual offenders. *International Journal of Offender Therapy and Comparative Criminology, 40*(4), 300-317.

Green, B.C., Johnson, K.A., & Bretherton, L. (2014). Pragmatic language difficulties in children with hyperactivity and attention problems: An integrated review. *International Journal of Language and Communication Disorders, 49*(1), 15-29.

Gregory, J. & Bryan, K. (2011). Speech and language therapy intervention with a group of persistent and prolific young offenders in a non-custodial setting with previously undiagnosed speech, language and communication difficulties. *International Journal of Language and Communication Disorders, 46*(2), 202-215.

Hagaman, J.L., Trout, A.L., DeSalvo, C., Gehringer, R., & Epstein, M.H. (2010). The academic and functional academic skills of youth who are at risk for language impairment in residential care. *Language, Speech, and Hearing Services in Schools, 41*(1), 14-22.

Hammill, D.R., Brown, V.L., Larsen, S.C., & Wiederholt, J.L. (1994). *Test of Adolescent and Adult Language*, 3rd ed. Austin, TX: Pro-Ed.

Hasan, H.A. & Harry, B. (1998). Understanding the gang culture and how it relates to society and school. In L.H. Meyer, H.S. Park, M. Grenot-Scheyer, & I.S. Schwartz (Eds), *Making Friends: The Influences of Culture and Development* (pp.263-293). Baltimore: Paul H Brookes.

HM Inspectorate of Prisons. (2002). A second chance. A review of education and supporting arrangements within units for juveniles managed by HM Prison Service: A thematic review carried out jointly with the Office for Standards in Education. London: HM Inspectorate of Prisons.

Hooper, S.J., Roberts, J.E., Zeisel, S.A., & Poe, M. (2003). Core language predictors of behavioural functioning in early elementary school children: Concurrent and longitudinal findings. *Behavioural Disorders, 29*(1), 10-21.

Hopkins, T., Clegg, J., & Stackhouse. J. (2016). Young offenders' perspectives on their literacy and communication. *International Journal of Language and Communication Disorders, 51*(1), 95-109.

Hopkins, T., Clegg, J., & Stackhouse, J. (2018). Examining the association between language, expository discourse and offending behaviour: An investigation of direction, strength and independence. *International Journal of Language & Communication Disorders, 53*(1), 113-129.

Hughes, H., Chitabesan, P., Bryan, K., Borschmann, R., Swain, N., Lennox, C., & Shaw, J. (2017). Language impairment and comorbid vulnerabilities among young people in custody. *The Journal of Child Psychology and Psychiatry, 58*, 1106-1113.

Johnson, C.J., Beitchman, J.H., & Brownlie, E.B. (2010). Twenty-year follow-up of children with and without speech-language impairments: Family, educational, occupational, and quality of life outcomes. *American Journal of Speech-Language Pathology, 19*(1), 51-65.

Kalberg, W.O., May, P.A., Blankenship, J., Buckley, D., Gossage, J.P., & Adnams, C.M. (2013). A practical testing battery to measure neurobehavioral ability among children with FASD. *The International Journal of Alcohol and Drug Research, 2*(3), 51-60.

Kennedy, E. (2013). Children and young people in custody 2012-13. London: HM Inspectorate of Prisons and Youth Justice Board.

Kippin, N.R., Leitão, S., Watkins, R., Finlay-Jones, A., Condon, C., Marriott, R., Mutch, R.C., & Bower, C. (2018). Language diversity, language disorder, and fetal alcohol spectrum disorder among youth sentenced to detention in Western Australia. *International Journal of Law and Psychiatry, 61*, 40-49.

Law, J., Garrett, Z., & Nye, C. (2010). Speech and language therapy interventions for children with primary speech and language delay or disorder. *Cochrane Database of Systematic Reviews 2003, 3.* Art. No: CD004110.

Law, J., Rush, R., Clegg, J., Peters, T., & Roulstone, S. (2015). The role of pragmatics in mediating the relationship between social disadvantage and adolescent behaviour. *Journal of Developmental and Behavioural Paediatrics, 36*(5), 389-398.

Letts, C., Edwards, S., Sinka, I., Schaefer, B., & Gibbons, W. (2013). Socio-economic status and language acquisition: Children's performance on the New Reynell Developmental Language Scales. *International Journal of Language & Communication Disorders, 48*(2), 121–143.

Locke, A., Ginsborg, J., & Peers, I. (2002). Development and disadvantage: Implications for the early years and beyond. *International Journal of Language and Communication Disorders, 37*(1), 3-15.

Loucks, N. (2007). No one knows: Offenders with learning difficulties and learning disabilities. Review of prevalence and associated needs. London: Prison Reform Trust.

Lum, J., Powell, M., Timms, L., & Snow, P. (2015). A meta-analysis of case-control studies investigating language in maltreated children. *Journal of Speech, Language and Hearing Research, 58*, 961-976.

Lynskey, M. & Hall, W., (2002). The effects of adolescent cannabis use on educational attainment: A review. *Addiction, 95*(11), 1621-1630.

Martin, A.J. (2014). The role of ADHD in academic adversity: Disentangling ADHD effects from other personal and contextual factors. *School Psychology Quarterly, 29*(4), 395-408.

McCool, S. & Stevens, I.C. (2011). Identifying speech, language and communication needs among children and young people in residential care. *International Journal of Language and Communication Disorders, 46*(6), 665-674.

McLeod, S. & McKinnon, D.H. (2007). Prevalence of communication disorders compared with other learning needs in 14,500 primary and secondary school students. *International Journal of Language and Communication Disorders, 42*(Suppl 1), 37-59.

Meyer, U. & Feldon, J. (2010). Epidemiology-driven neurodevelopmental animal models of schizophrenia. *Progress in Neurobiology, 90*(3), 285-326.

Miller, N., Noble, E., Jones, D., Allcock, L., & Burn, D.J. (2008). How do I sound to me? Perceived changes in communication in Parkinson's disease. *Clinical Rehabilitation, 22*(1), 14-22.

Mottram, P.G. (2007). HMP Liverpool, Styal and Hindley Study Report. Liverpool: University of Liverpool.

Mouridsen, S.E. & Hauschild, K-M. (2009). A long-term study of offending in individuals diagnosed with a developmental language disorder as children. *International Journal of Speech and Language Pathology, 11*(3), 171-179.

Nippold, M. (2007). *Later Language Development: School-age Children, Adolescents and Young Adults*, 3rd ed. Austin, TX: Pro-Ed.

O'Brien, G. & Bell, G. (2004). Learning disability, autism and offending behaviour. In S. Bailey & M. Dolan (Eds), *Adolescent Forensic Psychiatry* (pp.144-152). London: Oxford University Press.

Patten, P.L. (1998). The gangstas in our midst. *The Urban Review, 30*(1), 49-76.

Paul, R. & Norbury, C.F. (2012). *Language Disorders from Infancy through Adolescence*, 4th ed. St Louis, MS: Elsevier.

Putnins A.L. (1999). Literacy, numeracy and non-verbal reasoning skills of south Australian young offenders. *Australian Journal of Education*, 43(2), 157–171.

Quinton, D., Pickles, A., Maughan, S., & Rutter, M. (1993). Partners, peers and pathways: Assortative pairing and continuities in conduct disorder. *Development and Psychopathology*, 5(4), 763–783.

Ripley, K. & Yuill, N. (2005). Patterns of language impairment and behaviour in boys excluded from school. *British Journal of Educational Psychology*, 75, 37–50.

Roth, F.P., Speece, D.L., & Cooper, D.H. (2002). A longitudinal analysis of the connection between oral language and early reading. *The Journal of Educational Research*, 95(5), 259–272.

Roy, P. & Chiat, S. (2014). Developmental pathways of language and social communication problems in 9–11-year-olds: Unpicking the heterogeneity. *Research in Developmental Disabilities*, 35(10), 2534–2546.

Ryan, E.P. & Redding, R.E. (2004). A review of mood disorders among juvenile offenders. *Psychiatric Services*, 55(12), 1397–1407.

Sadock, B.J. & Sadock, V.A. (2007). *Kaplan and Sadock's Synopsis of Psychiatry*, 10th ed. Philadelphia: Wolters Kluwer.

Sanger, D., Creswell, J.W., Dworak, J., & Schultz, L. (2000). Cultural analysis of communication behaviors among juveniles in a correctional facility. *Journal of Communication Disorders*, 33(1), 31–57.

Sanger, D., Moore-Brown, B., Magnuson, G., & Svoboda, N. (2001). Prevalence of language problems among adolescent delinquents: A closer look. *Communication Disorders Quarterly*, 23(1), 17–26.

Sanger, D.D., Spilker, A., Scheffler, M., Zobell, A., & Belau, D. (2008). A comparison between juvenile delinquents' and teachers' opinions on metalinguistic and metacognitive skills. *Journal of Correctional Education*, 59(2), 145–171.

Semel, E., Wiig, E.H., & Secord, W.A. (2006). *Clinical Evaluation of Language Fundamentals* (CELF-4), 4th ed. London, UK: Harcourt Assessment.

Smart, D., Vassallo, S., Sanson, A., Richardson, N., Dussuyer, I., McKendry, W., Dussuyer, I., Marshall, B., Toumbourou, J., Prior, M., & Oberklaid, F. (2003). *Patterns and Precursors of Adolescent Antisocial Behaviour. Types, Resiliency and Environmental Influences.* Melbourne: Australian Institute of Family Studies.

Snow, P.C. (2009). Oral language competence in childhood and access to equity in education and health across the life span. In K. Bryan (Ed.), *Communication in Healthcare* (pp.101-134). Oxford: Peter Lang Publishers.

Snow, P. (2014). Oral language competence and the transition to school: Socio-economic and behavioural factors that influence academic and social success. *International Journal on School Disaffection*, 11(1), 3-24.

Snow, P. (2019). Speech-language pathology and the youth offender: Epidemiological overview and roadmap for future speech-language pathology research and scope of practice. *Language, Speech and Hearing Services in Schools, 50*, 324–339.

Snow, P.C. (2016). Elizabeth Usher Memorial Lecture: Language is literacy is language. Positioning Speech Language Pathology in education policy, practice, paradigms, and polemics. *International Journal of Speech Language Pathology, 18*(3), 216-228.

Snow, P.C. & Powell, M.B. (2004). Developmental language disorders and adolescent risk: A public-health advocacy role for speech pathologists? *International Journal of Speech Language Pathology, 6*(4), 221-229.

Snow, P.C. & Powell, M.B. (2005). What's the story? An exploration of narrative language abilities in male juvenile offenders. *Psychology, Crime and Law, 11*(3), 239-253.

Snow, P.C. & Powell, M.B. (2008). Oral language competence, social skills, and high-risk boys: What are juvenile offenders trying to tell us? *Children and Society, 22*(1), 16-28.

Snow, P.C. & Powell, M.B. (2011a). Oral language competence in incarcerated young offenders: Links with offending severity. *International Journal of Speech-Language Pathology, 13*(6), 480-489.

Snow, P.C. & Powell, M.B. (2011b). Youth (in)justice: Oral language competence in early life and risk for engagement in antisocial behaviour in adolescence. *Trends & Issues in Crime and Criminal Justice, 435*, 1-6.

Snow, P.C. & Woodward, M. (2017). Intervening to address communication difficulties in incarcerated youth: A phase 1 clinical trial. *International Journal of Speech-Language Pathology, 19*(4), 392-406.

Snow, P.C., Sanger, D.D., & Bryan, K. (2011). Listening to adolescents with speech, language and communication needs who are in contact with the youth justice system. In S. Roulstone & S. McLeod (Eds), *Listening to Children and Young People with Speech, Language and Communication Needs* (pp.111-120). Guildford: J&R Press.

Snow, P.C., Sanger, D.D., Caire, L., Eadie, P., & Dinslage, T. (2014). Improving communication outcomes for young offenders: A proposed Response to Intervention framework. *International Journal of Language and Communication Disorders, 50*(1), 1-13.

Snow, P.C., Woodward, M., Mathis, M., & Powell, M.B. (2015). Language functioning, mental health and alexithymia in incarcerated young offenders. *International Journal of Speech Language Pathology, 18*(1), 20-31.

Snowling, M. & Hulme, C. (2012). Annual Research Review: The nature and classification of reading disorders. A commentary on proposals for DSM-5. *The Journal of Child Psychology and Psychiatry, 53*(5), 593-607.

Snowling, M.J., Adams, J.W., Bishop, D.V.M., & Stothard, S. (2001). Educational attainments of school leavers with a preschool history of speech-language impairments. *International Journal of Language and Communication Disorders, 36*(2), 173-183.

Spencer, S., Clegg, J., & Stackhouse, J. (2012). Language and disadvantage: A comparison of the language abilities of adolescents from two different socioeconomic areas. *International Journal of Language & Communication Disorders, 47*(3), 274-284.

Spencer, S., Clegg, J., & Stackhouse, J., & Rush, R. (2017). Contribution of spoken language and socio-economic background to adolescents' educational achievement at age 16 years. *International Journal of Language and Communication Disorders, 52*(2), 184-196.

Starling, J., Munro, N., Togher, L., & Arciuli, J. (2011). Recognising language impairment in secondary school student populations. *Australian Journal of Learning Difficulties, 16*(2), 145-158.

St Clair, M.C., Pickles, A., Durkin, K., & Conti-Ramsden, G. (2011). A longitudinal study of behavioural, emotional, and social difficulties in individuals with a history of specific language impairment. *Journal of Communication Disorders, 44*(2), 186-199.

Stewart, A., Livingstone, M., & Dennison, S. (2008). Transitions and turning points: Examining the links between child maltreatment and juvenile offending. *Child Abuse & Neglect, 32*(1), 51-66.

Stringer, H. & Lozano, S. (2007). Under identification of speech and language impairment in children attending a special school for children with emotional and behavioural disorders. *Educational and Child Psychology, 24*(4), 9-19.

Talbot, J. (2010). Prisoners' voices: Experience of the criminal justice system by prisoners with learning disabilities. *Tizard Learning Disability Review, 15*(3), 33-41.

Tomblin, B., Records, N.L., Buckwalter, P., Zhang, X., Smith, E., & O'Brien, M. (1997). The prevalence of specific language impairment in kindergarten children. *Journal of Speech, Language and Hearing Research, 40*(6), 1245-1260.

Toumbourou, J.W., Williams, I.R., Snow, P.C., & White, V.M. (2003). Adolescent alcohol-use trajectories in the transition from high school. *Drug and Alcohol Review, 22*(2), 111-116.

Vallance, D.D., Im, N., & Cohen, N.J. (1999). Discourse deficits associated with psychiatric disorders and with language impairments in children. *Journal of Child Psychology and Psychiatry, 40*(5), 693-704.

Whitmire, K.A. (2000). Adolescence as a developmental phase: A tutorial. *Topics in Language Disorders, 20*(2), 1-14.

Winstanley, M., Webb, R.T., & Conti-Ramsden, G. (2018). More or less likely to offend? Young adults with a history of identified developmental language disorders. *International Journal of Language & Communication Disorders, 53*(2), 256-270.

Zucker, T.A., Cabell, S.Q., Justice, L.M., Pentimonti, J.M., & Kaderavek, J.N. (2013). The role of frequent, interactive prekindergarten shared reading in the longitudinal development of language and literacy skills. *Developmental Psychology, 49*(8), 1425-1439.

11 Communication and forensic psychiatry

Jane O'Connor

Introduction

Forensic psychiatry is a sub-speciality of psychiatry that deals with the assessment, treatment and rehabilitation of offenders with mental disorders. The clinical process involved in diagnosis in forensic psychiatry is the same as in other areas which concern mental health. What is different is the degree of detail, which often includes access to a wider range of collateral information. The diagnostic process concludes with an opinion about mental disorder that is legally defined, with reference to disturbance in thinking, perceiving, emotion or judgement. Patients engaged with forensic mental health services may have communication difficulties associated with, or intrinsic to, their mental disorder. Communication impairments impact participation in social, educational, vocational and therapeutic contexts. Language and communication needs of people with mental illness have been demonstrated (Walsh, Regan, Sowman, Parsons, & McKay, 2007). These are addressed in more detail in Chapter 3 (Walsh et al.) of this book.

People who work in forensic psychiatry are knowledgeable about the criminal justice system, mental health services and legal systems and the relationship between mental disorder and offending behaviour. They are concerned with risk assessment and risk management and their aim is to prevent future harm. Forensic mental health care involves the work of multiple disciplines within the forensic mental health services and collaboration with other agencies. Members of the multidisciplinary team (MDT) in forensic psychiatry must be aware of legal and psychiatric definitions of mental illness and disorder in the jurisdiction in which they work. Although some forensic psychiatry MDTs include Speech and Language Therapists, this is not the norm, despite the high demands on language and communication ability within the assessment, therapeutic and rehabilitative pathways. The role of the Speech and Language Therapist as a member of the MDT in forensic psychiatry is not new, with services in Broadmoor Hospital in the United Kingdom (UK) established in the 1990s. This chapter aims to provide an introduction to forensic services, particularly aimed at therapists entering this area of practice for the first time. The chapter will review the patients, settings and care pathways in forensic mental health services. Among other factors, the nature of patient impairments and the restrictions in the environments will help to demonstrate the importance of considering language and communication in this setting.

The patients

People with mental illness are over-represented in prison populations, with prisoners several times more likely to have psychosis and major depression than the general population (Fazel & Danesh, 2002). People with autism are also over-represented in the criminal justice system (King & Murphy, 2014). Attempts to quantify the prevalence of offending in people with intellectual disability have proven highly variable, their treatment within the criminal justice system depending on the extent to which their disability is recognized (Jones, 2007).

For someone accused of a crime, contact with the criminal justice system begins at the point of arrest. There are processes outside the scope of forensic psychiatry which impact on mentally disordered offenders from this point onwards. For example, at the point of arrest a 'formal caution' is given which may present the first formal communication dilemma. A number of procedural steps follow through the arrest and process of custodial detention and police interviews. At each point, there is no doubt that communication challenges arise. When mental disorder is suspected among people engaged within the criminal justice system, a referral to a forensic psychiatric service should follow. Such services provide assessment and treatment to people with a range of mental disorders including schizophrenia, bipolar affective disorder, intellectual disability, brain injury, autism spectrum disorder and other neurodevelopmental disorders. These presentations often coexist and may be complicated by substance misuse. In addition to mental disorder, those patients admitted to medium and high secure forensic units have a history of violence and pose a risk to the safety of the public.

Someone charged with an offence may be in the community, subject to certain restrictions, or on remand in prison. If a prisoner who is on remand presents as mentally disordered, their legal personnel or the court may ask a forensic psychiatrist to assess their fitness to plead to the charge. This means assessing the person's ability to understand and to follow the court proceedings; to make a proper defence; to know that they might challenge any jurors to whom they may object; to understand the evidence; to give appropriate instructions to their legal representatives. The assessment of fitness to plead places a demand on communication abilities. If found unfit, they may, pursuant to legislation in that jurisdiction, be committed to a forensic psychiatric hospital.

If someone was mentally unwell when they committed the offence, the person and their legal representative may ask the jury to consider using a special verdict and find the person 'not guilty by reason of insanity'. The legal criteria for reaching such a verdict include that at the time of the offence, the accused person was suffering from a mental disorder, and the mental disorder was such that they did not know the nature and quality of the act, or did not know that what they were doing was wrong, or were unable to refrain from committing the act. The special verdict is descended from the M'Naghten Rules (see Roche, 1959) and is applicable in countries in which the legal system developed from British law (e.g., Ireland, Australia, South Africa, India). This verdict results in placement in a secure psychiatric hospital and the period of time is not determined in advance, as it is dependent on recovery and risk assessment and management.

Patients receive assessment and treatment from forensic psychiatry teams if they are mentally unwell while in prison. If someone is on remand for a relatively minor offence and they are mentally ill, the forensic psychiatry team will work with the court and local psychiatric services to set up a diversion to general psychiatric services (Stevens & Rodin, 2011). If someone serving a prison sentence requires inpatient treatment it is likely they will be transferred to a forensic hospital, again pursuant to local legislation. A number of people in forensic hospitals have been referred from general psychiatric services, deemed to have exceeded the capacity of that service due to violence and dangerousness, and are therefore detained under civil, not criminal, legislation.

The forensic psychiatry inpatient population is composed largely of young men. The offences committed by people coming into contact with forensic psychiatry services are varied with approximately half detained for violent or sexual offences (Rutherford & Duggan, 2008). The purpose of forensic psychiatric admission is different to that of a general psychiatric admission, in that its aim is to treat the mental disorder and also address the offending behaviour. Therefore, the course and duration and aftercare planning of that admission is complex, and usually takes a greater amount of time (Davoren et al., 2015). A review of forensic services in the UK reported that while the majority of people are detained for less than five years, over a quarter were detained for over 10 years (Rutherford & Duggan, 2008). In the 2016 census in Ireland, 43% of patients detained in the Central Mental Hospital on the night of the census were detained for over five years (Daly & Craig, 2016).

The setting

Forensic psychiatric services may be provided in high secure hospitals, medium secure hospitals, forensic intensive care units or low secure units. Forensic psychiatry multidisciplinary teams are involved in treatment and supervision of community patients and provision of liaison services to general psychiatry departments and teams. Forensic psychiatry teams also work in non-clinical settings such as bail hostels, probation services and prisons (Berman, Minne, Attard, & Oyebode, 2012).

In forensic inpatient services, the patient follows a stratified pathway through levels of 'therapeutic security'. The stratification of levels of physical/ environmental, relational and procedural security is from acute unit (with high secure care), through to medium security (with medium secure care), onwards to low and minimal secure pre-discharge security (Kennedy, 2002). These levels of security are outlined below.

Physical security

Levels of physical security are clearly overt in forensic settings. Patients, staff and others can see much of the environmental or physical security employed; it is what greets one on arrival. It is the secure buildings, perimeter fences, secure outdoor spaces and alarm and monitoring systems. Secure forensic inpatient units are unlikely to have been purpose built, in the initial phase in any case, and challenges arise when competing goals of therapy and security, privacy and observability, are at play. The importance of fostering meaningful rehabilitative social interaction in psychiatric settings while maintaining privacy has been emphasized (Seppänen, Törmänen, Shaw, & Kennedy, 2018). The recognition of the importance of the physical environment in relation to social interaction in forensic settings has not yet translated into clear consideration of the communication environment.

Procedural security

Procedural security relates to the policies and practices for controlling risk, which are necessary at patient and systems level. These may be less visible but will be keenly felt by patients. These might include monitoring of communication, frequency and nature of visits, requirement for property searches or need for night confinement. Night confinement means locking of patient rooms at night and is in use in many psychiatric secure psychiatric hospitals. Assessments of the impact of night confinement have produced differing answers, ranging from 'no impact' (Hague, Chu, Wilkins, McNeill, & Wright, 2015) to considerable concern for human dignity and care (Velpry & Eyraud, 2014). The need for these practices may be very clear to management and staff, but represent a departure from usual hospital care for many patients. The challenge in communicating the practices and procedures to patients in a secure setting is therefore significant.

Relational security

Another level of security refers to 'relational security', which is the provision of high staff-to-patient ratios of well-trained staff. It has been found that this allows appropriate supervision and monitoring but also the opportunity for building good therapeutic relationships with patients, "which in a large part confers security" (Kennedy, 2002).

Admission units have high levels of therapeutic security (high levels of environmental protections, high staff-to-patient ratios, high levels of procedural security), while rehabilitation units have lower levels, and pre-discharge units would have the least therapeutic security. Patients move along this pathway through care so that the need for therapeutic security is matched to the individual assessment of risk, and the risk is managed in the appropriate setting (Pillay, Oliver, Butler, & Kennedy, 2014). It is recognized that staff will not be able to deliver therapeutic inputs in an environment in which they do not feel safe. It is also accepted that patients will not make optimal progress in an overly restrictive environment (Davison, 2004). The principle, therefore, is that patients should be treated in the least restrictive setting possible.

Legal contacts

People who access forensic mental health services will, by definition, come into contact with the Mental Health Commission (https://www.mhcirl.ie) and the criminal justice system of that jurisdiction on a regular basis. These are systems which they are required to navigate, and with whom they must communicate. Contact often involves participation in verbally-mediated interventions, either in one-to-one meetings or meetings with a number of people present (e.g., mental health tribunals, mental health review boards and court hearings). Much care and attention and no little expense is devoted to ensuring that the patient and their legal representative are present, but less attention is paid to whether the written and verbal information given to the patient is accessible to them in a communicative sense. The critical role of communication support and how this is achieved in mental health settings is discussed by Brophy and O'Connor in Chapter 9 of this volume, and many of these principles are applicable within forensic settings.

Engagement, treatment and recovery in forensic psychiatry

Engagement

Communication that is meaningful for patients, family and carers is required for successful engagement regarding mental health care. Autonomy and beneficence sometimes meet in the middle, and decisions are shared equally between the clinician and the patient. This is the 'shared decision making' model with the expert patient that has been widely endorsed by public health policy (Health Services Executive (HSE), 2017). However, this is not always the case. Often the two are unbalanced, with autonomy receding with advance of beneficence-based paternalism, to prevent harm by that patient. This is particularly so for patients in forensic psychiatry services. The patients' judgement is impacted by severe enduring mental illness, their autonomy eroded by their disorder, resulting in risk of or actual harm to the patient and/ or others. This unequal relationship between psychiatric multidisciplinary team and patient can impact on engagement by patients in care planning at all levels. Regarding engagement, patients, families and carers can be engaged in their own care planning and management at individual level, and also in local service delivery and development at the community level. They may be involved in the running of services or organizations and in policy development and implementation (Kennedy, Rafferty, & Price, 2017). To achieve this level of engagement, communication practices within the forensic context must be responsive to the communication needs of individual patients.

Recovery

Assessments and therapeutic inputs are delivered to patients in forensic mental health services in pursuit of recovery. Some key concepts provide the foundation of effective recovery work: hope, personal responsibility, education, self-advocacy and support (Jacobson & Greenley, 2001). Imperative to working with these concepts is communication that is meaningful. However, as outlined in the *National Framework for Recovery in Mental Health 2018–2020* (HSE-Mental Health Services, 2017, p.2) "...recovery is very much determined by what recovery means to an individual service user and through the articulation of their desires, beliefs and choices to realise their potential". In reviewing the paradigm of recovery in mental health services, the importance of delivering "care in a spirit of partnership, respect and involvement even when being coercive" captures the challenges inherent in the process (Simpson & Penney, 2011, p.304).

Recovery in forensic mental health can be considered across a number of domains and considers the application of the recovery principle to secure mental health care (Simpson & Penney, 2018). Broadly, the domains are personal recovery, symptomatic recovery, functional recovery and forensic recovery (Kennedy, 2018). Personal recovery relates to (re)gaining a sense of personal control or agency. Associated with this idea of recovery as 'agency' should be included authenticity and responsibility. Symptomatic recovery is concerned with improving symptoms and signs of mental illness or disorder, and/or distress associated therewith. Functional recovery is about the patient fulfilling roles in social, occupational and family domains, developing increasing independence. Forensic recovery is the ability to live safely with minimal secure care, with the patient achieving increasing autonomy and responsibility for themselves and their actions. Moving towards recovery in these domains requires multifaceted treatments, many of which are highly dependent on communication processes.

Assessment, treatment and the interaction with communication support needs

Patients in forensic mental health services have needs across a number of areas: mental health, physical health, drugs and alcohol misuse, problem behaviours, occupational activity, family and social relationships, self-care and activities of daily living (Gelder, Harrison, & Cowen, 2006; Gill, McKenna,

O'Neill, Thompson, & Timmons, 2010). Competent language skills, in both comprehension and expression, are necessary in order to engage effectively with the therapies available. The kind of communication and language needed will develop and change as a patient moves through a forensic mental health service towards recovery and eventual discharge.

Formulating an individual care and treatment plan requires a detailed forensic psychiatric assessment. As part of this assessment the patient will be asked for their own account of their early life including early home and family life, previous educational attainment, previous traumatic experiences, previous illnesses, past offences and circumstances leading up to their index offence. This information, along with collateral information from those who know the patient well, is necessary to develop an individual risk formulation. A patient with communication difficulties may struggle to structure and sequence information coherently to narrate these past events resulting in a case history and risk formulation that are incomplete.

A patient in the early stage of their admission may require an assessment of their communication needs. Impaired ability to verbally express feelings and emotions in an appropriate way may lead the person to use aggressive behaviour or acts, instead of words, to express themselves. They may also grapple when faced with the unit routine, 'unwritten rules' and nonverbal communication of others. They may also struggle to relate to others in socially acceptable ways, which in the restricted environment of a secure setting can lead to problems within the peer group.

Addressing not only the mental disorder, but also the harmful behaviour of patients, is integral to the work of forensic psychiatry. This work is carried out in a step-wise fashion, usually using verbally-mediated approaches. Some of the steps are completed as part of a group and some are individual sessions and programmes of sessions. The main theoretical models in this area are the *Risk Need Responsivity Model* (Polaschek, 2012) and *Good Lives Model* (Barnao, Robertson, & Ward, 2010). These are used in parallel with recovery principles as outlined above. The initial part of the work will include learning skills to manage oneself in social and challenging situations. These self-management skills will include problem solving work, distress tolerance, mindfulness, emotional recognition and regulation, anger but also assertiveness management, social skills training and perspective taking. More patient-specific work is then done with patients around their index offence and the factors contributing to same, including review of the Book of Evidence. The goal of this work is to understand why the offence occurred and reduce the risk of it happening again. The kind of language skills needed for this type of work are often very different to the communication repertoire in everyday use for that patient. A patient beginning to address their own harmful behaviour could benefit from developing language and communication skills necessary for reflection on their past actions.

Similarly, in the pre-discharge phase of treatment, patients will be encouraged, in keeping with their level of ability, to be as involved as possible in their own risk management and planning of discharge, onward placement, conditional discharge, or complete discharge. The efficacy and authenticity of communication between patient, forensic service and community service is important in achieving timely and appropriate discharge.

Patients in the pre-discharge part of the hospital should also benefit from speech and language therapy in order to learn to adjust from the institutional setting to the community setting, where communication demands and challenges may be increased. Given the aforementioned lengthy duration of admissions, this is particularly pertinent in relation to disclosure of information and (re) building social relationships (Gravell & France, 1991).

Clinical implications

The communication profiles of patients in forensic psychiatry services is likely to impact most aspects of their engagement with their families, friends, peers, court, legal, prison, nursing and multidisciplinary forensic psychiatry team members. This can range from deleterious, in the case of inappropriate expression of feelings such as frustration, to obfuscation, in the case of someone attending a group-based intervention without being able to engage meaningfully. It may be helpful to consider the clinical implications of communication problems as they impact specific groups of patients in forensic psychiatry settings.

Schizophrenia

At the time of writing, the majority of inpatients in Ireland's medium secure Central Mental Hospital have experienced psychosis (in excess of 80%) with over two-thirds of the patient population in the hospital having a diagnosis of schizophrenia. Many of those with schizophrenia in forensic psychiatry services have complex presentations, including negative symptoms and impaired cognition, with concomitant communication impairments. There is a growing body of research pertaining to the similarities between autism and schizophrenia in the areas of pragmatic use of language, social communication and reciprocity (Solomon et al., 2011). Of particular interest is the similarity in relation to social cognition exhibited by people with negative symptoms of schizophrenia and autism (Couture et al., 2009), discussed in Chapter 3 of this volume (Walsh et al.). Since communication needs and supports are accepted as part of autism, these developments serve to emphasize the importance of communication in forensic mental health settings.

Autism

People with autism are over-represented in the Criminal Justice System. If unfit to plead, or found 'not guilty by reason of insanity' of an offence, they may be detained in a forensic psychiatric hospital. This type of disposal for someone with autism leads to their placement in a restricted environment, restrictions which the person may struggle to come to terms with. Communication difficulties represent a constitutional aspect of autism spectrum disorder (ASD), comprising part of its diagnostic criteria. The fifth iteration of the *Diagnostic and Statistics Manual* (DSM-5, American Psychiatric Association, 2013) states that people with ASD have "persistent deficits in social communication and social interaction across multiple contexts, deficits in nonverbal communicative behaviours used for social interaction and deficits in developing, maintaining, and understanding relationships". As such, assessment of speech, language and communication needs, and provision of appropriate supports, is imperative to meet the needs of such patients. While awareness of communication needs of this group is high in disability and social care settings, it may not be thus in forensic settings. A review of forensic services for people with intellectual disability and/or autism spectrum disorder found that, aside from specialist in-patient units, staff and managers felt that people with learning disabilities and/or ASD "did not fit in easily with the core business of the secure settings" (Myers, 2004, p.1). The author went on to say that people with ASD across all settings were described by people working in forensic settings as "having needs beyond those which 'mainstream' services in the secure settings could meet" (Myers, 2004, p.1).

Intellectual disability

While some studies report a highly variable rate of people with intellectual disability in secure settings, they agree on the importance of identifying disability and associated needs and supports when someone with an intellectual disability offends. Between 50% and 90% of people with intellectual disability have communication difficulties (Emerson, Hatton, Felce, & Murphy, 2001). In a review in a National Health Service (NHS) Forensic Support Service for offenders with learning disabilities, a high percentage (approximately 80 percent) of service users referred to that service had communication difficulties, and between 79 percent and 84 percent of those service users identified as having a communication difficulty were thought to have offending behaviours linked to their communication impairments (McNamara, 2012).

Conclusions

While there are existing speech and language therapy services in some forensic settings, the need outweighs the current service structure. Developments to include speech and language therapists in forensic MDTs are welcomed. Given the high demands on communication with regards to assessment, engagement, treatment and recovery, speech and language therapy services offer the potential to increase the effectiveness of services for patients with communication support needs. Research exploring the impact of speech and language therapy support on engagement, understanding, frustration, the use of coercive treatments (such as restraint and seclusion), are all highly relevant within the forensic context. Exploring the impact of specialized language and communication assessments and supports on Quality of Life assessments, as distinct from Quality of Care measurements, will help to demonstrate the utility of such a service (Plimley, 2007), and should be prioritized as the provision of speech and language therapy services in forensic mental health settings continues to grow.

The opportunity to develop the role of speech and language expertise within forensic settings ranges from that first point of contact with the police, all the way through the therapeutic pathways that follow. This could lead to a rich inter-agency, as well as multidisciplinary, role for the Speech and Language Therapist and the clinical specialty itself. For example, input from a Speech and Language Therapist at the point of drafting policy documents, or indeed legislation, could greatly facilitate the experience of the mentally-disordered offender throughout these various processes. Each intervention will offer an opportunity for future research.

References

American Psychiatric Association. (2013). *Diagnostic and Statistical Manual of Mental Disorders*, 5th ed. Arlington, VA: American Psychiatric Publishing.

Barnao, M.T., Robertson, P., & Ward, T. (2010). Good Lives Model applied to a forensic population. *Psychiatry, Psychology and Law, 17*(2), 202-217. doi:10.1080/13218710903421274

Berman, J., Minne, C., Attard, S., & Oyebode, O. (2012). Forensic psychiatry. In P. Wright, J. Stern, & M. Phelan (Eds), *Core Psychiatry*, 3rd ed. (pp.471-486). Oxford: W.B. Saunders.

Couture, S.M., Penn, D.L., Losh, M., Adolphs, R., Hurley, R., & Piven, J. (2009). Comparison of social cognitive functioning in schizophrenia and high functioning autism: More convergence than divergence. *Psychological Medicine, 40*(4), 569-579. doi:10.1017/S003329170999078X

Daly, A. & Craig, S. (2016). Irish psychiatric units and hospitals census 2016. Retrieved from https://www.hrb.ie/fileadmin/publications_files/Irish_Psychaitric_Units_and_Hospitals_Census_2016_Main_Findings.pdf

Davison, S. (2004). Specialist forensic mental health services. *Criminal Behaviour and Mental Health, 14*(S1), S19-S24. doi:10.1002/cbm.604

Davoren, M., Byrne, O., O'Connell, P., O'Neill, H., O'Reilly, K., & Kennedy, H.G. (2015). Factors affecting length of stay in forensic hospital setting: Need for therapeutic security and course of admission. *BMC Psychiatry, 15*, 301-301. doi:10.1186/s12888-015-0686-4

Emerson, E., Hatton, C., Felce, D., & Murphy, G. (2001) *Learning Disabilities: The Fundamental Facts*. London: The Foundation for People with Learning Disabilities.

Fazel, S. & Danesh, J. (2002). Serious mental disorder in 23000 prisoners: A systematic review of 62 surveys. *The Lancet, 359*(9306), 545-550. doi:10.1016/S0140-6736(02)07740-1

Gelder, M., Harrison, P., & Cowen, P. (2006). *Shorter Oxford Textbook of Psychiatry*, 5th ed. Oxford, UK: Oxford University Press.

Gill, P., McKenna, P., O'Neill, H., Thompson, J., & Timmons, D. (2010). Pillars and pathways: Foundations of recovery in Irish forensic mental health care. *British Journal of Forensic Practice, 12*(3), 29-36.

Gravell, R. & France, J. (1991). *Speech and Communication Problems in Psychiatry*. London: Chapman & Hall.

Hague, A., Chu, S., Wilkins, T., McNeill, K., & Wright, K.M. (2015). The impact of a night confinement policy on patients in a UK high secure inpatient mental health service. *The Journal of Forensic Practice, 17*(1), 21-30. doi:10.1108/JFP-11-2014-0045

Health Services Executive. (2017). The National Framework for Recovery in Mental Health 2018-2020. Retrieved from Dublin, Ireland: https://www.hse.ie/eng/services/list/4/mental-health-services/advancingrecoveryireland/national-framework-for-recovery-in-mental-health/recovery-framework.pdf

Jacobson, N. & Greenley, D. (2001). What is recovery? A conceptual model and explication. *Psychiatric Services, 52*(4), 482-485. doi:10.1176/appi.ps.52.4.482

Jones, J. (2007). Persons with intellectual disabilities in the criminal justice system: Review of issues. *International Journal of Offender Therapy and Comparative Criminology, 51*(6), 723-733. doi:10.1177/0306624X07299343

Kennedy, H.G. (2002). Therapeutic uses of security: Mapping forensic mental health services by stratifying risk. *Advances in Psychiatric Treatment, 8*(6), 433-443. doi:10.1192/apt.8.6.433

Kennedy, L.A., Rafferty, M., & Price, A. (2017). Service user, family member and carer engagement in mental health services in Ireland – A review of the literature. Mental Health Engagement Office, HSE, St Loman's Hospital, Palmerstown, Dublin.

Kennedy, H.G. (2018). *Model of Care National Forensic Mental Health Service.* Central Mental Hospital Dublin, Ireland.

King, C. & Murphy, G.H. (2014). A systematic review of people with autism spectrum disorder and the criminal justice system. *Journal of Autism and Developmental Disorders, 44*(11), 2717-2733. doi:10.1007/s10803-014-2046-5

McNamara, N. (2012). Speech and language therapy within a forensic support service. *Journal of Learning Disabilities and Offending Behaviour, 3*(2), 111-117. doi:10.1108/20420921211280097

Mental Health Commission (https://www.mhcirl.ie)

Myers, F. (2004). On the borderline? People with learning disabilities and/or Autistic Spectrum Disorders in secure, forensic and other specialist settings. Retrieved from http://docs.scie-socialcareonline.org.uk/fulltext/asdsecure.pdf

Pillay, S.M., Oliver, B., Butler, L., & Kennedy, H.G. (2014). Risk stratification and the care pathway. *Irish Journal of Psychological Medicine, 25*(4), 123-127. doi:10.1017/S0790966700011228

Plimley, L.A. (2007). A review of quality of life issues and people with autism spectrum disorders. *British Journal of Learning Disabilities, 35*(4), 205-213. doi:10.1111/j.1468-3156.2007.00448.x

Polaschek, D.L.L. (2012). An appraisal of the risk–need–responsivity (RNR) model of offender rehabilitation and its application in correctional treatment. *Legal and Criminological Psychology, 17*(1), 1-17. doi:10.1111/j.2044-8333.2011.02038.x

Roche, P.Q. (1959). Psychiatry and the M'Naghten Rule. *The Journal of Criminal Law, Criminology, and Police Science, 50*(2), 160-162.

Rutherford, M. & Duggan, S. (2008). Forensic mental health services: Facts and figures on current provision. *The British Journal of Forensic Practice, 10*(4), 4-10.

Seppänen, A., Törmänen, I., Shaw, C., & Kennedy, H.G. (2018). Modern forensic psychiatric hospital design: Clinical, legal and structural aspects. *International Journal of Mental Health Systems, 12*(58), 1-12. https://doi.org/10.1186/s13033-018-0238-7

Simpson, A.I.F. & Penney, S. (2011). The recovery paradigm in forensic mental health services. *Criminal Behaviour and Mental Health, 21*(5), 299-306. doi: 10.1002/cbm.823

Simpson, A.I.F. & Penney, S.R. (2018). Recovery and forensic care: Recent advances and future directions. *Criminal Behaviour and Mental Health, 28*(5), 383-389. doi:10.1002/cbm.2090

Solomon, M., Olsen, E., Niendam, T., Ragland, J.D., Yoon, J., Minzenberg, M., & Carter, C.S. (2011). From lumping to splitting and back again: Atypical social and language development in individuals with clinical-high-risk for psychosis, first episode schizophrenia, and autism spectrum disorders. *Schizophrenia Research*, *131*(1–3), 146–151. doi:10.1016/j.schres.2011.03.005

Stevens, L. & Rodin, I. (2011). *Psychiatry*, 2nd ed. London: Churchill Livingstone.

Velpry, L. & Eyraud, B. (2014). Confinement and psychiatric care: A comparison between high-security units for prisoners and for difficult patients in France. *Culture, Medicine, and Psychiatry*, *38*(4), 550–577. doi:10.1007/s11013-014-9400-0

Walsh, I., Regan, J., Sowman, R., Parsons, B., & McKay, P. (2007). A needs analysis for the provision of a speech and language therapy service to adults with MHDs. *Irish Journal of Psychological Medicine*, 24(3), 89–93. doi:10.1017/S0790966700010375

Acknowledgement

I would like to acknowledge the support of Dr Paul O Connell, Consultant Forensic Psychiatrist, in the writing of this chapter. Any errors and misinterpretations that remain are my own.

12 Applications of Cognitive Behavioural Therapy to speech and language therapy practice in adult mental health

Jennifer Brophy

Introduction

Speech and language therapy for adults with mental health difficulties remains an emerging and evolving domain of clinical practice. The centrality of language and communication in mental health has been outlined in detail in Chapter 3 of this volume. The Speech and Language Therapist (SLT) has a specialist role in adult mental health services in relation to the identification, differential diagnosis and treatment of speech, language, communication and swallowing difficulties in adults in order to reduce risk and increase resilience and wellbeing (IASLT, 2015).

The main aim of assessment in this area is to create a comprehensive picture of the service user's communicative functioning and the factors which influence this, such that a management plan may be formulated and implemented by the SLT as part of the clinical team. One of the core benefits of SLT assessment is that it contributes to the client's, carer's and team's understanding of the communication factors which influence mental health difficulties and, therefore, lessen the chance of the client feeling "misunderstood, misinterpreted and mismanaged" (France, 2001, p.16).

While the evidence base for SLT intervention for adults with mental health difficulties remains limited, SLT interventions frequently focus on increasing insight into the relationship between communication ability and mental health difficulties and reducing frustration on the part of both service users and carers. As well as maintaining current communicative function, new skills, motivation and confidence are often developed. In essence, the aim of therapy is to

> ...facilitate clients in becoming more effective communicators in a general sense rather than people who are skilled in producing drilled components of communicative ability with the emphasis on listening and self-monitoring (Muir, 1997, p.126).

In addition, Byng and Duchan (2005, p.917) have advised that SLT interventions should involve meaningful contributions given that:

> ... the end product of therapy for most people needs to be that they feel more equipped to exchange opinions, negotiate, express affection, express needs and so on – the real life purposes to which most of us put our communication.

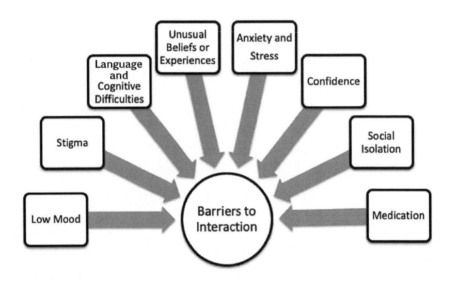

Figure 12.1 Barriers to relating for people with schizophrenia (adapted from Brophy, 2009).

Barriers to interaction for adults with mental health disorders

While there are many diagnostic labels which assist in defining and describing the experience of mental health difficulties, the impact of these difficulties on speech, language and communication functioning is highly individual and varied, as outlined in detail in Chapter 3 of this volume.

A study undertaken by Brophy (2009) which explored the experiences of people with schizophrenia of language and communication difficulties associated with or intrinsic to their diagnosis, highlighted a myriad of factors which impacted on the participants' communicative competence. Brophy (2009) concluded that there was a need for an acknowledgment within SLT practice of the variety of barriers to interaction for people with schizophrenia. Figure 12.1 illustrates the myriad of influences on the communicative competence of the person referred for speech and language therapy (Brophy, 2009).

As a result, SLTs working in mental health are required to see beyond the diagnostic label and formulate each client's communication support needs from a broad perspective incorporating considerations at the personal, environmental and community levels (IASLT, 2016).

Furthermore, Brophy (2009) emphasized the direct implications of these barriers to interaction for SLTs working in this domain of practice. For example, several of the participants in the study spoke of the impact of anxiety on their ability to interact with others. Anxiety represents a significant barrier to interaction and one that should be acknowledged and addressed as part of intervention programmes. For people with schizophrenia, the source of interpersonal difficulties can be those intrinsic to their diagnosis. However, it should be noted that affective states, such as anxiety and depression, also impact on their ability to engage in social interaction with others (Bellack, Mueser, Gingerich, & Agresta, 2004). Co-morbid anxiety disorders are reported in over 50% of people with schizophrenia (Pallanti, Quercioli, & Hollander, 2004). The presence of anxiety disorders in schizophrenia has been associated with poor social functioning and greater risk of relapse (Blanchard, Mueser, & Bellack, 1998). Of particular significance is the prevalence of social anxiety disorders which has been found to be in excess of 36% in outpatients with schizophrenia (Pallanti et al., 2004).

Given the social challenges of a communication disability, coupled with the feelings of fear and loss of control often inherent in the course of schizophrenia, the presence of anxiety symptoms has clinical implications for SLTs in terms of being adequately skilled to offer anxiety management as part of a holistic treatment programme. Granholm and colleagues (2005, p.521) highlight that:

> ... by challenging thoughts that interfere with skills execution in the real world (e.g. expectancies, delusional fears), social competence and functioning may be improved.

Just as anxiety is a barrier to relating, so is the effect of social isolation and withdrawal on communicative functioning. When confronted with a mental health difficulty a 'stepping back' can occur which can lead to both social isolation and loneliness. Often, stigma and discrimination result in people concealing their difficulties and becoming isolated (Gonzales-Torres, Oraa, Aristegui, Fernandez-Rivas, & Guimon, 2007). Professor Olds, of Harvard University, comments that in her experience "people are quite willing to say that they have a psychiatric problem but not that they are lonely" (Griffin, 2010, p.18). This experience of social isolation and loneliness can be perpetuated and reinforced by a cycle of thoughts, feelings and behaviours which influence the person's ability to engage and participate in social, vocational and community life.

The relationship between social competence and the process of thinking, feeling and behaving is reflexive. The nuances in relationships are almost limitless and the meaning that we construct in these relationships is important to our self-concept. Acknowledging and incorporating these influences on interaction into speech and language therapy clinical practice is recommended, in that it allows the person's difficulties to be formulated and addressed from a broad perspective which is helpful in managing the process of change. This is supported by Hayes and Collins (2001, p.284) who suggest that "communication skills work which has its sole emphasis on the acquisition of behavioural skills has often limited or short-lived effects". They conclude that "behavioural changes cannot be accomplished and maintained without concomitant changes in self-perception" (Hayes & Collins, 2001, p.284). Therefore, combining evidence-based psychological approaches with the communication skills work of the SLT in mental health has potential to yield positive outcomes.

Cognitive Behaviour Therapy: A useful approach in speech and language therapy practice

In this chapter, Cognitive Behavioural Therapy (CBT) is presented as a framework which allows the SLT to focus directly on supporting the client's speech, language and communication needs as well as addressing some of the psychological issues which will inevitably surface, either as a direct consequence of the communication difficulties or associated with them.

At this point it is useful to distinguish between the use of cognitive behavioural skills in routine clinical practice and Cognitive Behavioural Therapy as a psychotherapeutic intervention (Williams & Garland, 2002). Research findings have shown that a short, well-designed CBT skills programme can enable mental health staff to integrate basic CBT knowledge and skills into everyday practice, producing improvements in practice and patient care (Duffy, Gillespie, & O'Shea, 2013), a finding which may be equally applicable to SLTs. This chapter emphasizes the use of cognitive behavioural skills to help manage change in collaboration with the client. The use of these skills also has the advantage of assisting the SLT in conceptualizing their client's communication difficulties as being linked to, or influenced by, the person's unhelpful thinking styles or interpretation of themselves, of others and of the world, thus perpetuating their difficulties.

Perhaps the best way to conceptualize the use of cognitive behavioural skills in speech and language therapy practice is to view it as a frame of reference for understanding the client's view of the world. This approach is chosen as it is evidence based, pragmatic, collaborative and problem focused and, as such, mirrors some of the values core to SLT practice.

The cognitive model

The origins of Cognitive Behavioural Therapy (CBT) date back to the 1950s/60s with the work of Albert Ellis and Aaron T. Beck. Both were psychiatrists, trained in psychoanalysis, who became disillusioned by the slow progress of their clients. Through careful observation, they discovered that their clients tended to get better when they changed their ways of thinking about themselves, their problems and the world. Cognitive Therapy was developed by Beck in the early 1960s as a "structured, short-term, present oriented psychotherapy for depression, directed toward solving current problems and modifying dysfunctional thinking and behaviour" (Beck, 1995, p.1). The term Cognitive Behaviour Therapy came into use in the early 1990s, initially used by behaviourists to describe behaviour therapy with a cognitive component. However, in more recent years, the term 'CBT' has evolved into a generic term to include the whole of the cognitively-oriented psychotherapies.

CBT is one of the most extensively researched forms of psychotherapy. This approach has been shown to be effective for a wide variety of mental health problems, such as adult and adolescent unipolar depression, generalized anxiety disorder, panic disorder, social phobia, post-traumatic stress disorder and childhood depressive and anxiety disorders (Butler, Chapman, Forman, & Beck, 2006). Studies have demonstrated that CBTp can result in decreased positive symptoms, improvement in negative symptoms, and improved functioning (Burns et al., 2014; Turner et al., 2014, van der Gaag,2014)

Of note, CBT is more than just a set of techniques – it also encompasses comprehensive theories of human behaviour. CBT proposes a 'biopsychosocial' model of how humans come to feel and act as they do (Beck, 2011) (i.e., a combination of biological, psychological and social factors is involved). The most basic premise is that our emotions and behaviours are influenced by our *perceptions* of events. Cognitive theory purports that it is not the situation itself that determines what we feel, but rather it is the way we *think* about the situation (Beck, 2011). Very often, people conceptualize their distress as being directly related to the events and situations in their life: "I had an argument with my partner this morning and I'm still angry"; "My boss didn't give me any feedback on my work and I feel defeated". In each example, the person highlights that it is the situation which caused the emotional upset. However, what a person feels in response to a situation is determined not only by that situation but also by the meaning or perception attached to it.

The thoughts that go through our mind in any given situation are automatic and cause us to have different emotional responses. These automatic thoughts reflect the way in which we *interpret* and *think* about a situation, and have a major effect on the way we feel (Beck, 2011).

Within CBT, it is recognized that there are three levels of thinking which are accessible to the client (Beck, 2011):

1. **Automatic thoughts**: Automatic thoughts are generally very brief and are quickly subsumed by our awareness of the emotions that follow from them so they may not even be noticed (Beck, 2011). They have the quality of being habitual and plausible. A useful exercise suggested by Beck (2011) is to notice the responses to 'Reading this book':

Situation	Automatic thought	Feelings/actions
Reading this book →	"This is too hard" → "I'll never understand it"	Frustration/annoyance Close book

The ability to notice and evaluate automatic thoughts when in an upsetting situation is one of the core skills learned and practised in CBT. The client learns to ask, "What was going through my mind when I felt so upset earlier?"

Take a moment to try this CBT exercise now

Think of a time earlier today (as you read this chapter) or over the past few days when you noticed some kind of emotional upset such as sadness, anxiety or anger. Now try to recall what you were thinking about at the time. As you recall your thoughts during this event, you may begin to become aware of the automatic thoughts that were going through your mind, which you might not have noticed at the time as the feeling was too strong.

Automatic thoughts which are negative tend to reflect distortions in our thinking that can happen particularly at times of emotional distress (Beck, 2011). Table 12.1 highlights some of the more common types of unhelpful thinking.

While each person has their own way of seeing events and situations, when people experience anxiety or depression their automatic thoughts tend to take on a predictable pattern. A goal of CBT is to help people become aware of their negative automatic thoughts, and learn to stand back, evaluate and question these thoughts with a view to the possibility of an alternative explanation (Beck, 2011).

2. **Attitudes, rules and assumptions**: When we begin to become aware of the nature of automatic thoughts, we may begin to notice underlying patterns or themes. Lying beneath our automatic thoughts are the rules and assumptions we hold about ourselves (Beck, 1995) (e.g., "I must always be prepared"; "In order to be accepted, I must not make mistakes"). Figure 12.2 outlines an underlying rule or assumption which may influence the perception of the situation 'Reading this book' (adapted from Beck, 1995, p.18).

Rule/Assumption
If I don't/cannot understand things quickly, then there is something wrong with me

↓

Situation	Automatic thought	Feelings/actions
Reading this book →	"This is too hard" → "I'll never understand it"	Frustration/annoyance Close book

Figure 12.2 Attitudes, rules and assumptions (adapted from Beck, 1995, p.18).

Table 12.1 Description of common types of unhelpful thinking styles.

Distortion	Description	Examples
All or nothing thinking	Situations are perceived as 'black and white'	"If I am not perfect, then I am a total failure"
Mind reading	Assuming what others think without having to ask. Expectation that other people know what you are thinking	"I won't go to the party because I know they don't like me"
Discounting the positive	Positive and pleasant experiences are ignored for no reason. In this way negative thoughts are maintained despite being contradicted by everyday experiences	"This doesn't count, because anyone could get this kind of job"
Catastrophizing	Living the worst-case scenario – assuming a situation will be more difficult than it is likely to be	"This rash on my leg this morning means I have skin cancer. I need to get to the doctor now"
Personalizing	Feeling overly responsible if things do not turn out well and often carry the burden of this	"If I was a really good friend, talking to me would make her feel better. I'm obviously letting her down"
Jumping to conclusions	Making an interpretation of an event based on lack of definite facts	"She didn't say hello to me in the corridor, what have I done to upset her?"
Must/should statements	Focus on the way things should be, act, think or feel which often has standards which cannot be met	"I should be able to handle this better"
Mental filtering	Paying attention to small details which take on great importance	"I noticed that one person looked disinterested when I was speaking, it must have been very boring for everyone"

3. **Core beliefs (schema)**: Core beliefs are the building blocks of all thought processes (Beck, 1995). They provide the foundation of cognitive constructs about ourselves, others and the world and are less immediately accessible (Beck, 1995). It is thought that these beliefs are formed early in life as people try to make sense of their environment. Their interactions with other people and the world lead to certain understandings or learnings (i.e., their beliefs) which may vary in their accuracy and functionality (Beck, 1995). These are regarded by the person as absolute truths, just the way "I am" (e.g., "I am attractive", "I am unlovable", "I am smart"). In order to preserve certainty and predictability, our experiences are constantly filtered and distorted so that these core beliefs, our absolute truths, may remain intact. Figure 12.3 illustrates a core belief which may be relevant to the interpretation of the experience of 'Reading this book'.

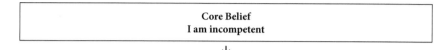

Core Belief
I am incompetent

↓

Rule/Assumption
If I don't/cannot understand things quickly, then there is something wrong with me

↓

Situation	Automatic thought	Feelings/actions
Reading this book →	"This is too hard" → "I'll never understand it"	Frustration/annoyance Close book

Figure 12.3 Core Beliefs (adapted from Beck, 1995, p.18).

The central process in CBT is to assist the person to understand the links between thoughts, feelings, physical sensations and behaviours. The client is then invited to conduct real-life experiments to test the accuracy and emotional consequences of certain ways of thinking (Beck, 2011). The person's experiences are frequently formulated using the 'vicious cycle' model illustrated in Figure 12.4.

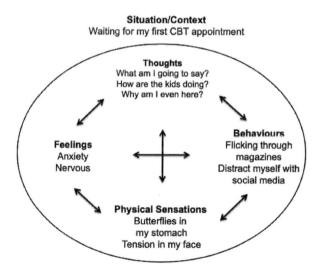

Figure 12.4. Basic CBT Formulation using example of waiting for first CBT appointment.

Each part of the vicious cycle is interconnected. It is understood that making a change in any one area will lead to changes in the others and bring symptom relief. For example, focusing on slowing and relaxation of the breath and the body when feeling anxious can reduce arousal levels and have a knock-on effect on the thoughts, emotions and behaviours that follow (Padesky & Mooney, 1990).

The usual course of therapy is to focus initially on the here and now identification of negative automatic thoughts (NATs) using the format above. Then the beliefs that underlie the NATs and are common to many situations become the focus of treatment such that a person's conclusions/perceptions of events can change. Finally, the deeper modification of more fundamental core beliefs is what reduces the chances of relapse into the future (Beck, 1995).

So, what makes CBT so effective? The following elements are common to effective psychosocial interventions and are core to a cognitive behavioural approach to treatment (Williams & Garland, 2002, p.173):

- Focus on the current problems most relevant to the client

- Clear underlying model of practice

- Structure or plan to the treatment offered

- Treatment is collaborative and delivered in the context of a sound therapeutic relationship

- It is focused on empowering the client with the skills to make changes in their everyday lives.

Cognitive Behaviour Therapy: Applications in speech and language therapy practice

Evidence from other domains of SLT practice

The use of CBT approaches in speech and language therapy practice is not new. There is evidence to show that using these approaches can enhance outcomes in people with fluency disorders (Menzies, Onslow, Packman, & O'Brien, 2009) and voice disorders (Butcher, Elias, & Cavalli, 2007; Daniilidou, Carding, Wilson, Drinnan, & Deary, 2007; Miller, Deary, & Patterson, 2014).

CBT approaches have also been shown to enhance the effectiveness of social skills interventions in other client groups. In the area of autism spectrum disorders (ASD), social skills interventions based on CBT framework are a promising treatment modality for the social communication skills difficulties in young people with ASD (Laugeson & Park, 2014). McLeod (2013) recently reviewed CBT for people with ASD in relation to the specific role of the SLT which included (i) enabling access for CBT-based interventions for young people with ASD by developing adaptations, and (ii) using CBT principles to complement the speech and language therapy work with young people with ASD.

The effectiveness of cognitive behavioural social skills training (CBSST) has been demonstrated in a randomized controlled trial in older adults with schizophrenia (Granholm et al., 2005, 2007). CBSST combines CBT and social skills training to target functional impairment in people with psychotic disorders. Through the CBT component, participants learn about their unhelpful thinking and beliefs (e.g., "I always fail" or "I can't learn anything") that interfere with goal-directed activities. Through the social skills training component, participants learn communication and problem-solving skills with a specific focus on using these skills to achieve their functional goals.

How can CBT be helpful in speech and language therapy practice in adult mental health?

CBT approaches in speech and language therapy practice in mental health can help identify unhelpful thoughts and appraisals around communication difficulties and understand how these affect feelings and behaviours. Incorporating CBT approaches into clinical practice can assist clinicians in gathering information about their clients' views of the world in a structured and evidence-based way. SLTs can then work with their clients in reviewing evidence for their thinking styles, consider alternative ways of viewing events, test hypotheses in order to experiment in new ways, and problem solve around setbacks (Menzies et al., 2009).

The following CBT approaches have been selected as being useful adjuncts to speech and language therapy practice:

1. **Formulation**: CBT can help to bring an understanding of our clients' perspectives in a structured way through the process of *formulation* (Kuyken, 2006).

2. **CBT interventions**: CBT can assist in working with clients to help them understand the link between thoughts, feelings and behaviours using (i) *cognitive strategies*, and (ii) *behavioural strategies* (Beck, 2011).

Formulation: Using the Five Areas Approach (Williams & Garland, 2002)

Case formulation is the cornerstone of evidence-based practice in CBT and is understood to be a provisional map of a person's presenting problems that describes the territory of the problems and explains the factors that cause and maintain the problem (Kuyken, 2006). It is the process by which a person's difficulties are presented and understood in CBT terms, which then informs the subsequent intervention.

In typical CBT sessions, case formulations are built gradually over the course of 12-16 hour-long sessions which allow time and space for the client to assimilate this new blueprint for themselves (Persons, 2008). This process, however, is often not available to everyone, due either to resource limitations or difficulty accessing the language and concepts of CBT. For clients with speech, language and communication needs, the language of CBT can be highly technical and inaccessible. It is often difficult to translate concepts such as 'negative automatic thoughts', 'overgeneralization', 'schema', 'thinking errors' into everyday language.

One way of making CBT accessible is to use the Five Areas Approach developed by Williams and Garland (2002). They present a "pragmatic and accessible model of assessment and management that uses CBT" (Williams & Garland, 2002, p.173). This approach has been used by a wide variety of healthcare practitioners including psychiatrists, nurses and allied health professionals. The aim of the Five Areas Approach is to "communicate fundamental CBT principles and key clinical interventions in a clear language. It is not a new CBT approach; rather it is a new way of communicating the existing evidence-based CBT approach for use in a non-psychotherapy setting" (Williams & Garland, 2002, p.74). It helps the practitioner see clearly what their client thinks about their situation, their physical and emotional feelings connected with that, as well as what they are doing as a result (altered behaviours).

The Five Areas Approach, as its name suggests, is comprised of five parts (Williams & Garland, 2002, p.176):

1. Life situation, relationship and practical problems
2. Altered thinking
3. Altered emotions (moods or feelings)
4. Altered physical feelings/sensations
5. Altered behaviours or activity levels.

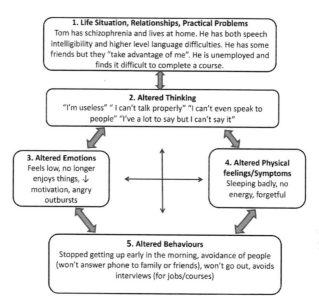

1. Life Situation, Relationships, Practical Problems
Tom has schizophrenia and lives at home. He has both speech intelligibility and higher level language difficulties. He has some friends but they "take advantage of me". He is unemployed and finds it difficult to complete a course.

2. Altered Thinking
"I'm useless" " I can't talk properly" "I can't even speak to people" "I've a lot to say but I can't say it"

3. Altered Emotions
Feels low, no longer enjoys things, ↓ motivation, angry outbursts

4. Altered Physical feelings/Symptoms
Sleeping badly, no energy, forgetful

5. Altered Behaviours
Stopped getting up early in the morning, avoidance of people (won't answer phone to family or friends), won't go out, avoids interviews (for jobs/courses)

Figure 12.5 Five Areas Assessment for Tom.

Figure 12.5 shows a Five Areas Assessment of a 24-year-old man, Tom, who was referred for speech and language therapy in his local mental health services. Tom has a diagnosis of schizophrenia with associated speech and higher-level language difficulties, which include difficulties with information processing and organization of language, such that his discourse is often difficult for the listener to follow. The assessment shows what Tom thinks about his situation and how he feels physically and emotionally as well as his altered behaviours.

Williams and Garland (2002) outline two primary reasons for working with clients to identify problems in each of the five areas. Firstly, it aids the clinician's understanding of the impact of their clients' circumstances on their subjective experience. Secondly, it can help in identifying clear target areas for intervention. As with the 'vicious cycle' model mentioned previously, making changes in any one of these areas leads to change in the other areas as well. A useful checklist for completing a Five Areas Assessment is provided in Williams and Garland (2002, pp.176–178).

CBT interventions

CBT involves helping the client to first notice and then challenge and modify his/her unhelpful thoughts and perceptions of events in their lives (Beck, 1995). Within CBT there are a variety of cognitive and behavioural interventions that can be used for this purpose.

Socratic dialogue

Socratic dialogue is a feature of CBT that permeates the entire course of treatment. Through the use of Socratic Questioning, there is an assumption that the client alone has the solutions to their difficulties (Beck, 1995). Socratic Questions are "open, collaborative, non-confrontational and asked with a spirit of enquiry and curiosity" (Turnbull & Stewart, 2013 p.10). These questions are asked with the aim of 'guiding discovery' and not with the aim of trying to persuade the client of the therapist's point of view (Turnbull & Stewart, 2013). Examples of Socratic Questions are shown in Table 12.3.

Cognitive restructuring

Early on in CBT, the client is asked to begin the process of self-monitoring and recording automatic thoughts and assumptions using a Thought Record (Beck, 1995). The client is asked to complete this between sessions, ideally directly after an event has occurred. The first three columns of the Thought Record are used to document the situation the person was in, the awareness and intensity of the emotional reaction and any automatic thoughts that arose. The example in Table 12.4 shows how Sarah reported on the experience of anxiety when thinking about an upcoming event.

Table 12.3 Examples of Socratic Questions (adapted from Paul & Elder, 2006).

Questions for clarification	What makes you say that? Can you give a specific example? Who? What? Why? Where? What did you do?
Questions that probe assumptions	What are you assuming when you say that? What do you make of this?
Questions that probe evidence	What is the evidence for that being true/not true? Are there any alternative explanations? Is this thought helpful?
Questions about viewpoints and perspectives	In relation to that situation, what do you know now that you didn't know then? What would you tell a friend who was in a similar situation?
Questions that probe implications and consequences	What is the worst thing that could happen, if this were true? If that did happen, what then?
Questions about the question	Why do you think I asked that question? How does being asked these questions feel?

Table 12.4. The Thought Record: Sarah.

Situation	Automatic thought	Emotion
Visited my mother. Listened to her talk badly of my sister. Wanted to tell her my opinion but didn't	I'm a walkover I'm an easy target	Angry (80%) Frustrated (100%) Sad (70%)

Now that Sarah has listed her automatic thoughts, the next step is for her to consider evidence that supports and does not support her thoughts to evaluate their accuracy, as shown in Table12. 5.

Table 12.5 Evaluating evidence for and evidence against: Sarah.

Evidence for	Evidence against
I do many favours for people and don't leave time for myself I spend a lot of time listening to other people's problems and don't have support for my own difficulties	I have voiced my opinion to my mother in the recent past I am disciplined with myself I can say 'No' to some people (e.g., my husband, sister) if I need to

By evaluating the evidence for and against her thinking, Sarah is able to come to a more balanced interpretation of this situation. As often happens, a small amount of new information can assist in a shift of perceptions and eventually lead to a more helpful and less restrictive perspective (Rector, 2010). A template of questions (Menzies et al., 2009, p.198), which can be used with clients in order to challenge their negative beliefs and assumptions, can be useful in this type of intervention.

Behavioural interventions

A powerful way of questioning and evaluating thoughts and assumptions is to test their validity in real-life situations through behavioural experiments. Bennett-Levy et al. (2004, pp.27-28) separate behavioural experiments into two types:

1. **Active**: Once an unhelpful thought has been identified, the client

deliberately acts or thinks differently in the difficult situation. For example, if a client has an underlying assumption that "If I speak in a group, people won't understand me and will think I'm stupid", you may ask them to engage in an experiment to determine what might actually happen when they speak in a group. This will only be done when the client is ready and after they have developed (i) a good understanding of why this would be helpful, and (ii) developed strategies to cope with the range of possible outcomes from these types of experiments. For example, the client may be asked to deliberately ask a question in a group context. This will allow him/her to see the extent to which: (a) he/she is understood; (b) other people's response (e.g., do others notice/look confused, take his comment/question seriously); and (c) how well he/she coped with the situation.

2. **Observational**: This type of experiment can be used when making a change to a thought or behaviour in a situation which is too anxiety provoking or where more information is needed. For example, the client who fears speaking in a group may spend time observing how other people respond to comments/questions in group contexts and document this to evaluate against underlying assumptions of judgement or ridicule.

A template (see Menzies et al., 2009, p.197), for recording observations during behavioural experiments can be useful in this type of intervention.

Application of CBT approaches in SLT practice: Case example

The case example below illustrates the assessment and intervention approach taken with a client, using a CBT approach.

Richard is a 20-year-old young man with a diagnosis of ASD and Generalized Anxiety Disorder (GAD), referred for speech and language therapy due to concerns regarding speech intelligibility and a queried diagnosis of cluttering. Collateral information revealed that Richard had been seen by SLTs previously. He had a history of developmental speech and feeding difficulties and presented with food and oral sensitivity (e.g., lumpy food textures, sensitive gag reflex when teeth brushing). He was in his second year of university and had settled in well with a group of friends. Richard reported that he avoided speaking in front of groups as he is afraid "I won't get the sound out". He felt embarrassed if he was asked to repeat himself in conversation. His experience of previous speech and language therapy sessions was "okay". He reported that the main focus was on "slowing down" but it "didn't really work". The observations of the SLT in the first session showed that Richard presented with mild phonological difficulties which were compensated for by a fast speaking rate. This was confirmed by Richard when he reported, "I speak fast to gloss over sounds I can't say". He reported a fear of others not understanding him in conversation and often gave short answers as a result.

Table 12.6 The Thought Record: Richard.

Situation	What was difficult about the interaction?	What did I do? (Behaviour)	How did I feel? (Emotion)	What went through my mind during and after?
Talking to an office worker	Responding to questions and explaining the situation – being sure I was understood	Attempted to speak more clearly than usual but this was difficult as long sentences were required	Embarrassed, unsure if I was understood or what the other person thought	I have difficulty communicating in work situations
Telling story/anecdote to friend while out	As above	As above Concentrated harder	Awkward Frustrated	Communication issues ruin a conversation I can't enunciate I can't get sentences across despite my focus on speaking
Introducing myself to new people at work (and in other social situations)	Nervous as new person less likely to be prepared to take in my speech patterns and I want to make a good impression	Struggled to get words out so decided not to say much	Embarrassed Annoyed	Hope I didn't seem rude/make a bad impression I can't handle these situations
Asking a conversational question to an acquaintance	Question 'garbled' and not understood	Had to repeat myself often	Uncomfortable	This damages the flow of conversation

Table 12.7 Evaluating evidence for and evidence against: Richard.

Evidence for	Evidence against
Conversations don't last long but maybe that's because I give short answers People ask me to repeat what I have said I look anxious when I meet them, even if I don't feel that way. That is because of my fast speech rate	I have made friends in my first year in college because I am: Interesting and interested in others Reliable and supportive A good listener Witty and have funny ideas Make an effort (even when I don't have energy to speak and feel tired) Other people have said that I am very pleasant and that I come across as friendly.
Balanced alternative: Even though I have some speech difficulties, I still make a good impression when I meet people as evidence by the information above.	

An adapted version of the Communication Attitude Test (Brutten & Vanryckeghem, 2010) was completed and showed that Richard presented with the following unhelpful automatic thoughts in speaking situations:

- "People won't understand me when I speak" (*All or nothing thinking*)

- "I wish I could talk like other people" (*Must/Should statement*)

- "People think I'm anxious when I speak, but I'm not" (*Mind reading*)

- "My classmates think I talk differently" (*Mind reading*)

- "I am not a good speaker" (*All or nothing thinking*)

- "It is harder for me to give a report in lectures than it is for most other people" (*Jumping to conclusions, Mind reading*).

In speech and language therapy sessions, these thoughts were discussed with Richard and explored based on his experiences of different speaking situations. Richard agreed that it was helpful to understand that there was more influencing his communication ability than just his speech intelligibility. He could see that his perception of himself as a speaker was also contributing to his confidence in interaction with others.

Richard agreed to complete a self-monitoring exercise between sessions. Table 12.6 illustrates how Richard documented his communication experiences, such that he and the SLT could understand how his interpretation of these experiences was relevant to the therapy process. It was clear that goal setting

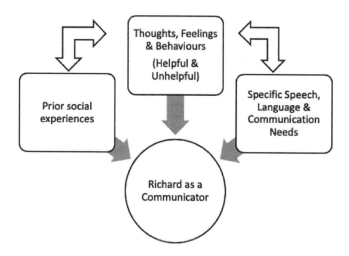

Figure 12.6 Illustration of factors influencing Richard as a communicator.

needed to include both speech/communication strategies *and* changes in his self-perception as a communicator.

In speech and language therapy sessions a recurrent theme was Richard's fear that "I never make a good impression". This was identified as a catastrophic thought which occurred when he met new people. This thought was investigated and evaluated by looking at the evidence for and against (Table 12.7).

Richard benefitted from a formulation of his communication difficulties in a broader context than just speech 'behaviours'. This formulation was helpful in order to plan a speech and language therapy intervention which took into account Richard's unique view of himself as a communicator. It meant that goals were focused both at the level of speech strategies and changes in his self-perception. Figure 12.6 illustrates the way that Richard and the SLT understood his communication difficulties and was helpful in planning treatment goals which were relevant to each domain.

Making CBT accessible for people with speech, language and communication needs

While this chapter has focused on the direct application of CBT approaches to enhance speech and language therapy practice in adults with mental health and communication difficulties, it is also within the scope of this topic to discuss the role of the SLT in making formal Cognitive Behaviour Therapy accessible for service users with speech, language and communication needs.

A significant cohort of service users present with complex mental health, communication and cognitive difficulties (see Chapter 3). The SLT has a unique role in the assessment and recommendations of communication supports for these service users. One benefit of assessment by an SLT is the potential to support access to evidence-based interventions, such as CBT, which may otherwise be inaccessible for them due to speech, language and communication needs.

The range of cognitive abilities required to engage in CBT include "emotion recognition, self-reflection and meta-cognition, perspective taking, verbal ability, short- and long-term memory and causal reasoning" (Lickel, MacLean, Blakeley-Smith, & Hepburn, 2012, p.992). Specifically, Sams, Collins and Reynolds (2006) found that the ability to link behaviours to emotions is linked with verbal ability and the identification of thoughts is associated with IQ. Therefore, the basis of the cognitive model (links between thoughts, feelings and behaviours) is more likely achievable by those with higher verbal ability and IQ.

Given the cognitive requirements necessary to engage in CBT, a pragmatic approach in the application of CBT to people with complex mental health, cognitive and communication needs must be taken. Hassiotis et al. (2012, p.18) recommend that "the first step any therapist should undergo is evaluating each client individually to assess whether or not he or she has prerequisite cognitive skills to undergo therapy". They suggest a template for this assessment which includes many areas in which speech and language therapy input is essential:

- Cognitive and language skills (including grammar and vocabulary)

- Memory

- Reading ability

- Writing ability

- Attention control

- Perception of control and self-efficacy

- Insight.

Following on from these assessments, the SLT can recommend specific strategies and communication supports that will allow access to CBT for the client Examples of these supports can be:

- Guidance on understanding a person with speech difficulties

- Guidance on using language appropriate to the client's level of comprehension (e.g., types of questions, concrete language, linking questions to everyday experiences)

- Visual supports (i.e., modified thought records, photo symbols, photographs of emotions).

Training and skills development

Cognitive Behaviour Therapy (CBT) is an evidence-based intervention which is effective for a wide range of psychosocial difficulties. The utility of this approach within mental health settings is clear. CBT as a therapeutic intervention is integral to the design and delivery of evidence-based, recovery focused mental health services (HSE, 2013). It is recognized that nurses, medical staff and health and social care professionals are well placed to deliver CBT interventions due to the direct involvement they have with delivery of care.

It has been recognized that a standardized framework is needed to ensure the safe and effective delivery of CBT interventions to people accessing mental health services. In Ireland, a Guidance Document has been produced which outlines a standardized approach to the education and training of nurses and health and social care professionals in *Basic Cognitive Behavioural Therapy Skills for Practice* (HSE, 2013). A structured education programme is described which focuses on "enhancing skills for clinical practice rather than creating specialists. Essentially, it aims to add some practical tools to the professionals' existing skill set" (HSE, 2013, p.3).

The CBT approaches described in this chapter are straightforward to implement and it is suggested that they can be incorporated usefully into speech and language therapy practice in mental health. However, caution is required in that they should only be used by SLTs with experience/training in CBT. In addition, they should also be delivered under the supervision of an appropriately qualified clinician and in accordance with the scope of practice guidelines of the SLT's professional body.

Conclusion

Using CBT approaches allows the SLT to focus both on supporting the service user's speech, language and communication needs and addressing some of the psychological issues which will inevitably surface, either as a direct consequence of the communication difficulties or associated with them. Using CBT approaches does not require the SLT to take on extra responsibility for solving the person's difficulties or become a 'mini' CBT therapist who can work with complex problems. The incorporation of CBT approaches is largely suited to people with mild-to-moderate difficulties and is not an alternative to referral to specialized services. Using CBT approaches can best be viewed as guided self-help to augment speech and language therapy practice rather than comprehensive one-to-one psychotherapy.

References

Beck, J. (1995). *Cognitive Therapy: Basics and Beyond*. London: Guildford Press.

Beck, J. (2011). *Cognitive Behaviour Therapy: Basics and Beyond*, 2nd ed. London: Guildford Press.

Bellack, A.S., Mueser, K.T., Gingerich, S., & Agresta, J. (2004). *Social Skills Training for Schizophrenia*, 2nd ed. London: Guildford Press.

Bennett-Levy, J., Butler, G., Fennell, M., Hackmann, A., Mueller, M., & Westbrook, D. (2004). *Oxford Guide to Behavioural Experiments in Cognitive Therapy*. Oxford: Oxford University Press.

Blanchard, J.J., Mueser, K.T., & Bellack, A.S. (1998). Anhedonia, positive and negative affect and social functioning in schizophrenia. *Schizophrenia Bulletin*, *24*, 413-424.

Boyle, M.P. (2011). Mindfulness training in stuttering therapy: A tutorial for speech-language pathologists. *Journal of Fluency Disorders*, *36*, 122-129.

Brophy, J. (2009). Working alongside people with schizophrenia: Directions for speech and language therapy practice. Unpublished MSc. thesis, Trinity College Dublin.

Butcher, P., Elias, A., & Cavalli, L. (2007). *Understanding and Treating Psychogenic Voice Disorders: A CBT Framework*. Chichester: John Wiley & Sons.

Butler, A.C., Chapman, J.E., Forman, E.M., & Beck, A.T. (2006). The empirical status of cognitive behaviour therapy: A review of meta-analyses. *Clinical Psychology Review*, *26*, 17-31.

Byng, S. & Duchan, J. (2005). Social model philosophies and principles: Their applications to therapies for aphasia. *Aphasiology*, *19*, 906-922.

Daniilidou, P., Carding, P., Wilson, J., Drinnan, M., & Deary, V. (2007). Cognitive behavioral therapy for functional dysphonia: A pilot study. *Annals of Otology, Rhinology and Laryngology*, *116*(10), 717-722.

Duffy, M., Gillespie, K., & O'Shea, J. (2013). How do trainees rate the impact of a short cognitive behavioural training programme on their knowledge and skills? *Behaviour and Cognitive Psychotherapy*, *42*, 653-667.

France, J. (2001). Disorders of communication and mental illness. In J. France & S. Kramer (Eds), *Communication and Mental Illness: Theoretical and Practical Approaches* (pp.15-26). London: Jessica Kingsley.

Gonzales-Torres, M.A., Oraa, R., Aristegui, M., Fernandez-Rivas, A., & Guimon, J. (2007). Stigma and discrimination towards people with schizophrenia and their family members: A qualitative study with focus groups. *Social Psychiatry and Psychiatric Epidemiology*, *42*, 14-23.

Granholm, E., McQuaid, J.R., McClure, F.S., Auslander, L.A., Perivoliotis, D., Pedrelli, P., Patterson, T., & Jeste, D.V. (2005). A randomised controlled trial of cognitive behavioural social skills training for middle aged and older outpatients with chronic schizophrenia. *American Journal of Psychiatry*, *162*, 520-529.

Granholm, E., McQuaid, J.R., McClure, F.S., Link, P.C., Perivoliotis, D., Gottlieb, J.D., Patterson, T., & Jeste, D.V. (2007). A randomised controlled trial of cognitive behavioural social skills training for middle aged and older outpatients with chronic schizophrenia: 12-month follow-up. *Journal of Clinical Psychiatry*, *68*, 730-737.

Griffen, J. (2010) *The Lonely Society Report*. London: Mental Health Foundation. Retrieved from www.mentalhealth.org.uk

Hassiotis, A., Serfaty, M., Azam, K., Martin, S., Strydom, A., & King, M. (2012). *A Manual of Cogntive Behavioural Therapy for People with Learning Disabilities and Common Mental Disorders: Therapist Version*. London: Camden & Islington NHS Foundation Trust and University College London. Retrieved from http://www.candi.nhs.uk/

Hayes, C. & Collins, L. (2001) Personal construct psychology. In J. France & S. Kramer (Eds), *Communication and Mental Illness: Theoretical and Practical Approaches* (pp.284-297). London: Jessica Kingsley.

HSE (2013). Certificate in Basic Cognitive Behavioural Therapy Skills for Practice: Guidance Document. Retrieved from https://www.hse.ie/eng/about/who/onmsd/nmpdu/nmpddn/guiding-framework.pdf

Irish Association of Speech & Language Therapists (IASLT) (2015). *Speech and Language Therapy in Mental Health Services: A Guidance Document*. Dublin: IASLT.

Jagoe, C. (2007). A descriptive study of the presentation of communication disorders in a psychiatric setting. Paper presented at the South African Neurological Rehabilitation Association (SANRA), Durban, South Africa.

Kuyken, W. (2006). Evidence-based case formulation: Is the emperor clothed? In N. Tarrier (Ed.), *Case Formulation in Cognitive Behaviour Therapy: The Treatment of Challenging and Complex Cases* (pp.12-36). London: Routledge.

Laugeson, E.A. & Park, M.A. (2014). Using a CBT approach to teach social skills to adolescents with autism spectrum disorder and other social challenges: The Peers Method. *Journal of Rational Emotional Cognitive Behaviour Therapy, 32*, 84‑97.

Lickel, A., MacLean, W.E., Blakeley‑Smith, A., & Hepburn, S. (2012). Assessment of the prerequisite skills for cognitive behavioral therapy in children with and without autism spectrum disorders. *Journal of Autism and Developmental Disorders, 42*(6), 992‑1000.

McLeod, A. (2013). CBT in Autism Spectrum Disorders: The role of the speech and language therapist. Paper presented at the Irish Association of Speech and Language Therapy Conference, Dublin, Ireland.

Menzies, R., Onslow, M., Packman, A., & O'Brien, S. (2009). Cognitive behaviour therapy for adults who stutter: A tutorial for speech‑language pathologists. *Journal of Fluency Disorders, 34*, 187‑200.

Miller, T., Deary, V., & Patterson, J. (2014). Improving access to psychological therapies in voice disorders: A cognitive behavioural therapy mode. *Current Opinion in Otolaryngology & Head and Neck Surgery, 34*, 201–205.

Muir, N. (2001). Introduction to management and patient care. In J. France & N. Muir (Eds), *Communication and Mental Illness*. London: Jessica Kingsley.

Padesky, C.A. & Mooney, K.A. (1990). Presenting the cognitive model to clients. *International Cognitive Therapy Newsletter, 6*, 13‑14. Retrieved from www.padesky.com

Pallanti, S., Quercioli, L., & Hollander, E. (2004). Social anxiety in outpatients with schizophrenia: A relevant cause of disability. *American Journal of Psychiatry, 161*, 53‑58.

Paul, R. & Elder, L. (2006). *The Art of Socratic Questioning*. Dillon Beach, CA: Foundation for Critical Thinking.

Persons, J.B. (2008). What is the case formulation approach to Cognitive‑Behavior Therapy? In J.B. Persons (Ed.), *The Case Formulation Approach to Cognitive‑Behavior Therapy: A Guide to Individualised, Evidence Based Treatment* (pp.1‑16). London: Guilford Press.

Rector, N. (2010). Cognitive Behaviour Therapy: An information guide. Centre for Addiction and Mental Health Canada. Retrieved from https://www.camh.ca/en/hospital/health_information/a_z_mental_health_and_addiction_information/Acute-Stress-Disorder/Documents/cbt_guide_en.pdf

Sams, K., Collins, S., & Reynolds, S. (2006) Cognitive therapy abilities in people with learning disabilities. *Journal of Applied Research in Intellectual Disabilities, 19*, 25‑33.

Turnbull, J. & Stewart, T. (2010) *The Dysfluency Resource Book*. Milton Keynes: Speechmark.

Williams, C. & Garland, A. (2002). A cognitive behavioural therapy assessment model for use in everyday clinical practice. *Advances in Psychiatric Treatment, 8*, 172‑217.

The Way Forward

Caroline Jagoe and Irene P. Walsh

Communication is unquestionably interwoven with mental health in a myriad of interesting and complex ways, as has been demonstrated across the chapters in this text. Interpersonal connections and relationships are dependent on communication and are critical for maintaining mental health. However, the 'protective effects' of social connections are not consistent across all populations (Kawachi & Berkman, 2001), and an underexplored area is how communication difficulties may influence the role of social ties in mental health. Communication is also central to clinical processes in mental health services. From diagnostic interviews, to conversations around treatment choices and adherence, talk-based therapies and service-user involvement, communication is the medium of consultation, assessment, management and collaboration. For service users with communication difficulties, full and positive participation in these processes may be hampered if their communication support needs are not addressed.

A lifespan perspective on communication and mental health is not only sensible but essential if those with communication difficulties are to fully access the supports and services they require. Communication disturbances in children with mental health difficulties have attracted much research and clinical attention, with speech and language therapy service provision being relatively strong and consistent for this group of young service users and their families. Historically, the same has not been true within the field of adult mental health disorders, where psychiatric and linguistic research has focused on language and communication impairments, yet clinical involvement has followed more slowly and remains inconsistent in many settings. This situation belies the lifespan perspective portrayed in this text. Children transitioning from child and adolescent mental health services or young offender services do not suddenly 'grow out of' their communication difficulties. A case in point is the particular burden carried by young offenders in terms of the prevalence of language and communication difficulties among these adolescents and young adults. However, this area of need is increasingly being recognized and again must be approached within a lifespan perspective. The communication support needs

- at the key transition points between child/adolescent mental health services and adult services - warrant further focused attention as the field continues to develop. In fact, we could perhaps predict that the number of individuals with communication difficulties may be greater in adult mental health services, as early adulthood is the time of onset for some of the major mental illnesses that may have associated language and communication disturbances. Mental health professionals, and specifically speech and language therapists, must be at the forefront of advocacy for communication support services within adult mental health, older adult services and forensic mental health.

The communication environment emerged as an important theme across many of the chapters of this text, from infancy (Mc Glinn, Chapter 1), to the potential role of empowering communication partners (Jagoe, Chapter 6) and the role of the SLT in environmental interventions (Brophy & O'Connor, Chapter 9), including within the forensic setting (O'Connor, Chapter 10). An explicit focus on assessment and intervention within the communication environment has been lacking in the field of mental health disorders, with domains of practice for people with aphasia and dementia being more advanced (Bruce, Brush, Sanford, & Calkins, 2013; Howe, Worrall, & Hickson, 2008; O'Halloran, Hickson, & Worrall, 2008; Threats, 2007). Addressing the communication environment, particularly within clinical contexts, has the potential to enhance interaction and care for all users of mental health services beyond only those with communication difficulties.

The nature of speech and language therapy intervention within mental health services is growing and developing in new and exciting ways. The developments in the field and the growth in practice centre around the ambition to improve services, specifically for mental health service users with communication difficulties. Improvement in complex systems is enormously challenging. We would argue that these challenges exist at the level of individual interventions within the complex contextually-bound nature of communication, as well as within the complexity of a healthcare system. The effective use of theory is one way in which improvement work can be enhanced:

> ...the explicit application of theory could shorten the time needed to develop improvement interventions, optimise their design, identify conditions of context necessary for their success, and enhance learning from those efforts (Davidoff, Dixon-Woods, Leviton, & Michie, 2015, p.228).

A strong argument was made for theory-based developments in Chapter 5

(Kellaghan) and Chapter 5 (Jagoe), in which the potential role of pragmatic theories to guide the design of communication intervention is explored. These theories could be conceptualized as informing programme theories, detailing the theory underpinning the design of a specific intervention (for example, Cognitive Pragmatics Theory underlying Cognitive Pragmatic Treatment). Situating speech and language therapy practice within mental health in the context of broader theories, such as theories of inequality, behaviour change, and implementation science, can only benefit the field. Indeed, some of the areas of 'growing practice' explored in Part 3 of this book may be enhanced in the future by increased systematic and careful application of theory.

Across the three parts of this book, an emphasis on the relevance of the speech and language therapist's skill-set in the mental health area emerged. Many of the approaches addressed in this book will be familiar to therapists who have never worked within the field of mental health. Although the diagnoses in mental health may be different from other populations with whom therapists work, the impact of the communication difficulties are common and recognizable. The notion of 'therapeutic borrowing' or 'therapeutic extension' - the idea that existing interventions may be applied or adapted by another profession or for a new clinical context – is one which warrants careful consideration and further discussion. Psychosocial difficulties, including difficulties in interpersonal interactions, have been shown to be common across neurological and psychiatric disorders, and have common determinants (Cieza et al., 2015). This critical research suggests that approaches to psychosocial difficulties, specifically approaches that address the environment, may be appropriate as cross-cutting interventions. The speech and language therapist, with a well-established role within neurological services and an ever-increasing evidence base within this domain, has highly pertinent skills and approaches to address the issues which are common in those with psychiatric diagnoses. In Chapter 6, Jagoe outlined, for example, how communication partner training may be an important approach within adult mental health, although it is not currently as routine as it would be in other domains of speech and language therapy practice. The principle extends beyond disorder-focused interventions to health promotion or risk-based preventative interventions, with a clear example from infant mental health (Chapter 1) where it was shown that the existing skills of speech and language therapists are highly relevant in the context of supporting families at risk, or in taking a broad health promotion perspective. Conversely, as the chapter on Cognitive Behavioural Approaches suggested, the speech and language therapist has much to gain from other professions whose tools may have relevance to language and communication-focused work. A particularly powerful concept, highlighted in Chapters 7 (Walsh), 8 (Jagoe et al.,) and 9 (Brophy & O' Conner.) is that of Recovery. The concept of personal recovery in mental health is in contrast to the understanding of the term within neurological rehabilitation, for example, where the focus is on "the return of some or all of the normal repertoire of behaviours" (Bernhardt et al., 2017, p.445). While psychosocial recovery in speech and language therapy may be framed more broadly, the profession may benefit from embracing definitions which explicitly articulate these more functional concepts evident in the mental health definition of "living a satisfying, hopeful and contributing life even with limitations caused by illness [...and] development of new meaning and purpose in one's life" (Anthony, 1993, p.17).

Communication is not only one of the most basic of human capacities, it is a human right. People with language and communication disorders intrinsic to (or associated with) their mental health disorder should get the tailored services they require to enable them to engage with society in as full a way as possible. Bhugra (2011, p.2) suggests that "the contract between psychiatry and its practitioners on the one hand and the society at large on the other is an implicit and not an explicit one". Perhaps it is time to make this 'contract' more explicit and visible in practice, as the contents of this text have aimed to do. People with mental health disorders have a right to full participation in their communities with equal access to services and yet risk remaining 'unheard'. Given the fact that mental health professionals are all in the business of communication (and dialogue), they each carry this responsibility to enable easy access to appropriate services for the individuals they work with. This responsibility involves considering not only the expertise of the 'client' but of their fellow healthcare professionals. The Speech and Language Therapist, as a core member of mental health teams, brings a carefully-focused lens through which communication, in all its wonderful and challenging complexity, can be appreciated and optimized.

References

Anthony, W.A. (1993). Recovery from mental illness: The guiding vision of the mental health service system in the 1990s. *Psychosocial Rehabilitation Journal, 4*(11–23). https://doi.org/10.1037/h0095655

Bernhardt, J., Hayward, K.S., Kwakkel, G., Ward, N.S., Wolf, S.L., Borschmann, K., ... Cramer, S.C. (2017). Agreed definitions and a shared vision for new standards in stroke recovery research: The Stroke Recovery and Rehabilitation Roundtable taskforce. *International Journal of Stroke*, 5(444–450). https://doi.org/10.1177/1747493017711816

Bruce, C., Brush, J., Sanford, J., & Calkins, M. (2013). Development and evaluation of the Environment and Communication Assessment Toolkit with Speech-Language Pathologists. *Seminars in Speech and Language*, 01(042–052). https://doi.org/10.1055/s-0033-1337394

Cieza, A., Anczewska, M., Ayuso-Mateos, J.L., Baker, M., Bickenbach, J., Chatterji, S., ... Consortium, P. (2015). Understanding the impact of brain disorders: Towards a 'horizontal epidemiology' of psychosocial difficulties and their determinants. PLOS ONE, *10*(9), e0136271. https://doi.org/10.1371/journal.pone.0136271

Davidoff, F., Dixon-Woods, M., Leviton, L., & Michie, S. (2015). Demystifying theory and its use in improvement. *BMJ Quality & Safety*, 3(228–238). https://doi.org/10.1136/bmjqs-2014-003627

Howe, T.J., Worrall, L.E., & Hickson, L.M.H. (2008). Interviews with people with aphasia: Environmental factors that influence their community participation. *Aphasiology*, 22(10), 1092–1120. https://doi.org/10.1080/02687030701640941

Kawachi, I. & Berkman, L. (2001). Social ties and mental health. *Bulletin of the New York Academy of Medicine*, 3(458–467). https://doi.org/10.1093/jurban/78.3.458

O'Halloran, R., Hickson, L., & Worrall, L. (2008). Environmental factors that influence communication between people with communication disability and their healthcare providers in hospital: A review of the literature within the International Classification of Functioning, Disability and Health (ICF) framework. *International Journal of Language & Communication Disorders*, 43(6), 601–632. https://doi.org/10.1080/13682820701861832

Threats, T. (2007). Access for persons with neurogenic communication disorders: Influences of Personal and Environmental Factors of the ICF. *Aphasiology*, 1(67–80). https://doi.org/10.1080/02687030600798303

Index